enVision® Integrated
MATHEMATICS I

Assessment Resources

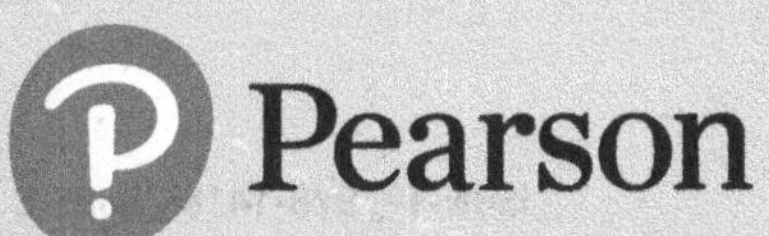

Boston, Massachusetts   Chandler, Arizona
Glenview, Illinois   New York, New York

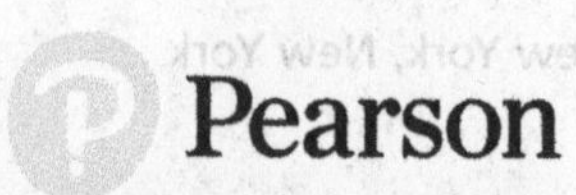

ISBN-13: 978-1418-28385-8
ISBN-10: 1418-28385-1

3 19

Contents

Name ____________________

Beginning-of-Year Assessment

1. Jacob's age is two years more than the sum of the ages of his siblings Becky and Micah. Which equation represents Jacob's age?

Ⓐ $z = x + y - 2$; x represents Micah's age, y represents Becky's age, and z represents Jacob's age.

Ⓑ $x = y + z + 2$; x represents Jacob's age, y represents Micah's age, and z represents Becky's age.

Ⓒ $x = 2 + y + z$; x represents Becky's age, y represents Jacob's age, and z represents Micah's age.

Ⓓ $y = x + z - 2$; x represents Jacob's age, y represents Becky's age, and z represents Micah's age.

2. What is the solution of $-83 = \frac{b}{4}$?

Ⓐ $b = -332$

Ⓑ $b = -87$

Ⓒ $b = -79$

Ⓓ $b = -20.75$

3. Ramona works in a clothing store where she earns a base salary of \$140 per day plus 14% of her daily sales. She sold \$600 in clothing on Saturday and \$1,200 in clothing on Sunday. How much did she earn over the two days?

Ⓐ \$252 Ⓒ \$392

Ⓑ \$291 Ⓓ \$532

4. Solve the equation below for y.

$6x - 3y = 36$

Ⓐ $y = 2x - 12$

Ⓑ $y = 12 - 2x$

Ⓒ $y = \frac{1}{2}x + 6$

Ⓓ $y = 6 - \frac{1}{2}x$

5. The equation $3w + 4j = 39$ is used to determine the number of water bottles w and the number of juice bottles j that can be bought for \$39. If you purchase 6 bottles of juice, how many bottles of water can you buy?

Ⓐ 3

Ⓑ 5

Ⓒ 15

Ⓓ 17

6. The formula for the area of a triangle is $A = \frac{1}{2}bh$, where b is the base of the triangle, and h is the height of the triangle. What is the length of the base if the area is 32 cm^2 and the height is 4 cm?

Ⓐ 4 cm

Ⓑ 8 cm

Ⓒ 16 cm

Ⓓ 18 cm

7. The formula for the volume V of a rectangular prism is $V = \ell wh$, where ℓ represents the length, w represents the width, and h represents the height. Rearrange the quantities in this formula to give a new formula for the width of the rectangular prism.

Ⓐ $w = \frac{Vh}{\ell}$

Ⓑ $w = \frac{\ell h}{V}$

Ⓒ $w = \frac{V\ell}{h}$

Ⓓ $w = \frac{V}{\ell h}$

8. Which number is a solution of the inequality $8 - \frac{1}{4}b \geq 27$?

Ⓐ −76

Ⓑ −80

Ⓒ −86

Ⓓ −140

9. Suppose it takes you 12 min to walk from home to school at a rate of 260 ft/min. Your friend lives closer to school than you do. Which inequality represents the distance d (in feet) that your friend lives from school?

Ⓐ $d < 260$

Ⓑ $d > 260$

Ⓒ $d > 3120$

Ⓓ $d < 3120$

10. What are the solutions of the compound inequality $2d + 3 \leq -11$ or $3d - 9 > 15$?

Ⓐ $d \leq -7$ or $d > 8$

Ⓑ $d \leq -4$ or $d > 2$

Ⓒ $d \leq -7$ or $d > 2$

Ⓓ $d \leq -4$ or $d > 8$

11. What are the solutions of $|3x + 2| > 9$?

Ⓐ $x > -\frac{11}{3}$ or $x > \frac{7}{3}$

Ⓑ $x < -\frac{11}{3}$ or $x > \frac{7}{3}$

Ⓒ $x > -\frac{11}{3}$ or $x < \frac{7}{3}$

Ⓓ $x < -\frac{11}{3}$ or $x < \frac{7}{3}$

12. Which function describes the table of values?

x	−2	0	2	4
$f(x)$	−7	−1	5	11

Ⓐ $f(x) = 1 - 3x$

Ⓑ $f(x) = x - 5$

Ⓒ $f(x) = 3x - 1$

Ⓓ $f(x) = 4x + 1$

13. A catalog-printing company receives a total amount C for each print job, which includes a setup charge S and a \$0.06 charge per page p for each job. Which rule describes the situation?

Ⓐ $C = 0.06p$

Ⓑ $C = S + 0.06p$

Ⓒ $C = 0.06S + p$

Ⓓ $C = 0.06(S + p)$

14. Dylan walks into a video arcade with a pocketful of quarters. He spends them at a rate of nine every half hour until he runs out. If the number of quarters Dylan has is graphed over time, which feature of the graph corresponds to Dylan's initial number of quarters before he spends the first one?

Ⓐ the *y*-intercept

Ⓑ the slope

Ⓒ the *x*-intercept

Ⓓ the minimum value

15. The changing speed of a car is modeled by the function $S(t) = -4t + 35$, where *t* is time in seconds. Interpret the model.

Ⓐ The car has an initial speed of 0 units and is speeding up to a speed of 35 units by 4 units per second.

Ⓑ The car has an initial speed of 4 units and is speeding up by 35 units per second.

Ⓒ The car has an initial speed of 35 units and is slowing down by 4 units per second.

Ⓓ The car has an initial speed of 35 units and is speeding up by 4 units per second.

16. Which of the following is an equation of the line that passes through the point (−2, 3) and is perpendicular to the graph of the equation $y = 3x - 2$?

Ⓐ $y = -\frac{1}{3}x + \frac{7}{3}$

Ⓑ $y = -\frac{1}{3}x + \frac{11}{3}$

Ⓒ $y = 3x + 9$

Ⓓ $y = 3x - 3$

17. Holly is trying to save $25,000 to put a down payment on a condominium. If she starts with $10,000 saved and saves an additional $750 each month, which equation represents how far Holly is from her goal of reaching $25,000? Let *x* stand for months and *y* stand for dollars.

Ⓐ $y = 25{,}000 - 750x$

Ⓑ $y = 15{,}000 - 750x$

Ⓒ $y = 750x - 10{,}000$

Ⓓ $y = 750x + 10{,}000$

18. What is the solution of the system of linear equations in the graph shown?

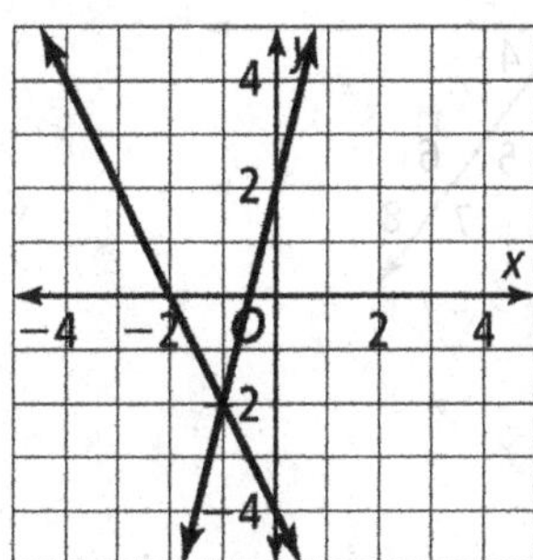

Ⓐ (−2, −1)

Ⓑ (−2, 0)

Ⓒ (−1, −2)

Ⓓ (0, 2)

19. Suppose you have 20 coins that total \$3.00. Some coins are nickels and some are quarters. Which of the following pairs of equations can you use to find out how many of each coin you have?

Ⓐ $n + q = 30$
$5n + 25q = 20$

Ⓑ $n + q = 30$
$n + q = 3.00$

Ⓒ $n + q = \frac{3.00}{20}$
$0.05n + 0.25q = 3.00$

Ⓓ $n + q = 20$
$5n + 25q = 300$

20. Compare the line passing through the points (−2, −9) and (4, 6) with the line given by the equation $y = \frac{2}{5}x - 4$.

Ⓐ They have the same slope.

Ⓑ They have the same x-intercept.

Ⓒ The two lines are perpendicular.

Ⓓ They have the same y-intercept.

21. Which angles are congruent to ∠3?

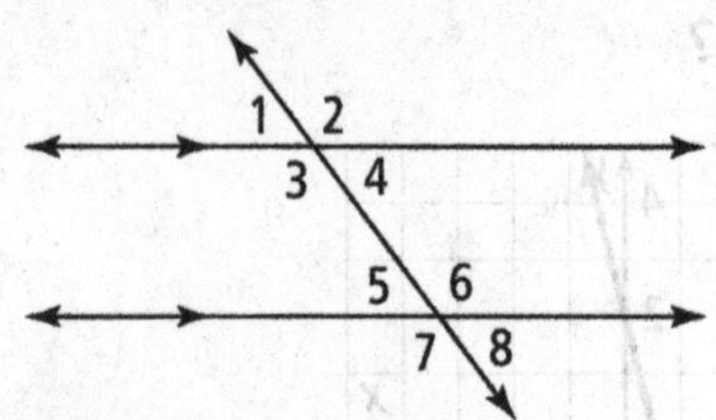

Ⓐ ∠2

Ⓑ ∠2, ∠6

Ⓒ ∠6

Ⓓ ∠2, ∠6, ∠7

22. Which term best describes the quadrilateral formed by $A(2, 3)$, $B(4, 6)$, $C(8, 9)$, and $D(5, 5)$?

Ⓐ quadrilateral

Ⓑ parallelogram

Ⓒ rhombus

Ⓓ kite

23. Which theorem can be used to show that $\triangle ABC \cong \triangle DEC$?

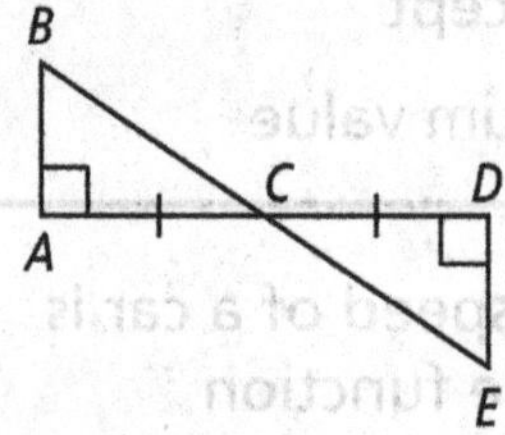

Ⓐ HL

Ⓑ ASA

Ⓒ AAS

Ⓓ SAS

24. The coordinates of points A and B are $A(4, -2)$ and $B(12, 10)$. What are the coordinates of the point that is $\frac{1}{4}$ of the way from A to B?

Ⓐ (1, −0,5)

Ⓑ (6, 1)

Ⓒ (10, 7)

Ⓓ (3, 2.5)

25. Line $\overleftrightarrow{TS}$ is the perpendicular bisector of $\overline{QR}$. Which of the following must be true?

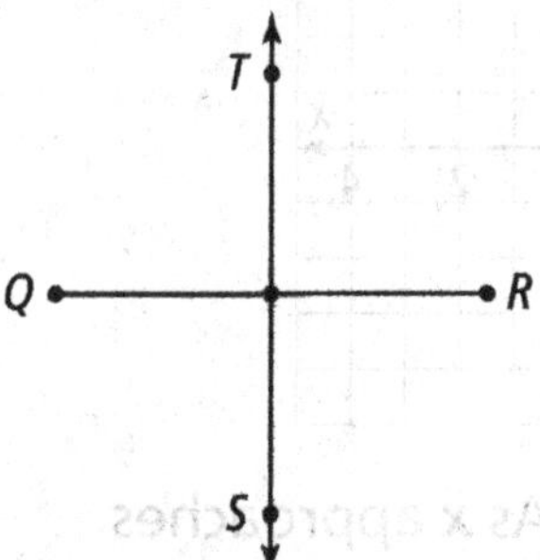

Ⓐ $\overline{QR} \cong \overline{TS}$

Ⓑ $\overline{TQ} \cong \overline{TR}$

Ⓒ $\overline{QT} \cong \overline{QS}$

Ⓓ $\overline{TR} \cong \overline{QS}$

26. In parallelogram *ABCD*, $\overline{AC} \perp \overline{BD}$. What is the most specific name for *ABCD*?

Ⓐ parallelogram

Ⓑ rectangle

Ⓒ square

Ⓓ rhombus

27. Which statement is not true?

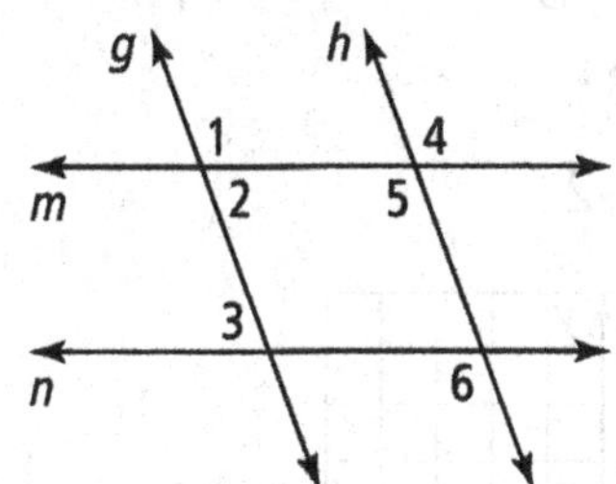

Ⓐ If $\angle 1 \cong \angle 4$, then $g \parallel h$.

Ⓑ If $\angle 2 \cong \angle 3$, then $m \parallel n$.

Ⓒ If $\angle 2 \cong \angle 5$, then $g \parallel h$.

Ⓓ If $\angle 4 \cong \angle 6$, then $m \parallel n$.

28. The vertices of $\triangle DEF$ are $D(1, 19)$, $E(16, -1)$, and $F(-8, -8)$. What type of triangle is $\triangle DEF$?

Ⓐ right

Ⓑ equilateral

Ⓒ isosceles

Ⓓ scalene

29. If $FN = 29$, what is the value of r?

Ⓐ 4

Ⓑ 5

Ⓒ 6

Ⓓ 7

30. Line p intersects lines a and b. $a \parallel b$. By which theorem is $\angle 1 \cong \angle 8$?

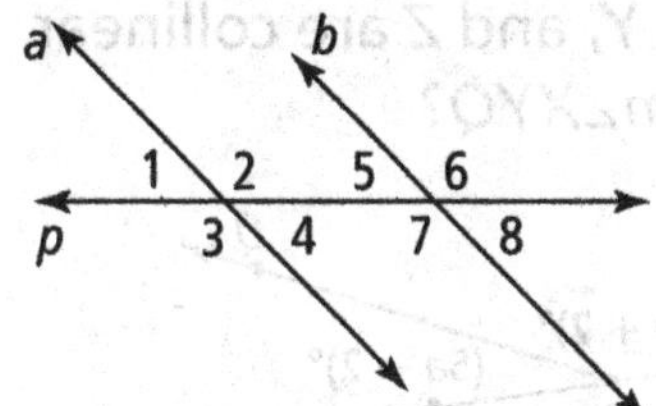

Ⓐ Alternate Exterior Angles Theorem

Ⓑ Alternate Interior Angles Theorem

Ⓒ Corresponding Exterior Angles Theorem

Ⓓ Corresponding Interior Angles Theorem

31. What is the distance between points $A(3, 12)$ and $B(6, 15)$? Round to the nearest tenth.

32. Which could be the first step of an indirect proof of the statement below? Select all that apply.

If the sum of the interior angles of a figure is 180°, then the figure is a triangle.

Ⓐ If a figure is not a triangle, then the sum of the interior angles is not 180°.

Ⓑ If the sum of the interior angles of a figure is 180°, then the figure is a triangle.

Ⓒ Assume that the figure is not a triangle and the sum of the interior angles is not 180°.

Ⓓ Assume that the sum of the interior angles of a figure is 180° and the figure is not a triangle.

33. Points X, Y, and Z are collinear. What is $m\angle XYQ$?

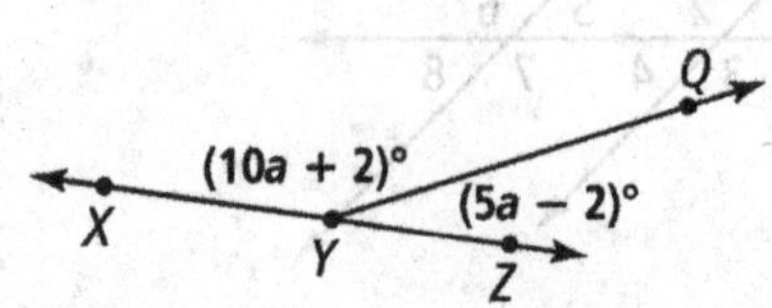

34. Graph $f(x) = 2^x$.

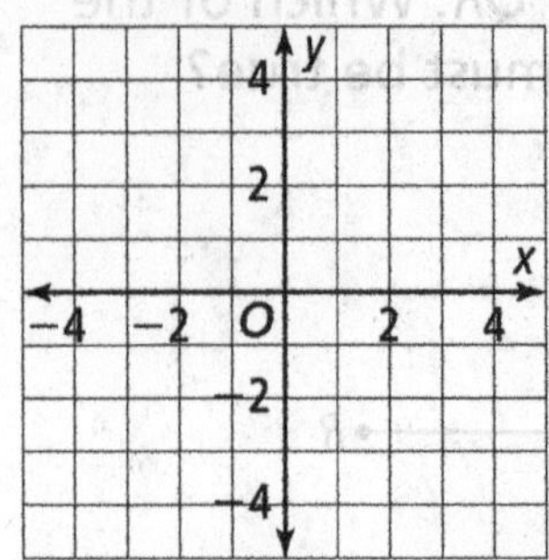

Complete: As x approaches negative infinity, $f(x)$ approaches ________________. As x approaches infinity, $f(x)$ approaches ________________.

35. The population of a town is 7,000, and it grows at a rate of 4.6% per year. What will the population be in 10 years?

Ⓐ about 10,975

Ⓑ about 3,220

Ⓒ about 73,220

Ⓓ about 7,733

36. Graph the system of inequalities.

$2x - y \leq 3$

$x - 2y \geq -2$

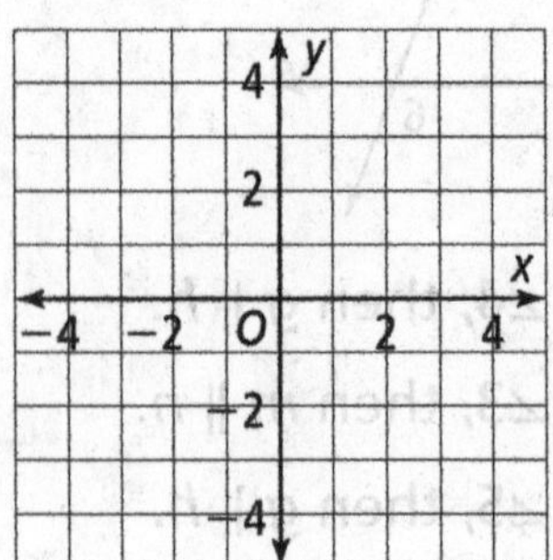

Name ______________________________

1 Readiness Assessment

1. Which list shows numbers ordered from least to greatest?

Ⓐ $1.01, \frac{21}{19}, 1.\overline{01}$

Ⓑ $\frac{21}{19}, 1.01, 1.\overline{01}$

Ⓒ $1.01, 1.\overline{01}, \frac{21}{19}$

Ⓓ $1.\overline{01}, 1.01, \frac{21}{19}$

2. Which statement is true?

Ⓐ $-17 > -20$

Ⓑ $\frac{1}{2} = \frac{8}{4}$

Ⓒ $8.01 < 8.001$

Ⓓ $-\frac{2}{3} < -6$

3. Which statement about the number −3 is true? Select all that apply.

Ⓐ It is a natural number.

Ⓑ It is a whole number.

Ⓒ It is an integer.

Ⓓ It is a rational number.

Ⓔ It is an irrational number.

4. Which statement is true?

Ⓐ All integers are whole numbers.

Ⓑ All whole numbers are natural numbers.

Ⓒ Some rational numbers are integers.

Ⓓ Some irrational numbers are rational numbers.

5. Solve $h - 104 = 7$.

6. If $\frac{k}{3} - 9 = 12$, what is the value of k?

Ⓐ 1

Ⓑ 7

Ⓒ 9

Ⓓ 63

7. Which properties can be used to solve $7y - 15 = -29$? Select all that apply.

Ⓐ Identity Property of Multiplication

Ⓑ Addition Property of Equality

Ⓒ Distributive Property

Ⓓ Inverse Property of Multiplication

Ⓔ Commutative Property of Addition

8. Where is $\sqrt{95}$ located on a number line?

Ⓐ between 7 and 8

Ⓑ between 8 and 9

Ⓒ between 9 and 10

Ⓓ between 10 and 11

9. Simplify $|-3 - 8|$.

10. Which of the following is equivalent to the expression $|-24 + 2| - 10$?

Ⓐ -32

Ⓑ -12

Ⓒ 12

Ⓓ 32

11. Evaluate $\left|2\frac{5}{6} + y\right|$ for $y = \frac{7}{4}$.

Ⓐ $2\frac{2}{5}$

Ⓑ $3\frac{1}{5}$

Ⓒ $3\frac{4}{5}$

Ⓓ $4\frac{7}{12}$

12. Solve and graph the solution to $x + 1 < 5$.

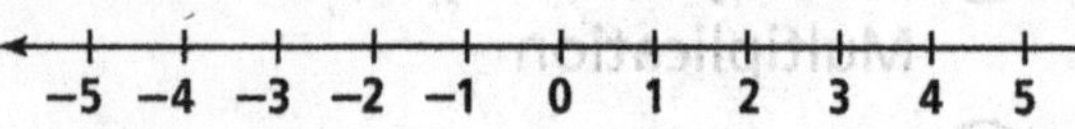

13. Which expression is equivalent to $\frac{1}{3}x(9y - 12)$?

Ⓐ $3xy - 4$

Ⓑ $3xy - 4x$

Ⓒ $3xy - 12$

Ⓓ $3y - 4x$

14. Which of the following statements is true if $x = -2$ and $y = 8$? Select all that apply.

Ⓐ $|x| \leq |y|$

Ⓑ $|y| \geq |x|$

Ⓒ $|x| > |y|$

Ⓓ $|y| < |x|$

15. Which expression is equivalent to the sum of x and five divided by twelve?

Ⓐ $\frac{x + 5}{12}$

Ⓑ $\frac{x}{5 + 12}$

Ⓒ $x + \frac{5}{12}$

Ⓓ $\frac{x}{5} + 12$

16. What is the value of $\left|-\frac{8}{9}\right|$?

17. What unit of time will make the statement true?

$$\text{seconds} + \frac{\text{seconds}}{?} \cdot \text{day} = \text{seconds}$$

18. If $C = 2\pi r$ and $C = 24$, what is the value of r?

Ⓐ $r = 12\pi$

Ⓑ $r = \frac{24}{2\pi}$

Ⓒ $r = 48\pi$

Ⓓ $r = \frac{48}{\pi}$

Name ______________________________

1-1 Lesson Quiz

Solving Linear Equations

1. What is the value of x in the equation $4x - 2(x + 3) = 8$?

Ⓐ $x = 1$

Ⓑ $x = 2.5$

Ⓒ $x = 3.5$

Ⓓ $x = 7$

2. Six friends all use $2-off coupons to buy themselves movie tickets. They spend a total of $42. What is the price of one movie ticket without the coupon?

Ⓐ $5

Ⓑ $7

Ⓒ $9

Ⓓ $11

3. The sum of two consecutive even integers is 74. What are the two numbers?

4. A scientist needs 10 liters of a 20% acid solution for an experiment, but she has only a 5% solution and a 40% solution. To the nearest tenth of a liter, about how many liters of the 5% and the 40% solutions should she mix to get the solution she needs? Write and solve an equation to match the situation.

Equation: ______________________________

Solution: ______ liters of 5% and ______ liters of 40%

5. Venetta buys 2 pounds of pistachios and 3 pounds of almonds. The pistachios cost $4 more per pound than the almonds. She pays a total of $48. Which of the following are true? Select all that apply.

Ⓐ One pound of pistachios plus 1 pound of almonds cost $20.

Ⓑ The pistachios cost twice as much per pound as the almonds.

Ⓒ Reducing the number of pounds of almonds by one results in a total cost of $40.

Ⓓ The cost a, in dollars, of 1 pound of almonds is modeled as $2(a - 4) + 3a = 48$.

Ⓔ The cost p, in dollars, of 1 pound of pistachios is modeled as $2p + 3(p - 4) = 48$.

1-2 Lesson Quiz

Solving Equations With a Variable on Both Sides

1. How many solutions does the equation $4x + 2(x - 5) = 3(2x - 4)$ have?

Ⓐ no solution

Ⓑ exactly one solution

Ⓒ at least two solutions

Ⓓ infinitely many solutions

2. Cranberry juice costs $6.30 per quart and apple juice costs $3.60 per quart. Terrence wants to make a mixture of apple and cranberry juice that sells for $4.50 per quart. How many quarts *q* of cranberry juice should he mix with 4 quarts of apple juice to make cranberry-apple juice at that price? Which equation below represents the situation?

Ⓐ $3.60(q - 4) + 25.20 = 4.50q$

Ⓑ $3.60q + 25.20 = 4.50(q + 4)$

Ⓒ $6.30(q - 4) + 14.40 = 4.50q$

Ⓓ $6.30q + 14.40 = 4.50(q + 4)$

3. What is the value of *x* in the equation $\frac{3}{2}(4x - 1) - 3x = \frac{5}{4} - (x + 2)$?

4. Which of the equations shown have infinitely many solutions? Select all that apply.

Ⓐ $3x - 1 = 3x + 1$

Ⓑ $2x - 1 = 1 - 2x$

Ⓒ $3x - 2 = 2x - 3$

Ⓓ $3(x - 1) = 3x - 3$

Ⓔ $2x + 2 = 2(x + 1)$

Ⓕ $3(x - 2) = 2(x - 3)$

5. Tonya's dog-walking service charges a flat rate of $20 per month, plus $3 per mile that each dog is walked. Beth does not charge a monthly fee for her dog-walking service, but she charges $5 per mile that each dog is walked. Write and solve an equation to find the number of miles *m* for which Tonya and Beth would charge the same amount.

1-3 Lesson Quiz

Literal Equations and Formulas

1. Solve the equation $a = m - n$ for the variable n.

   Ⓐ $n = a + m$ Ⓑ $n = m - a$

   Ⓒ $n = a - m$ Ⓓ $n = -m - a$

2. Deon plans to ride a 15-mi bicycle trail. If his average speed is 20 mi/h, which equation can he use to find the time t, in hours, for the ride?

   Ⓐ $t = 20 \cdot 15$

   Ⓑ $t = \frac{20}{15}$

   Ⓒ $t = 20 - 15$

   Ⓓ $t = \frac{15}{20}$

3. In physics, the Ideal Gas Law describes the relationship among the pressure, volume, and temperature of a gas sample. The law is represented with the formula $PV = nRT$, where P is the pressure, V is the volume, T is the temperature, n is the amount of gas, and R is a physical constant. Which of the equations below are equivalent to the formula $PV = nRT$? Select all that apply.

   Ⓐ $P = VnRT$

   Ⓑ $V = \frac{nRT}{P}$

   Ⓒ $n = \frac{PV}{RT}$

   Ⓓ $R = PVnT$

   Ⓔ $T = \frac{nR}{PV}$

4. The formula for the volume V of a cylinder is $V = \pi r^2 h$, where r is the radius of the base and h is the height of the cylinder. Solve the formula for h. Then find the height of a cylinder with a volume of 36π cm^3 and a base with a radius of 3 cm.

5. The temperature in degrees Kelvin is 273 degrees more than the temperature in degrees Celsius. Use the formula $C = \frac{5}{9}(F - 32)$ to write a formula for the temperature in degrees Fahrenheit F in terms of the temperature in degrees Kelvin K.

Name ____________________

1-4 Lesson Quiz

Solving Inequalities in One Variable

1. Which number line shows the solution to the inequality $-2(3x - 1) < 8$?

Ⓐ 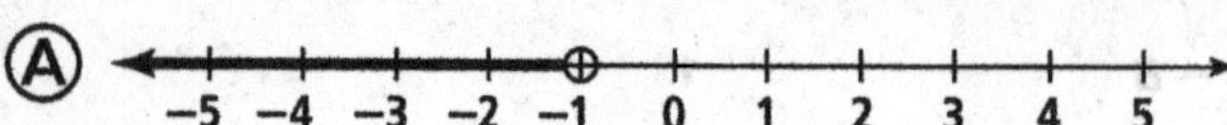

Ⓑ 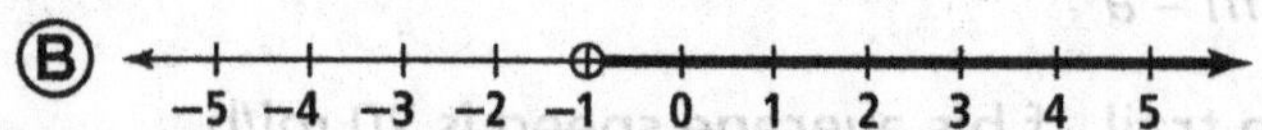

Ⓒ 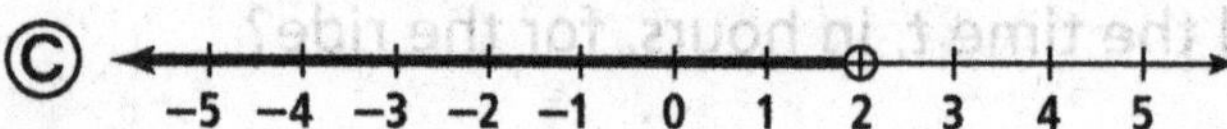

Ⓓ 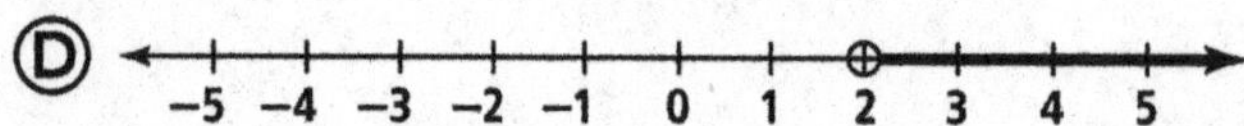

2. Solve the inequality $3(x - 2) + 1 \geq x + 2(x + 2)$.

Ⓐ $x \leq 4$

Ⓑ $x \geq -5$

Ⓒ no solution

Ⓓ all real numbers

3. Graph the solution of the inequality $-3(x + 1) \leq 6$ on the number line.

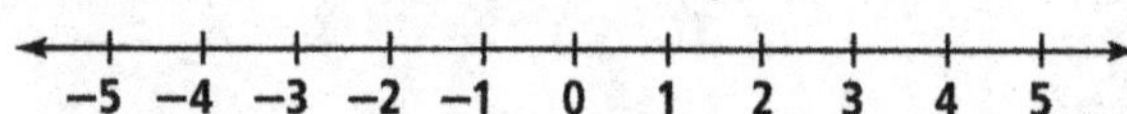

4. Graph the solution of the inequality $2x - (3 - x) > x + 1$ on the number line.

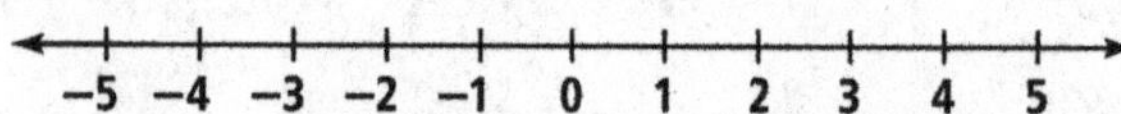

5. A video streaming company offers two monthly plans.

Plan A: \$3 per video viewed, plus a flat rate of \$8 per month

Plan B: \$5 per video viewed and no additional flat rate

Write an inequality to determine when the cost of viewing *n* videos using Plan A is less than the cost of viewing *n* videos using Plan B.

Inequality: ____________

Plan A is less expensive when ____________.

Name ______________________

enVision Integrated MATHEMATICS I

PearsonRealize.com

1-5 Lesson Quiz

Compound Inequalities

1. Which compound inequality describes the solutions graphed below?

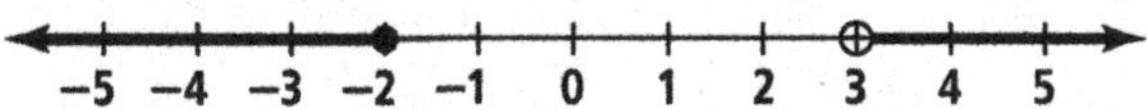

Ⓐ $x \leq -2$ or $x > 3$

Ⓑ $x \geq -2$ or $x < 3$

Ⓒ $x \leq -2$ and $x > 3$

Ⓓ $x \geq -2$ and $x < 3$

2. Solve the compound inequality $2x - 3 < 7$ and $5 - x \leq 8$.

Ⓐ $x \geq 3$ and $x < 2$

Ⓑ $x \geq 3$ and $x < 5$

Ⓒ $x \geq -3$ and $x < 2$

Ⓓ $x \geq -3$ and $x < 5$

3. Write a compound inequality for the graph shown.

4. Graph the solution on the number line.

$3(x + 3) - 2 < 4$ or $1 - x \leq -1$

–5 –4 –3 –2 –1 0 1 2 3 4 5

5. Values for the area A of the rectangle shown are $12 \leq A \leq 36$.
Write and solve a compound inequality for the value of x.

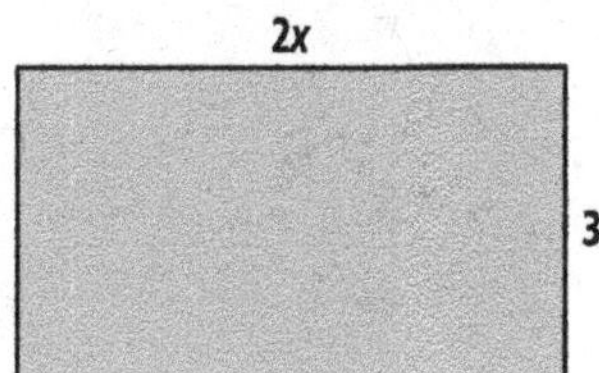

1-6 Lesson Quiz

Absolute Value Equations and Inequalities

1. Solve the absolute value equation $|x| - 2 = 5$.

Ⓐ $x = 3$ and $x = -3$

Ⓑ $x = 7$ and $x = -7$

Ⓒ $x = -7$ and $x = 3$

Ⓓ $x = -3$ and $x = 7$

2. Russel wants to buy 3 identical gift cards. He wants to make sure his total cost is no more than \$2 above or below \$60. Which of the following inequalities represents his situation?

Ⓐ $|3c - 60| \leq 2$

Ⓑ $|60 + 3c| \leq 2$

Ⓒ $|3c - 2| \leq 60$

Ⓓ $|3c + 2| \leq 60$

3. Solve and graph the solutions of the equation $2|x - 2| - 12 = 0$.

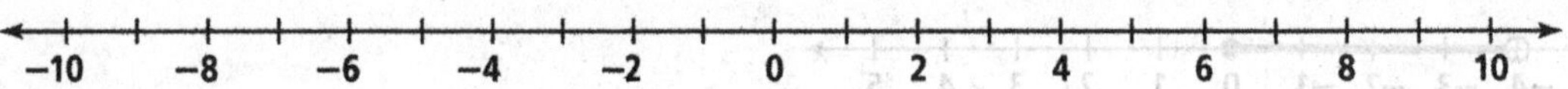

4. What are the minimum and maximum values of t for which $|t + 3| \leq 2$?

minimum: ____________

maximum: ____________

5. Solve and graph the solutions of the inequality $-|x - 2| + 9 > 6$.

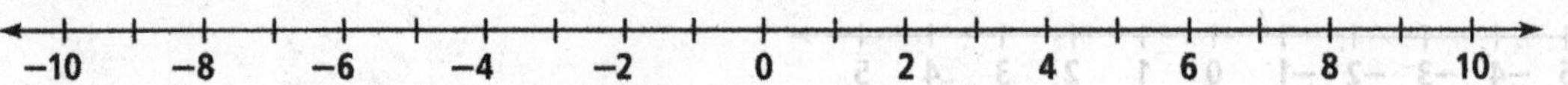

Name ______________________________

1 Topic Assessment Form A

1. What is the value of x in this equation?

$5x - 2(2x - 1) = 6$

Ⓐ 3
Ⓑ 4
Ⓒ 7
Ⓓ 8

2. The sum of three consecutive odd integers is 105. What are the three numbers?

3. Jacinta buys 4 pounds of turkey and 2 pounds of ham. She pays a total of \$30, and the turkey costs \$1.50 less per pound than the ham. What would be the combined cost of 1 pound of turkey and 1 pound of ham?

Ⓐ \$7.50　Ⓑ \$9.50
Ⓒ \$10.50　Ⓓ \$15.00

4. How many solutions are there to this equation?

$7x - 3(x - 1) = 2(2x + 3)$

Ⓐ no solution
Ⓑ exactly one solution
Ⓒ at least two solutions
Ⓓ infinitely many solutions

5. Teo makes a necklace of x wooden beads at \$0.50 each and 6 glass beads at \$1.25 each. The average cost of the beads in the necklace is \$0.75. Write an equation to model the situation.

6. Find the value of x in this equation.

$\frac{1}{3}(6x - 5) - x = \frac{1}{3} - 2(x + 1)$

7. Solve the equation $y = ax - b$ for the variable x.

Ⓐ $x = \frac{y}{a} + b$　Ⓑ $x = \frac{a + b}{y}$
Ⓒ $x = y + \frac{b}{a}$　Ⓓ $x = \frac{y + b}{a}$

8. Coulomb's Law $F = k\frac{qQ}{r^2}$ relates the force F between two charges q and Q, which are a distance of r units apart. Solve the formula for k.

9. Write the formula for the volume of a cone $V = \frac{1}{3}\pi r^2 h$ in terms of h. Find the height h of a cone with volume $V = 32\pi$ cm^3 and radius $r = 4$ cm.

Formula:

Height:

10. Solve the inequality.

$4(x + 3) - 7 \geq x + 3(x + 1)$

Ⓐ $x < 5$

Ⓑ $x > 3$

Ⓒ no solution

Ⓓ all real numbers

11. Graph the solution of the inequality on the number line.

$x - (5 - 3x) \leq 2x - 1$

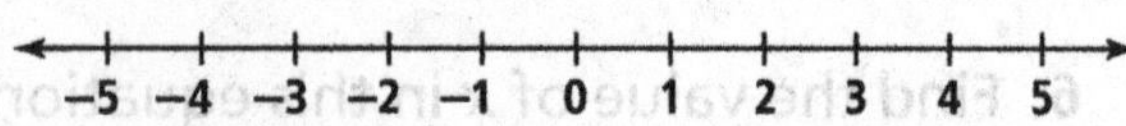

12. Solve the compound inequality.

$3x - 4 > 5$ or $1 - 2x \geq 7$

Ⓐ $x \leq -3$ or $x > 3$

Ⓑ $x < -3$ or $x \geq 3$

Ⓒ $x \geq -3$ or $x < 3$

Ⓓ $x > -3$ or $x \leq 3$

13. Write a compound inequality for the graph below.

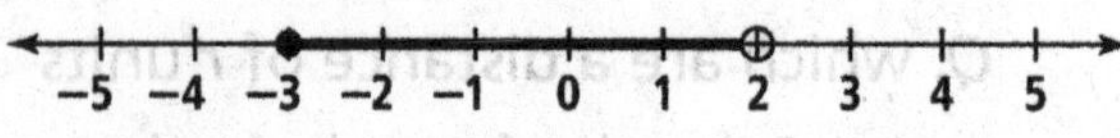

14. The area A of the rectangle shown is described with the inequality $100 \leq A \leq 1{,}000$. Write and solve a compound inequality for x.

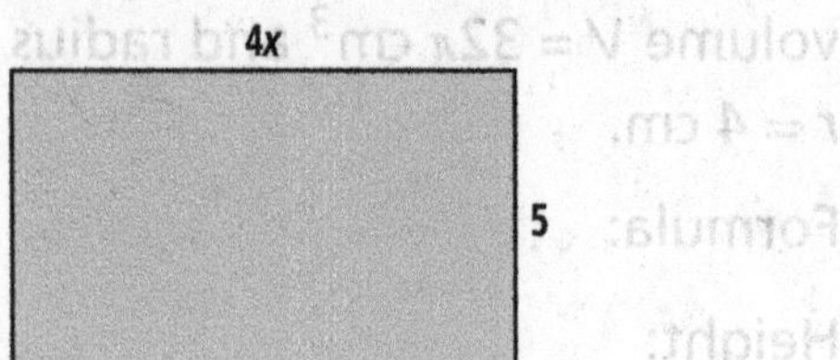

15. Solve the absolute value equation.

$4 - |x| = 1$

Ⓐ $x = \pm 3$ Ⓑ $x = \pm 5$

Ⓒ $x = -5, 3$ Ⓓ $x = -3, 5$

16. Jamie is buying 5 concert tickets, and he wants his total cost to be no more than \$4 above or below \$80. Which inequality models the cost x, in dollars, of a ticket?

Ⓐ $|5x + 4| \leq 80$ 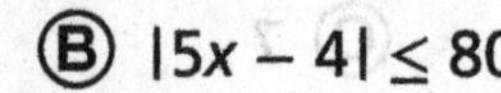 Ⓑ $|5x - 4| \leq 80$

Ⓒ $|80 - 5x| \leq 4$ 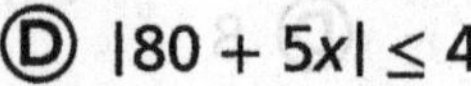 Ⓓ $|80 + 5x| \leq 4$

17. Graph the solution of the absolute value inequality on the number line.

$4 > |x + 1| + 2$

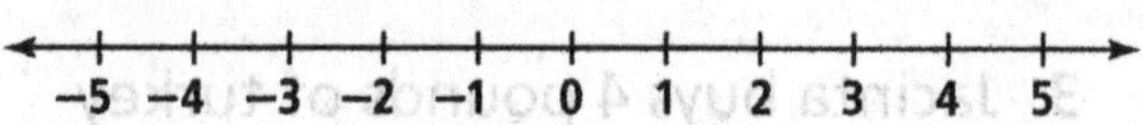

Name ______________________________

1 Topic Assessment Form B

1. What is the value of x in this equation?

$3(2x - 5) - 4x + 8 = -1$

Ⓐ -6
Ⓑ -2
Ⓒ 3
Ⓓ 4

2. The sum of three consecutive even integers is 72. What are the three numbers?

3. LaTanya buys 5 yards of blue fabric and 8 yards of green fabric. The blue fabric costs $2 more per yard than the green fabric. She pays a total of $62. What would be the combined cost of 1 yard of blue fabric and 1 yard of green fabric?

Ⓐ $6 Ⓑ $10
Ⓒ $9 Ⓓ $14

4. How many solutions are there to this equation?

$5x + 2 - 2(x - 1) = 3x + 4$

Ⓐ no solution
Ⓑ exactly one solution
Ⓒ at least two solutions
Ⓓ infinitely many solutions

5. Corey combines x pounds of herbal tea at $12 per pound with 8 pounds of regular tea at $9 per pound. He makes a mixture that averages $10.50 per pound. Write an equation to model the situation.

6. Find the value of x in this equation.

$\frac{3}{4}(6x + 1) - 3x = \frac{1}{4}(2x - 1)$

7. Solve the equation $s = a + lw$ for the variable w.

Ⓐ $w = \frac{s - a}{l}$ Ⓑ $w = \frac{s}{l} - a$
Ⓒ $w = \frac{s}{l} + a$ Ⓓ $w = \frac{a - s}{l}$

8. The velocity v that an object r units from Earth's center must have in order to escape Earth's gravity is given by $v^2 = \frac{2GM}{r}$, where G is a constant. Solve for the object's mass M.

9. Write the formula for the volume of a square prism, $V = \frac{1}{3}s^2h$, in terms of h. Then find the height h of a square prism with volume $V = 60\text{ cm}^3$ and side length $s = 6$ cm.

Formula:

Height:

10. Solve the inequality.

$-2(x - 3) - 4 \geq 3x - 5(x - 1)$

Ⓐ $x \geq 2$

Ⓑ $x \geq 5$

Ⓒ no solution

Ⓓ all real numbers

11. Graph the solution of the inequality on the number line.

$-2x + 5(x - 2) > 7x - 6$

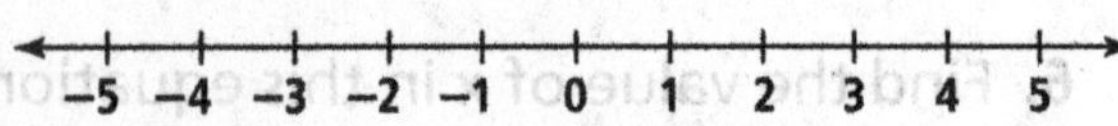

12. Solve the compound inequality.

$2(x - 2) + 7 > -1$ and $5 - 4x > 9$

Ⓐ $x < -2$ and $x < 1$

Ⓑ $x > -2$ and $x < 1$

Ⓒ $x < -2$ and $x < -1$

Ⓓ $x > -2$ and $x < -1$

13. Write a compound inequality for the graph below.

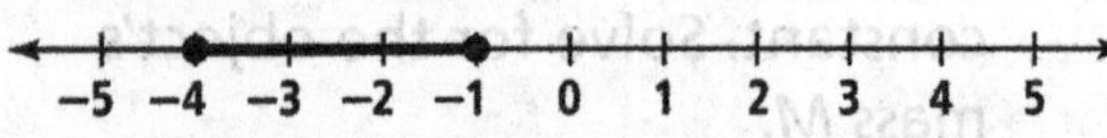

14. The area A of the rectangle shown is described with the inequality $36 \leq A \leq 72$. Write and solve a compound inequality for x.

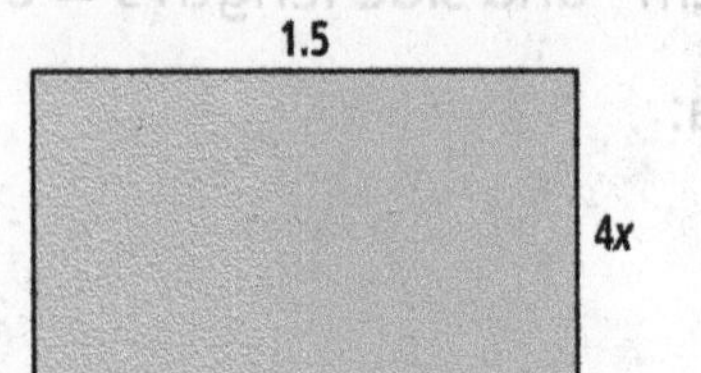

15. Solve the absolute value equation.

$3 = |6 - x|$

Ⓐ $x = \pm 3$ Ⓑ $x = \pm 9$

Ⓒ $x = 3, 9$ Ⓓ $x = -3, 9$

16. Isabel is buying 6 angelfish, and she wants her total cost to be no more than $2 above or below $36. Which inequality models the cost x, in dollars, of an angelfish?

Ⓐ $|36 + 6x| \leq 2$ Ⓑ $|6x + 2| \leq 36$

Ⓒ $|6x - 2| \leq 36$ Ⓓ $|36 - 6x| \leq 2$

17. Graph the solution of the absolute value inequality on the number line.

$2|x + 3| + 1 > 3$

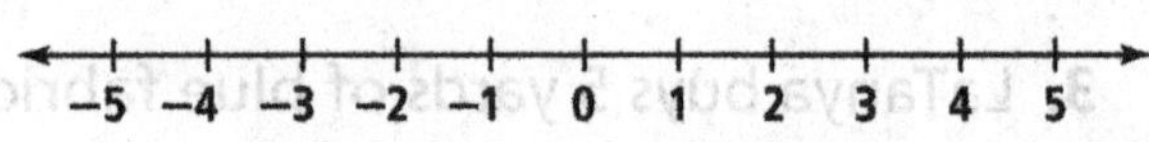

Name ______________________

enVision Integrated MATHEMATICS I

PearsonRealize.com

1 Performance Assessment Form A

Kelsey has designed a pendant, shown here, that hangs from a chain. She makes pendants by bending silver wire into circles. She plans to sell the pendants at a craft fair, and her goal is to make a minimum profit of $50 at the fair.

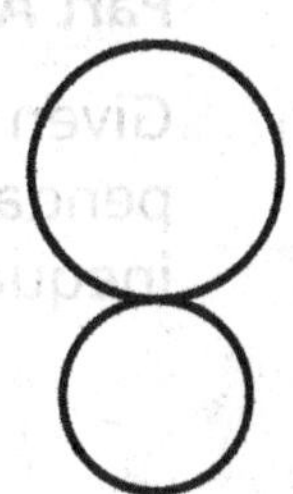

1. Kelsey's pendant design connects one circle made from a wire 6 cm long to a second circle made from a wire 8 cm long.

   The height of the pendant is determined by using the formula for the circumference of a circle, $C = \pi d$. Find the total height of the pendant design from top to bottom in terms of π. Then find the height rounded to the nearest tenth of a centimeter. Use 3.14 for π. Justify your answer.

2. Kelsey has to pay $200 to rent a booth at the craft fair. The materials for each pendant cost $7.80, and she plans to sell each pendant for $13.50. To make a profit, she must make more money than she spends. Kelsey has already made 10 pendants.

Part A

Given that Kelsey has already made 10 pendants, how many additional pendants must she make and sell in order to make a profit? Write and solve an inequality to answer that question. Show the steps of your solution.

Part B

Given that Kelsey has already made 10 pendants, how many additional pendants must she make and sell to make a profit of $50? Justify your answer.

Part C

It takes Kelsey 5 hours to make 12 pendants. If she works 8 hours per day for 3 days before the craft fair, can she make enough additional pendants to sell so that she can make a profit of at least $50? Explain.

Name ______________________

1 Performance Assessment Form B

Prizes Based on Money Raised	
$50 to $99.99	T-shirt
$100 to $124.99	T-shirt, backpack
$125 to $249.99	T-shirt, backpack, sports ball
$250 to $344.99	T-shirt, backpack, sports ball, travel mug
$345 or more	T-shirt, backpack, sports ball, travel mug, headphones

Ms. Smith's class will participate in an Algebra-Thon to raise money for a class trip. The Algebra-Thon workbook has 100 math problems. Students can raise money based on the number of math problems they answer correctly or by accepting a donation without regard to the number of math problems answered correctly. As shown in the table, prizes are awarded to students who raise $50 or more. Benjamin, a student in the class, answers 80 math problems correctly. His grandmother pays $0.25 per correct answer. His uncle gives him a donation.

1. If Benjamin receives $45 from his grandmother and uncle, how much money does his uncle give him? Explain.

2. Benjamin wants to win headphones. In addition to his grandmother and uncle, some friends of his agree that each one will give him a $20 donation. Some other friends agree that each one will pay him $0.25 for every correct answer. The number of friends who donate $20 to Benjamin is 4 times the number who pay him for correct answers. Write and solve an inequality to find the least number of friends who must pay him $0.25 for each correct answer in order for Benjamin to meet his goal. Justify your answer.

3. Tyler is also in Ms. Smith's algebra class. He wants to win a T-shirt, a backpack, and a sports ball.

Part A

Write and graph a compound inequality that represents the amount of money Tyler needs to collect to win the prize of a T-shirt, backpack, and sports ball.

Part B

Tyler receives $100 in donations. His aunt will pay him $0.50 for each correct answer to a math problem. Write and solve a compound inequality to find the number of questions that Tyler must answer correctly to win the prize he wants. Explain.

4. The number of questions Tyler answers correctly is within 2 of the number of Benjamin's correct answers.

Part A

Write and solve an absolute value inequality to determine the number of questions Tyler answers correctly.

Part B

Based on your answer to Part A, what prizes will Tyler win? Explain.

Name ______________________________

2 Readiness Assessment

1. What is the slope *m* of the graphed line?

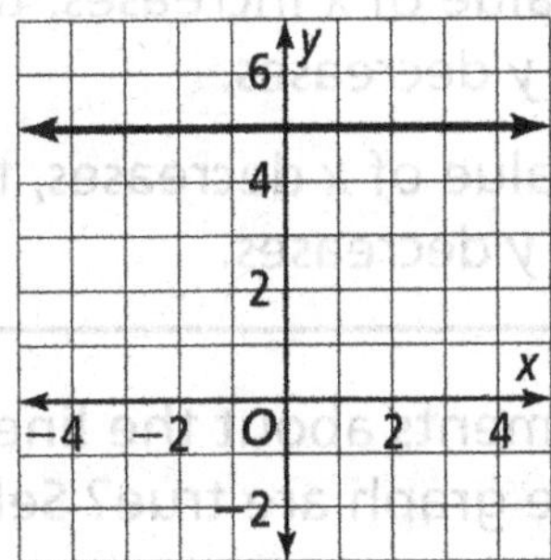

Ⓐ $m = 0$ Ⓑ $m = 5$

Ⓒ $m = \frac{1}{5}$ Ⓓ $m = -\frac{1}{5}$

2. What is the slope of the line that passes through the points shown in the table?

x	y
−1	−5
0	−3
1	−1
2	1

3. What is the slope of the line that passes through the points (0, −7) and (−4, 3)?

4. Which of the following ordered pairs represent points that lie on a horizontal line?

Ⓐ (−2, 3), (−5, 3)

Ⓑ (2, 3), (−2, 4)

Ⓒ (−2, 3), (−2, 4)

Ⓓ (2, −3), (5, 3)

5. A number *y* is 5 times the value of a number *x*. A line graphed in a coordinate plane represents the relationship between *x* and *y*. What is the slope of the line?

6. Which ordered pair gives the coordinates of a point that lies on the line shown in the graph?

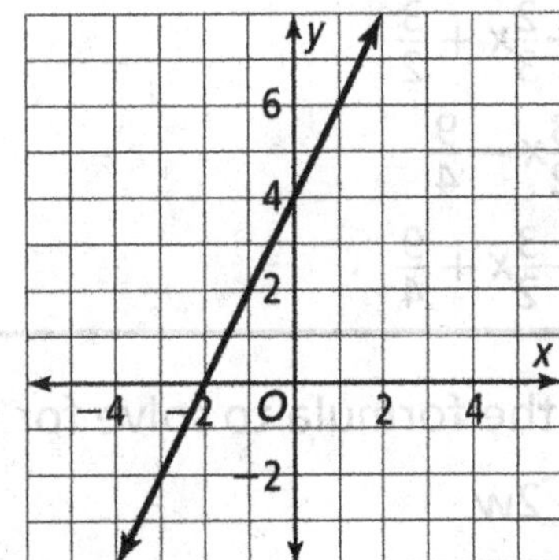

Ⓐ (0, 2) Ⓑ (−2, 0)

Ⓒ (2, 0) Ⓓ (0, −2)

7. Which of the following equations contain the ordered pairs shown in the table?

x	y
−1	5
0	1
1	−3
2	−7

Ⓐ $y = 4x + 1$

Ⓑ $y = \frac{1}{4}x + 1$

Ⓒ $y = -4x + 1$

Ⓓ $y = -\frac{1}{4}x + 1$

8. Which ordered pair is a solution of the equation $-\frac{1}{4}x + 6 = y$?

Ⓐ (4, 7) Ⓑ (2, 5)

Ⓒ (6, 0) Ⓓ (12, 3)

9. Does the equation $y = 2x$ represent a *linear* or a *nonlinear* function?

10. Which of the following equations is equivalent to the equation $4x - 6y = 9$?

Ⓐ $y = \frac{2}{3}x - \frac{3}{2}$

Ⓑ $y = -\frac{2}{3}x + \frac{3}{2}$

Ⓒ $y = \frac{3}{2}x - \frac{9}{4}$

Ⓓ $y = -\frac{3}{2}x + \frac{9}{4}$

11. Rewrite the formula to solve for *w*.

$P = 2\ell + 2w$

12. How can you find the reciprocal of 0.8? Select all that apply.

Ⓐ Solve the equation $0.8x = 1$.

Ⓑ Solve the equation $0.8 + x = 1$.

Ⓒ Divide 1 by 0.8.

13. What is the reciprocal of $\frac{2}{3}$?

Ⓐ $-\frac{3}{2}$ Ⓑ $-\frac{2}{3}$

Ⓒ $\frac{1}{3}$ Ⓓ $\frac{3}{2}$

14. Write the opposite of the reciprocal of −2.4.

15. Which statement about the function $y = -\frac{1}{4}x - 2$ is true?

Ⓐ As the value of *x* increases, the value of *y* increases.

Ⓑ As the value of *x* decreases, the value of *y* stays the same.

Ⓒ As the value of *x* increases, the value of *y* decreases.

Ⓓ As the value of *x* decreases, the value of *y* decreases.

16. Which statements about the lines shown in the graph are true? Select all that apply.

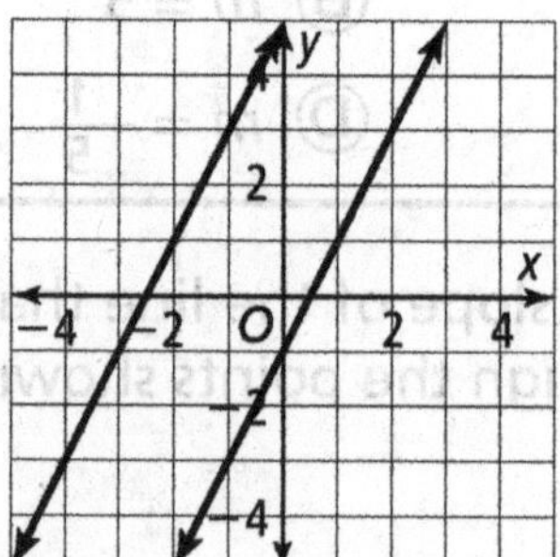

Ⓐ The lines are parallel.

Ⓑ The lines have different slopes.

Ⓒ The lines do not intersect.

Ⓓ The lines are nonvertical.

17. In Item 16, what is the slope of the line that has a *y*-intercept of −1?

18. Which statements about the graphs of the equations $y = 2x + 4$ and $y = -x + 4$ are true? Select all that apply.

Ⓐ The graphs intersect the *x*-axis at the same point.

Ⓑ The graphs intersect the *y*-axis at the same point.

Ⓒ The graphs have different slopes.

Ⓓ The graphs are parallel lines.

Name ______________________________

2-1 Lesson Quiz

Slope-Intercept Form

1. Which graph represents the equation $y = -\frac{4}{3}x - 2$?

Ⓐ
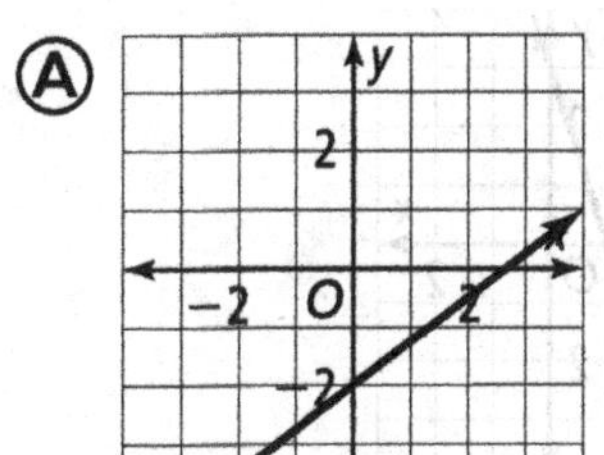

Ⓑ
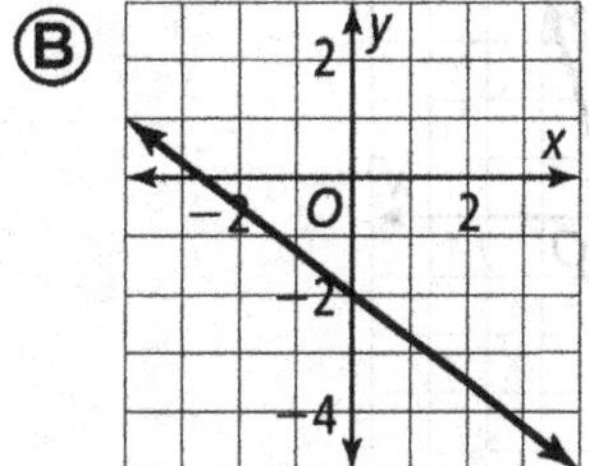

Ⓒ
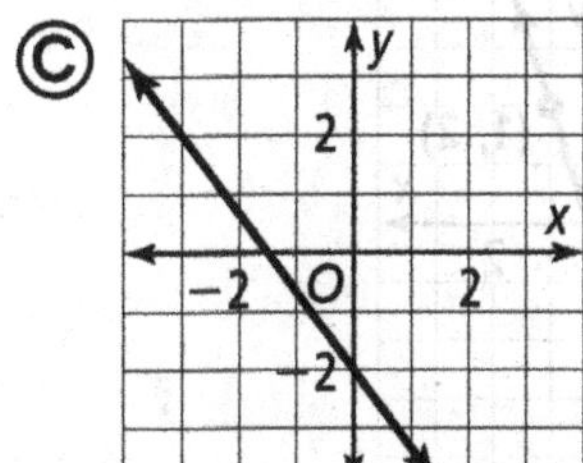

Ⓓ
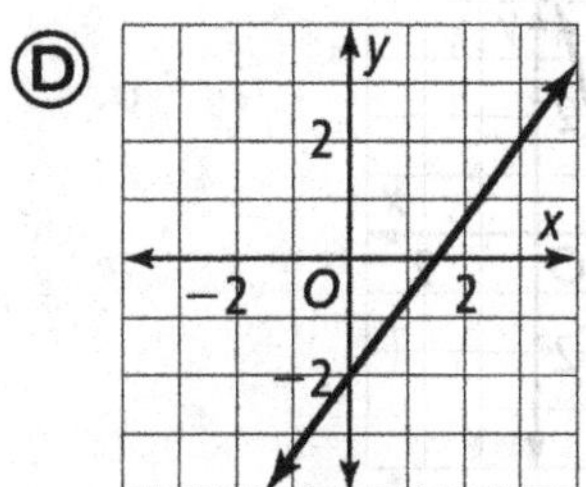

2. What is the slope of the line $y = -3x + 7$?

3. Which statements about the line that passes through (−2, 0) and (2, −4) are true? Select all that apply.

Ⓐ The slope of the line is 1.

Ⓑ The line intersects the y-axis at (0, −2).

Ⓒ The equation of the line is $y = -x - 2$

Ⓓ The line intersects the x-axis at (−2, 0).

4. Rachel hikes at a steady rate from a ranger station to a campground that is 20 mi away. After 2 h, she is 13 mi from the campground. After 4 h, she is 6 mi from the campground. A graph shows her distance y from the campground, in miles, after x hours. What is the slope of the graph, and what does it represent?

Ⓐ 20; Rachel's initial distance from the campground

Ⓑ −3.5; the rate at which Rachel's distance from the campground changes per hour

Ⓒ 3.5; Rachel's initial distance from the campground

Ⓓ 20; Rachel's final distance from the campground

5. Write the slope-intercept form of an equation for a line with y-intercept −5 and slope 2.

2-2 Lesson Quiz

Point-Slope Form

1. Which is the graph of the line $y - 2 = 3(x - 1)$?

Ⓐ 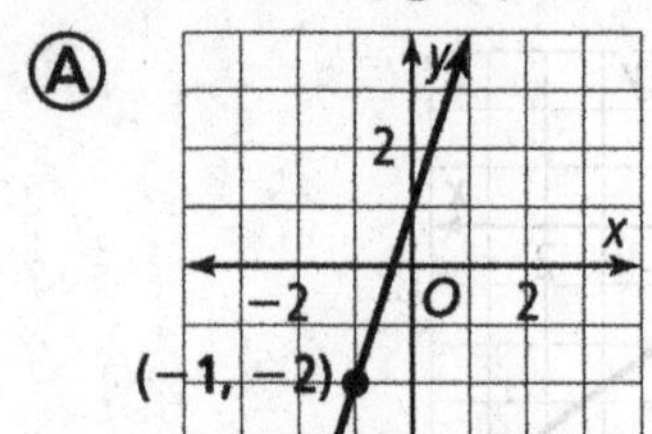

Ⓑ 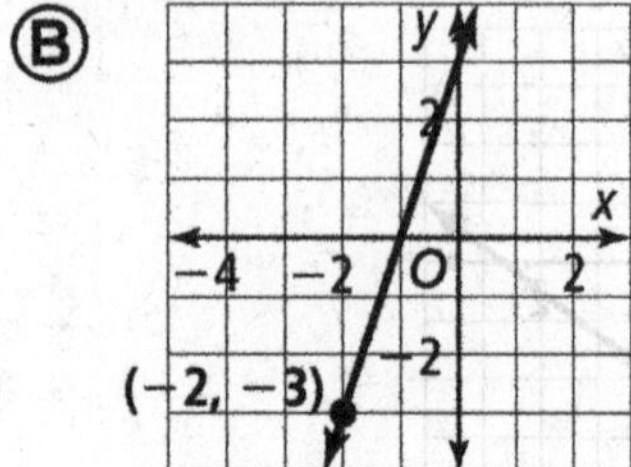

Ⓒ 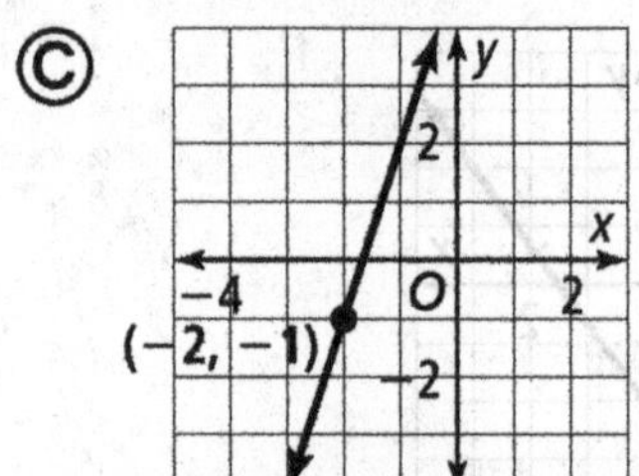

Ⓓ 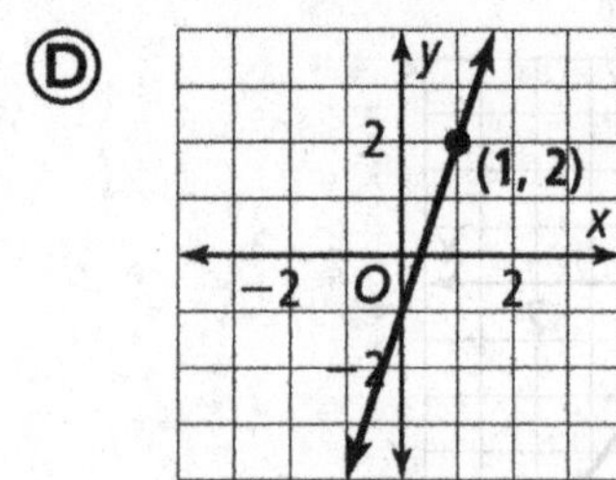

2. What is the equation in point-slope form of the line that passes through the point (1, −1) and has a slope of 4?

3. The graph of the equation $y - 1 = -2(x - 2)$ contains which set(s) of ordered pairs? Select all that apply.

Ⓐ (0, −2) and (1, 3)

Ⓑ (0, 5) and (−2, 9)

Ⓒ (−1, 7) and (2, 1)

Ⓓ (3, −1) and (2, −1)

4. Which equation represents the graphed line?

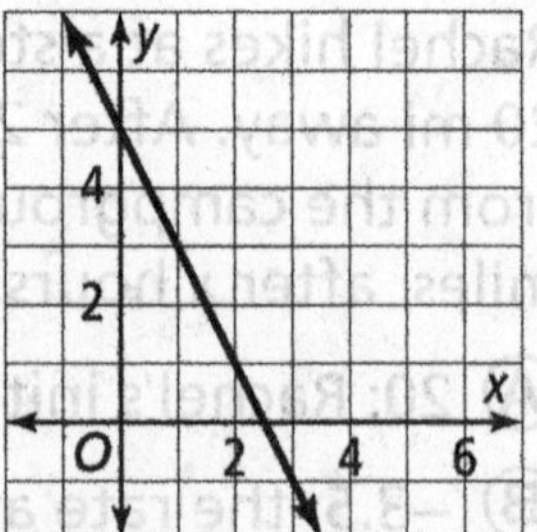

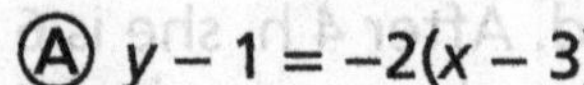

Ⓐ $y - 1 = -2(x - 3)$

Ⓑ $y - 1 = -2(x + 3)$

Ⓒ $y + 1 = -2(x - 3)$

Ⓓ $y + 1 = -2(x + 3)$

5. Which of the following equations could represent the points in the table? Select all that apply.

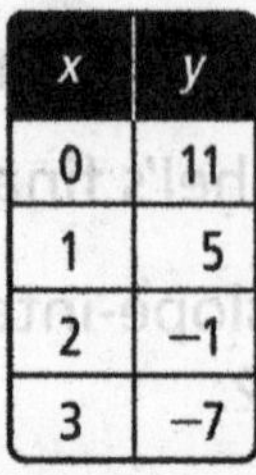

x	y
0	11
1	5
2	−1
3	−7

Ⓐ $y - 11 = -6(x - 0)$

Ⓑ $y - 1 = -6(x + 5)$

Ⓒ $y + 1 = -6(x - 2)$

Ⓓ $y - 7 = -6(x - 3)$

Name 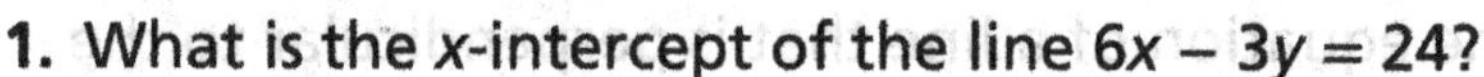

2-3 Lesson Quiz

Standard Form

1. What is the x-intercept of the line $6x - 3y = 24$?

2. Which of the following is an equation of the line in the graph?

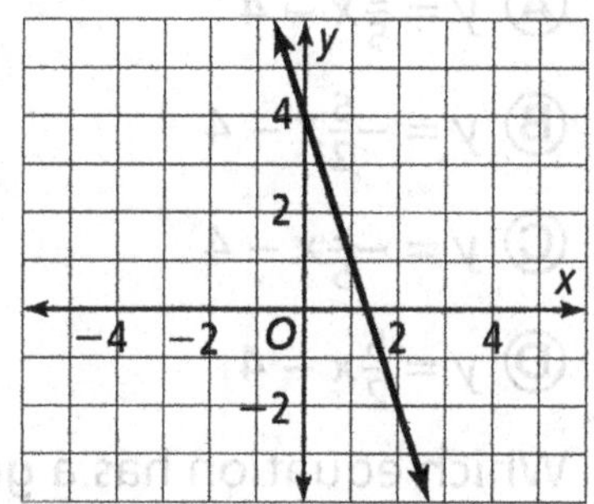

Ⓐ $3x - y = 4$
Ⓑ $3x + y = 4$
Ⓒ $-3x - y = 4$
Ⓓ $-3x + y = 4$

3. Which equation is equivalent to $y = \frac{2}{3}x - 6$?

Ⓐ $2x + 3y = -6$
Ⓑ $3x - 2y = 6$
Ⓒ $3x - 2y = 12$
Ⓓ $2x - 3y = 18$

4. Which statement about the lines below is true?

$4y = -16$ and $3x = 27$

Select all that apply.

Ⓐ Line $4y = -16$ is horizontal.
Ⓑ Line $3x = 27$ is vertical.
Ⓒ For both lines, all points on the line have an x- and a y-coordinate.
Ⓓ For either line, one of the coordinates of all the points is always the same value.

5. The glee club has \$90 to spend on pens and pencils. Each pen costs \$0.75 and each pencil costs \$0.15. Let x represent the number of pens, and let y represent the number of pencils. Write an equation that describes the number of pens and pencils that the glee club can buy. What is the greatest number of each type of writing tool that the club can buy?

Equation: ____________________

Greatest number of pens: ____________________

Greatest number of pencils: ____________________

Name ______________________________

2-4 Lesson Quiz

Parallel and Perpendicular Lines

1. Which of the following is the equation of a line that is perpendicular to the graph of $y = \frac{2}{5}x - 1$?

Ⓐ $y = \frac{2}{5}x - 4$

Ⓑ $y = -\frac{5}{2}x - 4$

Ⓒ $y = -\frac{2}{5}x - 4$

Ⓓ $y = \frac{5}{2}x - 4$

2. Which equation has a graph that is parallel to the graph of $2x - y = -1$?

Ⓐ $2x + y = 8$

Ⓑ $y = -\frac{1}{2}x + 3$

Ⓒ $y - 1 = 2(x - 3)$

Ⓓ $y = -2x - 1$

3. What is the equation in slope-intercept form of a line that passes through (–2, 2) and is perpendicular to the graph of $y = \frac{1}{2}x - 3$?

4. Are the lines $x - 2y = 4$ and $y = 2x - 2$ *parallel*, *perpendicular*, or *neither*?

5. Two ships are sailing parallel to each other. The path of Ship A is represented on a coordinate plane as the line $y = -\frac{1}{3}x + 4$. The path of Ship B passes through the point (3, 5). Graph the paths of the two ships.

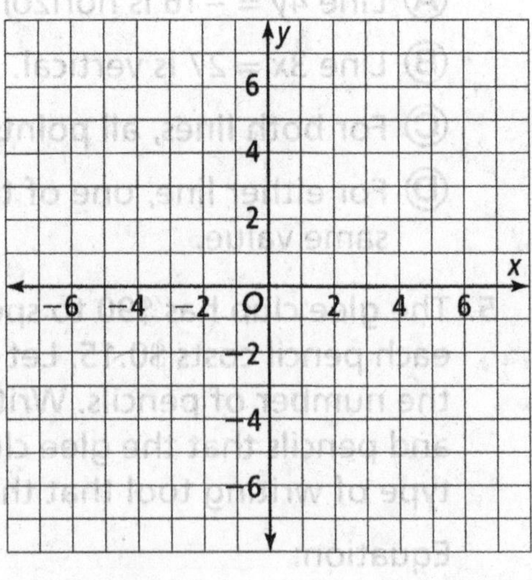

2 Topic Assessment Form A

1. What is the graph of $y = -4x - 1$?

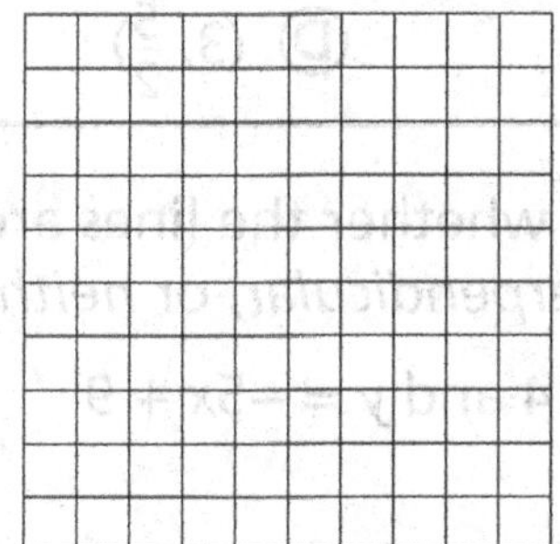

2. Which of the following is an equation of the line through (2, 3) and (–1, –12)?

   Ⓐ $y = \frac{1}{5}x + \frac{13}{5}$ Ⓑ $y = -\frac{1}{5}x + \frac{17}{5}$

   Ⓒ $y = 5x - 7$ Ⓓ $y = -5x + 7$

3. Yuson must complete 30 hours of community service. She does 2 hours each day. Write a linear equation to represent the hours Yuson has left after *x* days.

4. For the graph of the equation you wrote in Item 3, what does the *y*-intercept represent?

   Ⓐ hours left to complete

   Ⓑ total hours of service

   Ⓒ hours completed each day

   Ⓓ days it takes to complete 30 hours

5. What is an equation of the horizontal line that passes through (5, –7)?

6. For which values of *A*, *B*, and *C* will $Ax + By = C$ be a vertical line through the point (8, 6)?

   Ⓐ $A = 1, B = 0, C = 6$

   Ⓑ $A = 1, B = 0, C = 8$

   Ⓒ $A = 0, B = 1, C = 6$

   Ⓓ $A = 0, B = 1, C = 8$

7. What is an equation in point-slope form of the line shown in the graph, using the point (2, 2)?

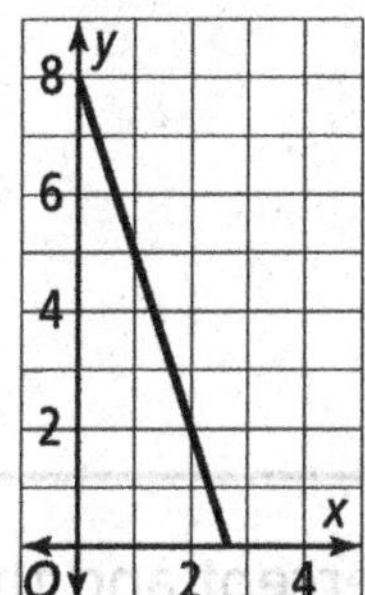

8. What is an equation in point-slope form of the line that passes through the point (4, –1) and has slope 6?

   Ⓐ $y + 1 = 6(x - 4)$

   Ⓑ $y + 1 = -6(x - 4)$

   Ⓒ $y - 1 = 6(x + 4)$

   Ⓓ $y - 1 = -6(x + 4)$

9. What is an equation in point-slope form of the line that passes through (–7, 1) and (–3, 9)?

   Ⓐ $y + 3 = 2(x - 9)$

   Ⓑ $y - 3 = 2(x + 9)$

   Ⓒ $y + 9 = 2(x - 3)$

   Ⓓ $y - 9 = 2(x + 3)$

10. What is the graph of $4x + 3y = -24$?

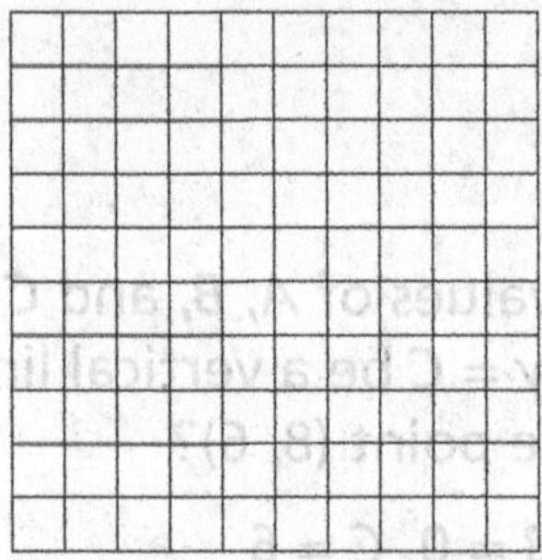

11. Write the equation in standard form of the line that has x-intercept 3 and y-intercept 5.

12. What is the equation in standard form of the line $y = \frac{1}{9}x + 5$?

Ⓐ $x = 9y - 45$

Ⓑ $x - 9y = -45$

Ⓒ $9y = x + 45$

Ⓓ $9y - x = 45$

13. What are the x-intercept and the y-intercept of the graph of $9x - 7y = -63$?

Ⓐ x-intercept: 7; y-intercept: −9

Ⓑ x-intercept: −7; y-intercept: 9

Ⓒ x-intercept: 9; y-intercept: −7

Ⓓ x-intercept: −9; y-intercept: 7

14. Derek has \$20 to spend on used books. Hardcover books cost \$5 each and paperbacks cost \$2 each. What equation in standard form determines the number x of hardcover books and the number y of paperback books he can buy?

15. For the situation in Item 14, which of the following represents a possible combination of books that Derek can buy? Select all that apply.

Ⓐ (−2, 15) Ⓑ (0, 10)

Ⓒ (2, 5) Ⓓ $(3, \frac{5}{2})$

16. Determine whether the lines are *parallel*, *perpendicular*, or *neither*.

$5x + 2y = 14$ and $y = -5x + 9$

17. Which lines are parallel to $8x + 2y = 7$? Select all that apply.

Ⓐ $y - 1 = 4(x + 8)$

Ⓑ $y = -4x + 15$

Ⓒ $16x + 4y = 9$

Ⓓ $y = -4x$

18. Write the equation in slope-intercept form of the line that passes through (6, −11) and is parallel to the graph of $y = -\frac{2}{3}x + 12$.

19. Line v passes through point (6, 6) and is perpendicular to the graph of $y = \frac{3}{4}x - 11$. Line w is parallel to line v and passes through point (−6, 10). What is the equation in slope-intercept form of line w?

20. What is the y-intercept of the line $y + 11 = -2(x + 1.5)$?

Name ______________________________

2 Topic Assessment Form B

1. What is the graph of $y = 2x + 3$?

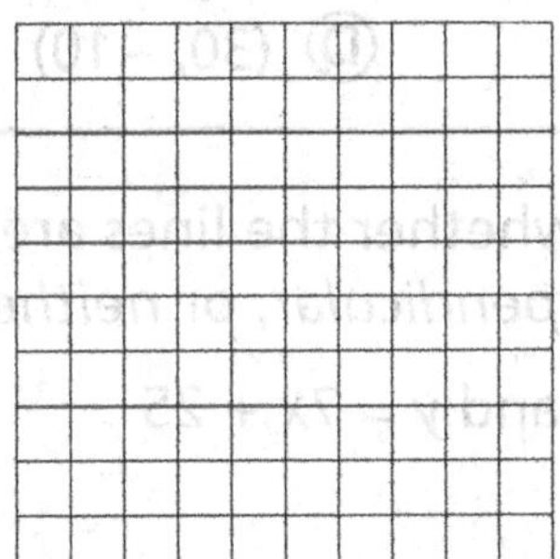

2. Which of the following is an equation of the line through (3, −1) and (−2, 14)?

Ⓐ $y = \frac{1}{3}x - 2$ Ⓑ $y = -\frac{1}{3}x$

Ⓒ $y = 3x - 10$ Ⓓ $y = -3x + 8$

3. Each day, Lourdes reads 30 pages of a 450-page book. Write a linear equation to represent the number of pages Lourdes has left to read after *x* days.

4. For the graph of the equation you wrote in Item 3, what does the *y*-intercept represent?

Ⓐ pages already read

Ⓑ pages in the book

Ⓒ pages read each day

Ⓓ days it takes to finish the book

5. What is an equation of the vertical line that passes through (−2, −9)?

6. For which values of *A*, *B*, and *C* will $Ax + By = C$ be a vertical line through the point (9, 3)?

Ⓐ $A = 1, B = 0, C = 3$

Ⓑ $A = 0, B = 1, C = 3$

Ⓒ $A = 1, B = 0, C = 9$

Ⓓ $A = 0, B = 1, C = 9$

7. What is an equation in point-slope form of the line shown in the graph, using the point (−2, −1)?

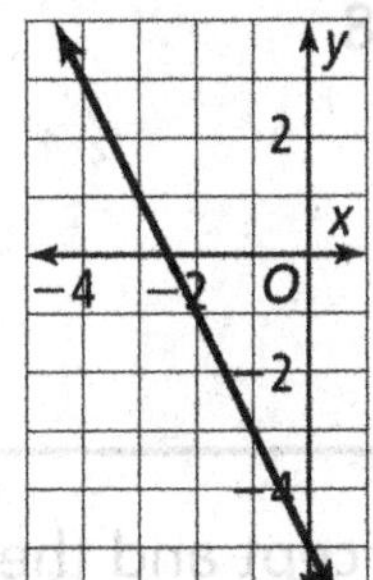

8. What is an equation in point-slope form of the line that passes through the point (−2, 10) and has slope −4?

Ⓐ $y + 10 = 4(x - 2)$

Ⓑ $y + 10 = -4(x - 2)$

Ⓒ $y - 10 = 4(x + 2)$

Ⓓ $y - 10 = -4(x + 2)$

9. What is an equation in point-slope form of the line that passes through (−1, −4) and (2, 5)?

Ⓐ $y + 1 = 3(x + 4)$

Ⓑ $y - 1 = 3(x - 4)$

Ⓒ $y + 4 = 3(x + 1)$

Ⓓ $y - 4 = 3(x - 1)$

10. What is the graph of $4x + 8y = 16$?

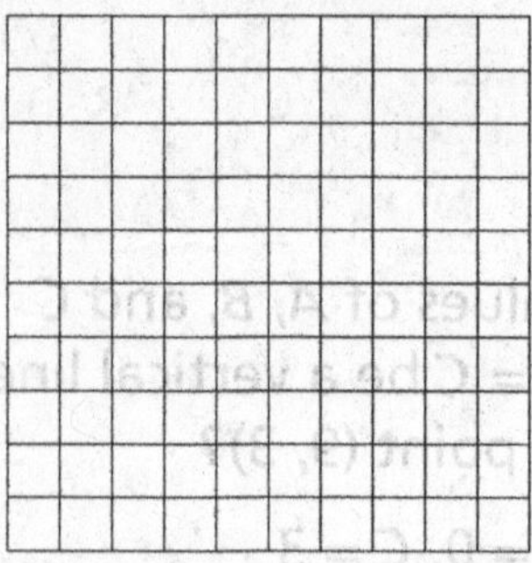

11. Write the equation in standard form of the line that has x-intercept 6 and y-intercept -2.

12. What is the equation in standard form of the line $y - 5 = \frac{3}{2}(x + 6)$?

Ⓐ $2y - 10 = 3x + 18$

Ⓑ $2y = 3x + 28$

Ⓒ $3x - 2y = -28$

Ⓓ $3x = 2y - 28$

13. What are the x-intercept and the y-intercept of the graph of $5x + 8y = 20$?

Ⓐ x-intercept: $\frac{5}{2}$; y-intercept: 4

Ⓑ x-intercept: 4; y-intercept: $\frac{5}{2}$

Ⓒ x-intercept: 5; y-intercept: 8

Ⓓ x-intercept: 8; y-intercept: 5

14. Jake needs to buy 120 beverages for a party. What equation, in standard form, determines the number x of 8-packs of juice and the number y of 12-packs of water that Jake can buy?

15. For the situation in Item 14, which of the following represents a combination of juice and water that Jake can buy? Select all that apply.

Ⓐ (0, 10) Ⓑ $(7\frac{1}{2}, 5)$

Ⓒ (12, 2) Ⓓ (30, −10)

16. Determine whether the lines are *parallel*, *perpendicular*, or *neither*.

$x + 7y = -3$ and $y = 7x + 25$

17. Which lines are perpendicular to $6x + 18y = 5$? Select all that apply.

Ⓐ $y = 3x - 10$

Ⓑ $x = 3$

Ⓒ $y + 6 = 3(x - 15)$

Ⓓ $3x + 9y = 8$

18. Write the equation in slope-intercept form of the line that passes through (−1, 11) and is parallel to the graph of $y = -8x - 2$.

19. Line j passes through point (2, 0) and is perpendicular to the graph of $y = \frac{1}{4}x - 3$. Line k is parallel to line j and passes through point (−1, 6). What is the equation in slope-intercept form of line k?

20. What is the y-intercept of the line $y + 4 = -4(x + 3.5)$?

2 Performance Assessment Form A

Suppose you are the diving officer on a submarine conducting diving operations. As you conduct your operations, you realize that you can relate the submarine's changes in depth over time to some linear equations. The submarine descends at different rates over different time intervals.

1. The depth of the submarine is 50 ft below sea level when it starts to descend at a rate of 10.5 ft/s. It dives at that rate for 5 s.

Part A

Draw a graph of the segment showing the depth of the submarine from 0 s to 5 s. Be sure the graph has the correct axes, labels, and scale. What constraints should you take into consideration when you make the graph?

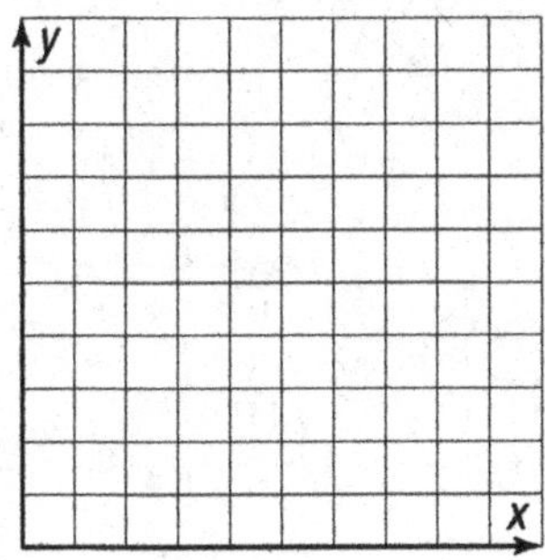

Part B

You want to model the segment in Part A with a linear equation. Determine the slope and the *y*-intercept. Then write the equation in slope-intercept form for depth *y*, in feet, below sea level over time *x*, in seconds.

2. After the initial 5-second descent, the submarine increases its rate of descent to 20 ft/s for 5 s.

Part A

Sketch a second segment on the graph from Item 1 that represents a descent of 20 ft/s for 5 s.

Part B

What is the point-slope form of a linear equation that models the situation described in Item 2, Part A? Why does it make sense to use slope-intercept form for the equation you wrote in Item 1, and point-slope form for the equation in Item 2?

3. At the surface of the ocean, the water pressure on the submarine is the same as the air pressure above the water—about 15 lb/in.^{2}. Below the surface, the water pressure increases by about 9 lb/in.^{2} for every 20 ft of descent.

Part A

Write an equation in slope-intercept form showing the pressure p, in pounds per square inch, on the submarine at different depths d, in feet. Then graph the equation.

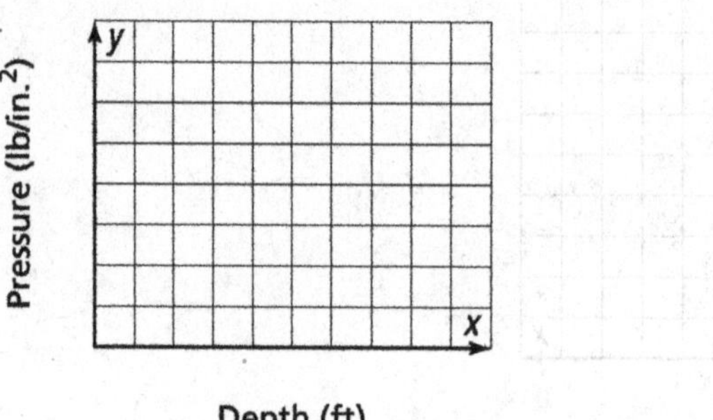

Part B

On another dive, the submarine descends at a steady rate from sea level. After 20 s the pressure gauge reads 100 lb/in.^{2}. What is the rate of descent for the submarine? Show the steps of your solution. If necessary, round answers to the nearest tenth.

2 Performance Assessment Form B

The table shows the average wholesale prices that a manufacturer charges for different types of computer products. Enrique wants to purchase some of those products for a store he owns. The store will then sell the computer products to customers.

Wholesale Technology Prices

Product	Price per Item ($)
Desktop computer	800
Laptop	850
Netbook	425
Notebook	600
Smartphone	450
Tablet	400

1. Enrique wants to spend $20,000 on the wholesale purchase of desktop computers and tablets only.

Part A

Write a linear equation in standard form that shows the number x of desktop computers and the number y of tablets that Enrique can buy. Explain why it is helpful to use the standard form of a linear equation for this situation.

Part B

Graph the equation from Part A. Describe the steps you used to make the graph.

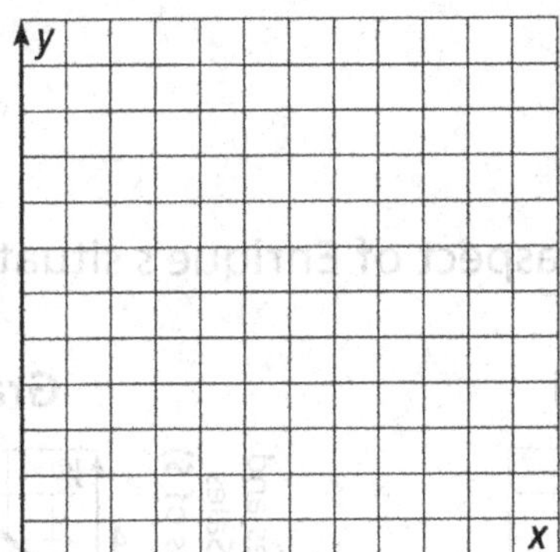

Part C

From Part B, how can Enrique determine how many units of each type of product he can buy? Explain your thinking.

2. Enrique predicts that he can make additional money from sales of accessories and services for computer products sold by his store. The table at the right shows predicted percent returns for such sales. For example, if the store makes x dollars selling computer products, Enrique predicts the store will make $0.05x$ dollars from selling accessories.

Return on Store Sales

Product	%
Accessories	5.0
Protection plans	7.5
Maintenance and repairs	2.5

Part A

In January and February of this year, the store made $2,500 from sales of accessories and services. Let x represent the amount the store will make from sales of computer products from March through December. Write an equation that represents the predicted amount y that the store will make from sales of accessories and services for the entire year. If Enrique predicts sales from accessories and services for the entire year will be $5,000, about how much money must be made from computer product sales from March through December? Explain.

Part B

What are the slope and y-intercept of the graph of the equation from Part A? What do the slope and y-intercept represent in this situation? Explain.

Part C

Which of the graphs shown could represent an aspect of Enrique's situation? Explain why you chose the graph you did.

Graph I

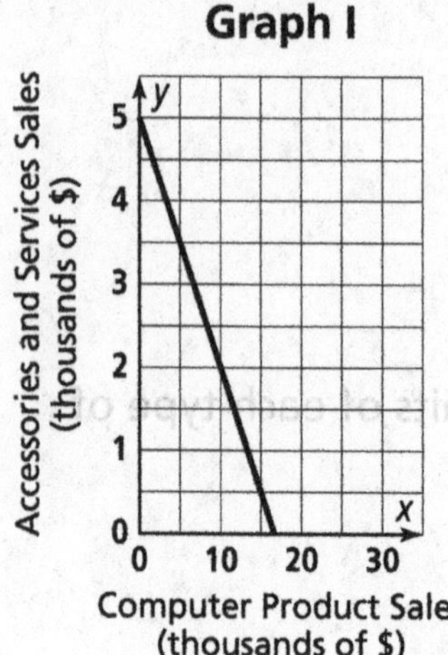

Graph II

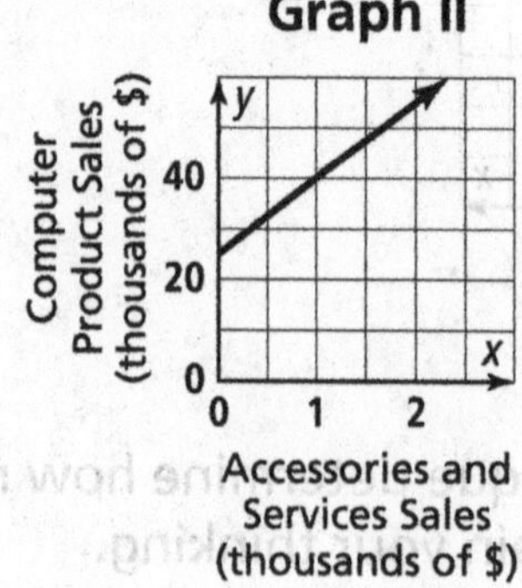

Graph III

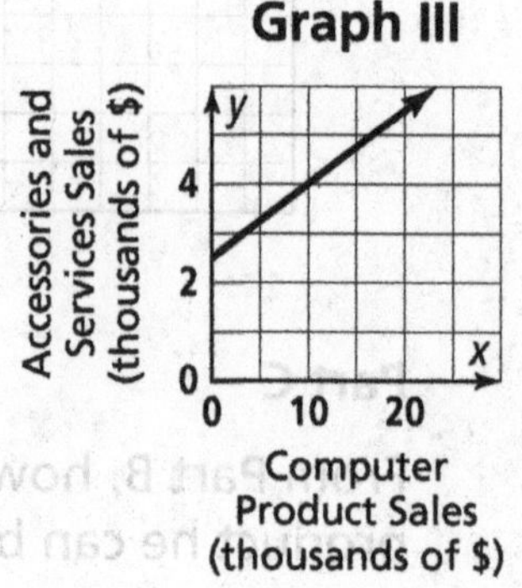

Name ____________________

Benchmark Test 1

1. What is the value of x in the equation?

   $4x + 2 - (3 + 3x) = 7$

   Ⓐ $\frac{8}{7}$

   Ⓑ $\frac{13}{10}$

   Ⓒ 6

   Ⓓ 8

2. The sum of three consecutive odd numbers is 51. What are the three numbers?

3. Melissa buys $2\frac{1}{2}$ pounds of salmon and $1\frac{1}{4}$ pounds of swordfish. She pays a total of \$31.25, and the swordfish costs \$0.20 per pound less than the salmon. What would be the combined cost of 1 pound of salmon and 1 pound of swordfish?

   Ⓐ \$15.60

   Ⓑ \$15.80

   Ⓒ \$16.60

   Ⓓ \$16.80

4. Terrell arranges x roses at \$3.50 each with 10 carnations at \$2.25 each. He makes a bouquet of flowers that averages \$3.00 per flower. Write an equation to model the situation.

5. Find the value of x in the equation.

   $\frac{3}{4}(8x - 6) - 2 = \frac{1}{2} - x$

6. Solve the equation $E = v + Ir$ for r.

   Ⓐ $r = \frac{E - v}{I}$

   Ⓑ $r = I(E - v)$

   Ⓒ $r = \frac{v + I}{E}$

   Ⓓ $r = E - v - I$

7. The formula for the volume of a square pyramid is $V = \frac{1}{3}s^2h$. Rewrite the formula in terms of h. Then find the height of a square pyramid with volume $V = 400$ cm^3 and side length $s = 10$ cm.

8. Solve the inequality.

$5(x + 1) - 10 \geq 2x + 3(x + 2)$

Ⓐ $x \geq -5$

Ⓑ $x \leq 6$

Ⓒ no solution

Ⓓ all real numbers

9. Solve the compound inequality.

$9 - 4x \geq 5$ or $4(-1 + x) - 6 \geq 2$

Ⓐ $x \geq 1$ or $x \geq 3$

Ⓑ $x \leq 1$ or $x \geq 3$

Ⓒ $x \leq -1$ or $x \leq 3$

Ⓓ $x \geq -1$ or $x \geq 3$

10. Write a compound inequality for the graph below.

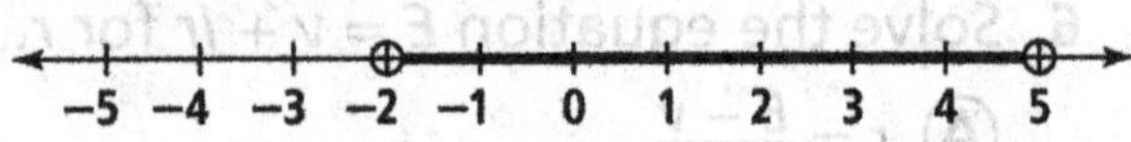

11. Solve the absolute value equation.

$8 = |5 - x|$

Ⓐ $x = \pm 3$

Ⓑ $x = \pm 13$

Ⓒ $x = 3, 13$

Ⓓ $x = -3, 13$

12. Graph the solution of the absolute value inequality on the number line.
$|2x - 3| - 1 > 4$

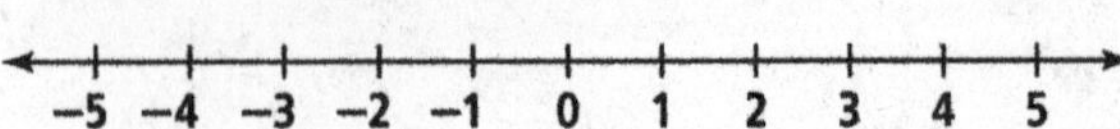

13. Graph the equation $y = 3x - 2$.

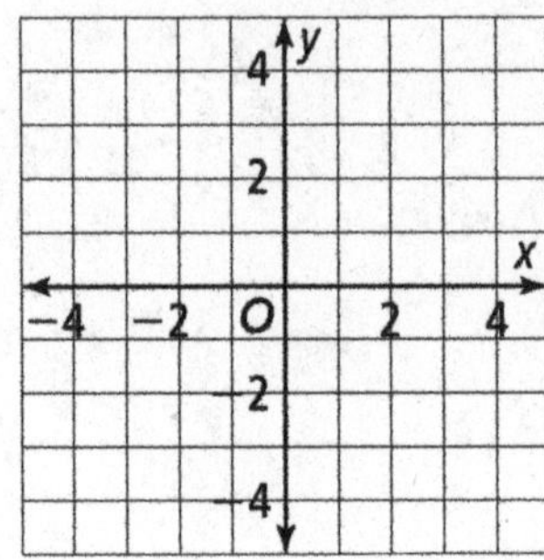

14. What is the equation of the line that passes through (–5, 0) and (4, 3)?

Ⓐ $y = \frac{1}{3}x + \frac{5}{3}$

Ⓑ $y = -\frac{1}{3}x - 5$

Ⓒ $y = 3x + 15$

Ⓓ $y = -3x - 15$

15. Denzel must practice the piano for 210 min each week. He practices for 30 min each day. Write a linear equation to represent the number of minutes Denzel still has to practice after *x* days.

16. For the graph of the equation you wrote in Item 15, what does the y-intercept represent?

Ⓐ number of days practicing each week

Ⓑ number of minutes practicing each day

Ⓒ number of hours practiced each week

Ⓓ number of minutes practiced each week

17. For which values of A, B, and C will $Ax + By = C$ be a horizontal line through the point $(-4, 2)$?

Ⓐ $A = 1, B = 0, C = 2$

Ⓑ $A = 1, B = 0, C = -4$

Ⓒ $A = 0, B = 1, C = 2$

Ⓓ $A = 0, B = 1, C = -4$

18. What is an equation of the line shown on the graph in point-slope form, using the point $(1, -1)$?

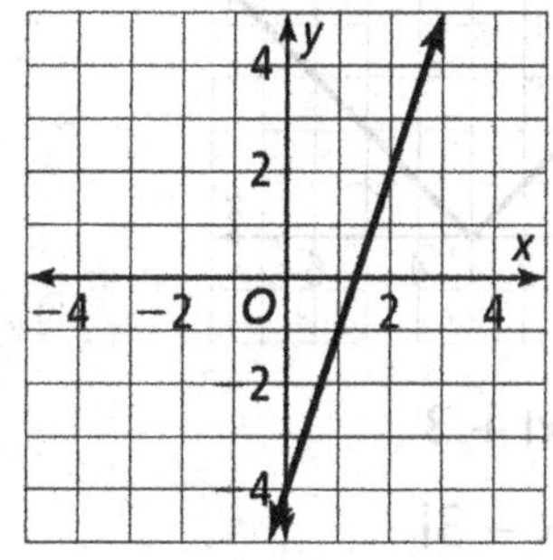

19. What is an equation in point-slope form of the line that passes through $(-3, -1)$ and has a slope of 2?

Ⓐ $y - 1 = 2(x - 3)$

Ⓑ $y + 1 = 2(x + 3)$

Ⓒ $y - 1 = 2(x + 3)$

Ⓓ $y + 1 = 2(x - 3)$

20. What is an equation for the absolute value function shown in the graph?

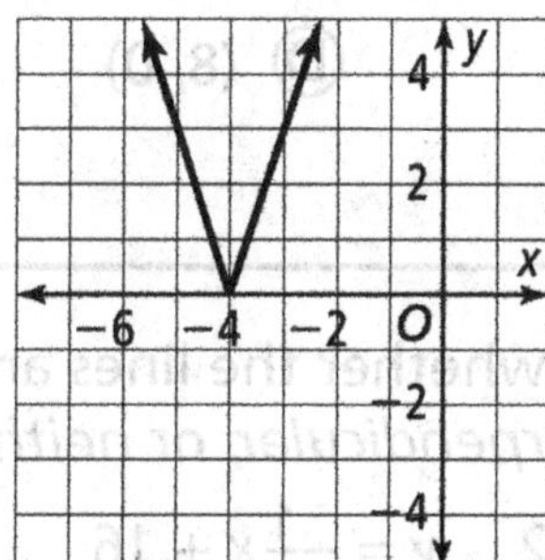

21. What is the equation in standard form of the line that has x-intercept -4 and y-intercept 3?

22. What are the x-intercept and the y-intercept of the graph of $12x - 4y = 48$?

Ⓐ x-intercept: 3; y-intercept: -12

Ⓑ x-intercept: 4; y-intercept: 12

Ⓒ x-intercept: 4; y-intercept: -12

Ⓓ x-intercept: 3; y-intercept: 12

23. Dwayne has \$80 to spend on video games. Used video games cost \$10 each, and new video games cost \$20 each. What equation in standard form determines the number x of used video games and the number y of new video games he can buy?

24. For the situation in Item 23, which of the following represent possible combinations of video games that Dwayne can buy? Select all that apply.

Ⓐ (0, 4)

Ⓑ (2, 3)

Ⓒ (7, 2)

Ⓓ (8, 0)

25. Determine whether the lines are *parallel, perpendicular,* or *neither.*

$2x + 4y = 32 \quad y = -\frac{1}{2}x + 16$

26. Which lines are perpendicular to $3x - y = 10$? Select all that apply.

Ⓐ $y = 3x + 5$

Ⓑ $y = -\frac{1}{3}x + 17$

Ⓒ $x + 3y = 27$

Ⓓ $y - 2 = \frac{1}{3}(3x + 36)$

27. Line m passes through point $(-2, -1)$ and is perpendicular to the graph of $y = -\frac{2}{3}x + 6$. Line n is parallel to line m and passes through the point $(4, -3)$. What is the equation in slope-intercept form of line n?

28. What is the y-intercept of the line $y - 14 = 6(x - 2.5)$?

29. Which inequality does the graph represent?

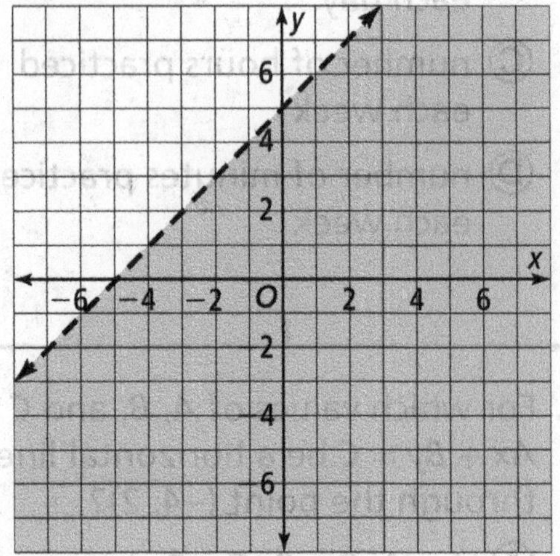

Ⓐ $y \leq x + 5$

Ⓑ $y > x + 5$

Ⓒ $y < x + 5$

Ⓓ $y \geq x + 5$

30. Which function is shown in the following graph?

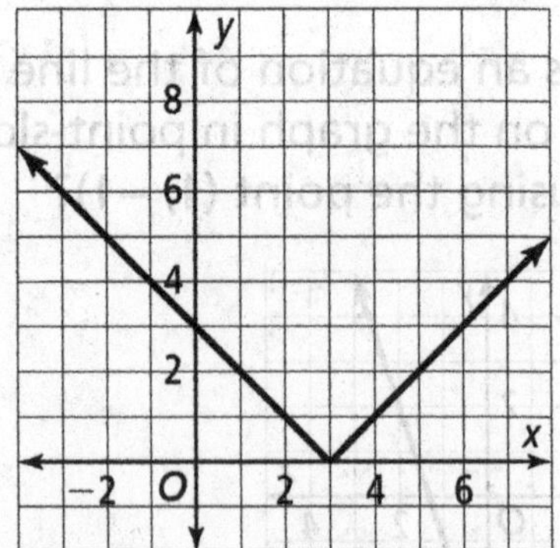

Ⓐ $f(x) = |x| + 3$

Ⓑ $f(x) = |x - 3|$

Ⓒ $f(x) = |x + 3|$

Ⓓ $f(x) = |x| - 3$

3 Readiness Assessment

1. In the group of ordered pairs shown, the x-values are inputs and the y-values are outputs. Which statements are true about the inputs and outputs? Select all that apply.

(2, 4), (6, 3), (5, 4), (7, 3), (8, 2)

Ⓐ There is only one input for every output.

Ⓑ There is only one output for every input.

Ⓒ There is more than one output for some inputs.

Ⓓ There is more than one input for some outputs.

2. Which equations have exactly one y-value for any given x-value? Select all that apply.

Ⓐ $y = -x$ Ⓒ $y = x^2$

Ⓑ $x = 4$ Ⓓ $y = x^3$

3. How many y-values are there for each x-value in the function represented by the graph?

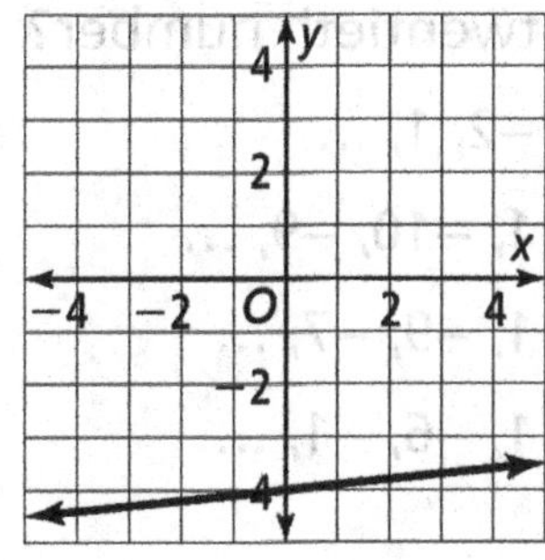

Ⓐ 0 Ⓒ 2

Ⓑ 1 Ⓓ infinitely many

4. Which statements about the function in Item 3 are true? Select all that apply.

Ⓐ Some input values are negative.

Ⓑ Some output values are negative.

Ⓒ Some input values are integers.

Ⓓ Some output values are integers.

5. Which ordered pair is a solution of the equation $y = -\frac{5}{4}x - 2$?

Ⓐ (−8, 8) Ⓒ (−8, −12)

Ⓑ (8, −8) Ⓓ $\left(1, -\frac{15}{4}\right)$

6. The ordered pair below represents a point on the line $3y + 4x = 5$. What is the missing y-coordinate of this point?

$\left(-\frac{1}{4}, __\right)$

7. A line passes through the points (−6, −3) and (6, −3). Which of the following points is also on the line?

Ⓐ (−3, 0) Ⓒ (0, −3)

Ⓑ (6, 0) Ⓓ (−6, 0)

8. Graph the linear equation $y = 2x + 3$.

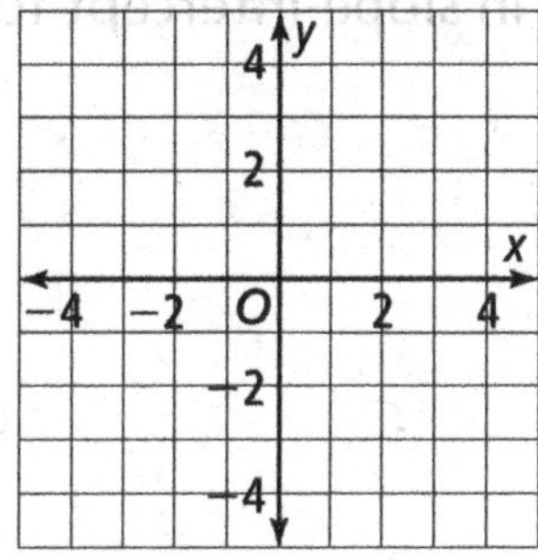

9. Find the slope and the y-intercept of the graph of $y = \frac{3}{2}x - 4$.

slope: ____ y-intercept: ____

---

10. Which of the following equations has a graph with a slope of $\frac{2}{3}$ and a y-intercept of -2?

Ⓐ $y - 2 = \frac{2}{3}x$ Ⓒ $y = -2 + \frac{2}{3}x$

Ⓑ $x = \frac{2}{3}y - 2$ Ⓓ $y = -2x + \frac{2}{3}$

---

11. What is an equation in slope-intercept form for the graph shown?

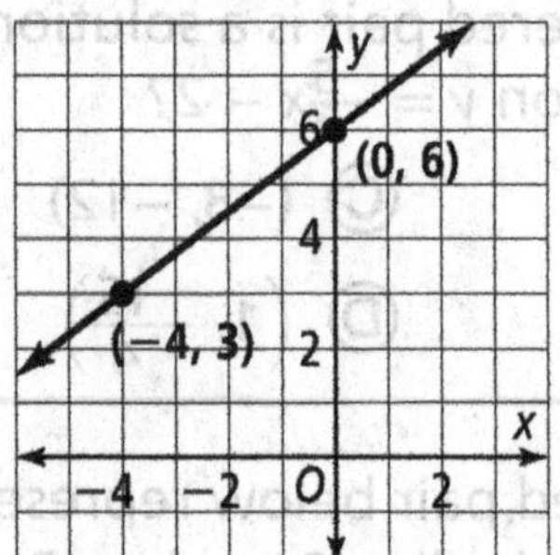

---

12. The graph of a linear equation has the same slope as the graph in Item 11, but its y-intercept is 7 less than the y-intercept of the line in Item 11. What is the equation for this graph?

---

13. Rewrite the linear equation $2x = \frac{1}{3}y - 9$ in slope-intercept form.

14. Which statement about the graph of a horizontal line is true?

Ⓐ Its slope is positive.

Ⓑ Its slope is negative.

Ⓒ Its slope is 0.

Ⓓ Its slope is undefined.

---

15. Each number in a list of numbers is 3 more than the number before it. The first number in the list is −4. What is the fifth number?

Ⓐ 8 Ⓒ 6

Ⓑ 7 Ⓓ 5

---

16. Fill in the missing number in the pattern shown:

8, 5, 2, ____, −4, −7, ...

---

17. Each number in a list of numbers can be found using the expression $6 - \frac{2}{3}(n - 1)$, where n is a positive integer that gives the position of the number in the list. What is the thirteenth number in the list?

Ⓐ −8 Ⓒ 8

Ⓑ −2 Ⓓ 13

---

18. Compare the twentieth entries in each list of numbers. Which list has the largest twentieth number?

Ⓐ −8, −5, −2, 1, ...

Ⓑ −12, −11, −10, −9, ...

Ⓒ −13, −11, −9, −7, ...

Ⓓ −16, −11, −6, −1, ...

Name ___________________________

enVision Integrated MATHEMATICS I

PearsonRealize.com

3-1 Lesson Quiz

Relations and Functions

1. Identify the domain and range of the relation.

x	−5	−2	1	5
y	10	11	4	10

domain: ______________ range: ______________

2. Which of these statements best describes the relation shown in Item 1?

Ⓐ a function that is one-to-one
Ⓑ a function that is many-to-one
Ⓒ a function that is one-to-many
Ⓓ a relation that is not a function

3. Which relations are functions? Select all that apply.

Ⓐ (3, 2), (−1, 7), (−3, 1), (0, 9), (2, −4)

Ⓑ 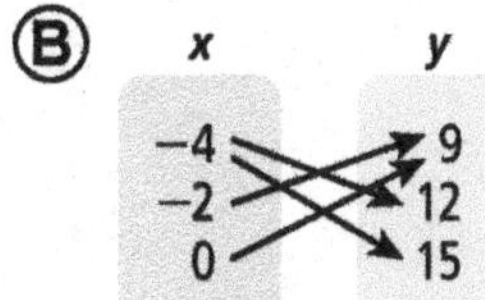

Ⓒ

x	1	2	3	4
y	2	4	6	13

Ⓓ 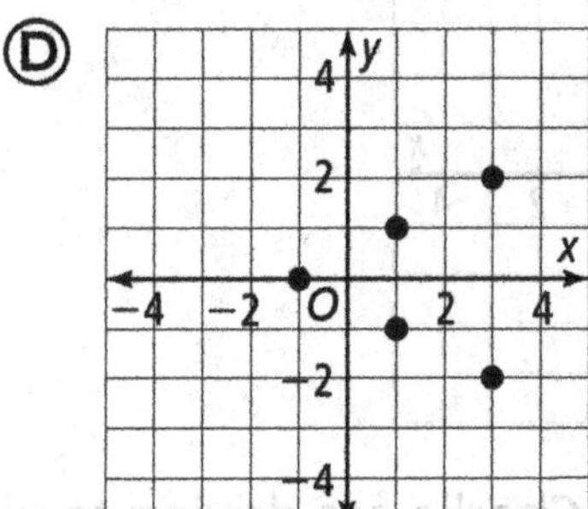

4. At a summer camp, 6-year-olds are in Group A, 7-year-olds are in Group B, and 8-year-olds are in Group C. Is the group assignment a function of age? If so, is the function one-to-one or many-to-one?

Ⓐ yes; many-to-one
Ⓑ yes; one-to-many
Ⓒ yes; one-to-one
Ⓓ no; not a function of age

5. Elijah is keeping track of his baby sister's shoe size at different ages. Which statements about the relationship between Elijah's sister's shoe size and her age are true? Select all that apply.

Ⓐ The relationship is a continuous function.
Ⓑ The relationship is a discrete function.
Ⓒ The domain and range are restricted to positive numbers.
Ⓓ The domain and range are restricted to positive integers.

3-2 Lesson Quiz

Linear Functions

1. Find the value of $f(-2)$ for the function $f(x) = 4x + 10$.

Ⓐ –3
Ⓑ –2
Ⓒ 2
Ⓓ 18

2. Write a linear function rule for the data in the table.

x	0	1	2	3	4
y	3	1	–1	–3	–5

Ⓐ $f(x) = 2x + 3$
Ⓑ $f(x) = -2x + 3$
Ⓒ $f(x) = 2x - 6$
Ⓓ $f(x) = -2x - 6$

3. Graph $f(x) = 3x - 4$.

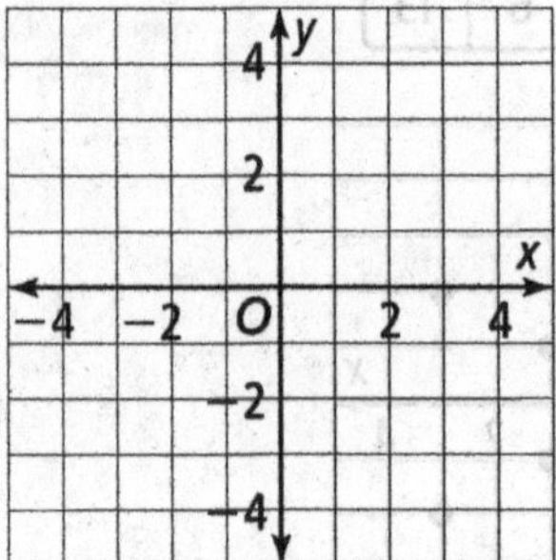

4. Aubrey and Charlie are driving to a city that is 120 miles from their house. They have already traveled 20 miles, and they are driving at a constant rate of 50 mi/h. Write a function that models the distance they drive as a function of time. What is a reasonable domain for this situation?

Function notation in slope-intercept form: ___

A reasonable domain is ___ $\leq x \leq$ ___.

5. Use the function you wrote in Item 4 to complete the following:

$f(1.5) =$ ___. The value indicates that after ___ hours of driving, Aubrey and Charlie will have traveled ___ miles.

Name ______________________________

3-3 Lesson Quiz

Transforming Linear Functions

1. Given $g(x) = f(x) + k$, what value of k transforms function f into g?

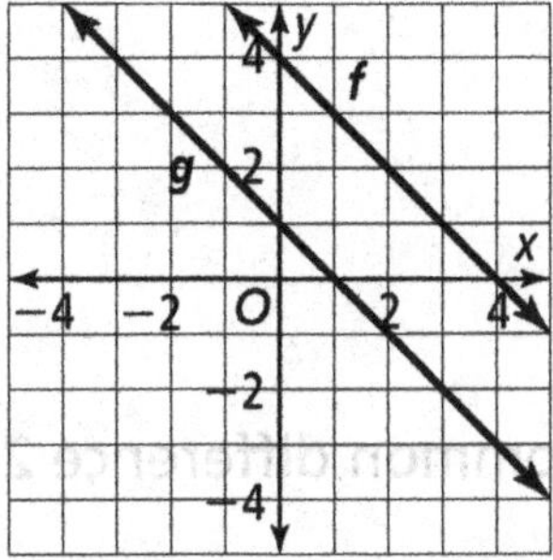

2. Given $f(x) = -7x + 9$ and $h(x) = -5f(x)$, what are the slope and y-intercept of the graph of function h?

slope = ______ y-intercept = ______

3. Graph the function $f(x) = \frac{1}{3}x + 1$ and the function $g(x) = f(6x)$.

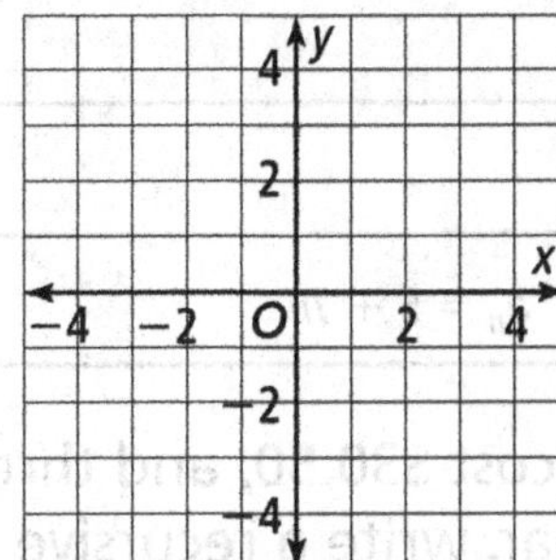

4. Given $f(x) = 8x + 1$ and $g(x) = f(x - 2)$, which equation represents g?

Ⓐ $g(x) = 6x + 1$

Ⓑ $g(x) = 6x - 1$

Ⓒ $g(x) = 8x + 15$

Ⓓ $g(x) = 8x - 15$

5. Keenan buys an embroidery machine for \$1,400. He uses it to embroider T-shirts. His total profit in dollars from selling the T-shirts is represented with the function $f(x) = 12x - 1{,}400$. When the machine breaks, he pays \$135 to have it fixed. How does that cost affect a graph of Keenan's profit function?

Ⓐ The graph is translated up 135 units.

Ⓑ The graph is translated down 135 units.

Ⓒ The graph is translated left 135 units.

Ⓓ The graph is translated right 135 units.

3-4 Lesson Quiz

Arithmetic Sequences

1. Which statement describes the sequence −9, −3, 3, 9, 15, ...?

Ⓐ an arithmetic sequence with common difference −9

Ⓑ an arithmetic sequence with common difference 3

Ⓒ an arithmetic sequence with common difference 6

Ⓓ not an arithmetic sequence

2. Which of the following is an arithmetic sequence with common difference 2?

Ⓐ 1, −3, 5, −7, 9, ... Ⓒ 10, 8, 6, 4, 2, ...

Ⓑ 2, 4, 8, 16, 32, ... Ⓓ 13, 15, 17, 19, 21, ...

3. Complete the table.

Sequence	Recursive Formula	Explicit Formula
0, 4.5, 9, 13.5, 18, ...		
	$a_n = a_{n-1} - 11; a_1 = 68$	
		$a_n = 5 + 7n$

4. Buying one movie ticket online costs $16.50, two tickets cost $30.50, and three tickets cost $44.50. Assuming that the relationship is linear, write a recursive formula and a function to represent the cost *C* of *n* tickets bought online. Give the domain of the function.

recursive formula: ______________________

function: ______________________ domain: ______________________

5. The table shows the cost of renting ski equipment at a ski lodge. Write a linear function *f* for the sequence. Then graph the function.

Number of Days Rented	1	2	3	4
Rental Cost ($)	12	17	22	27

function: ______________________

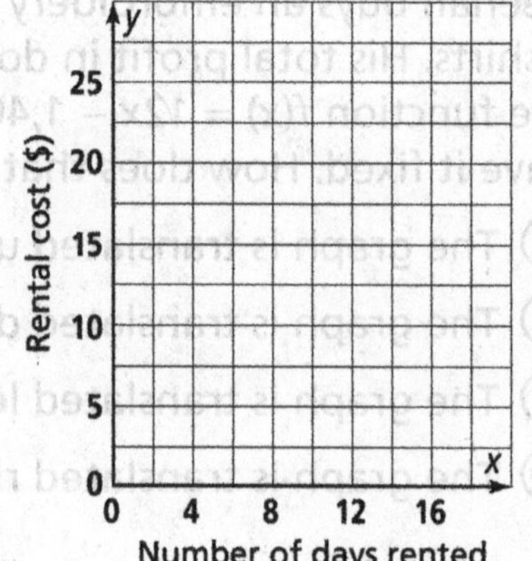

Name ____________________

3-5 Lesson Quiz

Scatter Plots and Lines of Fit

1. What type of association is shown by the data in the scatter plot?

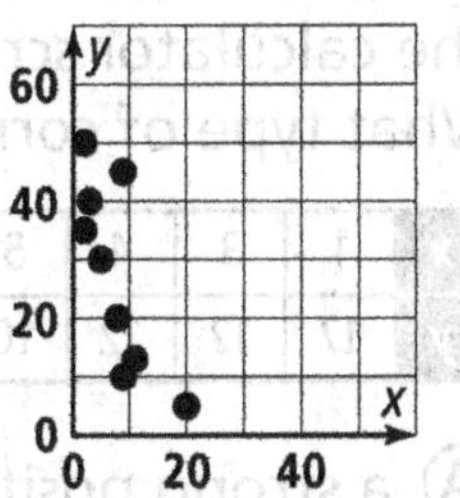

Ⓐ positive association

Ⓑ negative association

Ⓒ no association

Ⓓ trend association

2. Which equation best models the data shown in the scatter plot?

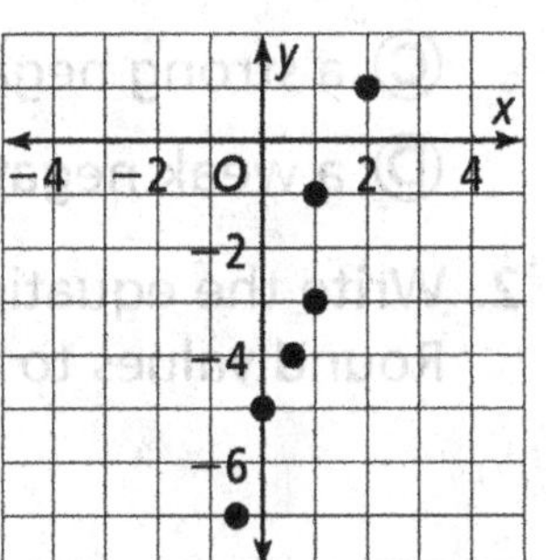

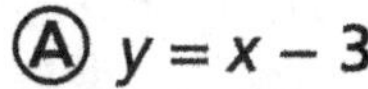
Ⓐ $y = x - 3$

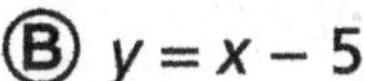
Ⓑ $y = x - 5$

Ⓒ $y = 3x - 3$

Ⓓ $y = 3x - 5$

3. When Hana goes to the mall, she always buys the same lunch and also buys some books. The table shows the number of books she buys x and the total amount of money she spends y. Make a scatter plot of the data. Tell whether there is a *positive correlation*, a *negative correlation*, or *no correlation*. Then, if possible, draw a trend line.

x	1	2	2	3	4
y	17	21	23	26	34

y
30
20
10
O
2
4
x

correlation: ____________

4. Which statements about the trend line in Item 3 are true? Select all that apply.

Ⓐ The slope is the cost of one book.

Ⓑ The slope is the cost of Hana's lunch.

Ⓒ The y-intercept is the cost of one book.

Ⓓ The y-intercept is the cost of Hana's lunch.

5. Hana draws a trend line for the scatter plot in Item 3 and writes the equation $y = 5.5x + 11$ to represent the line. Use her equation to predict how much she will spend if she buys 8 books.

Name

3-6 Lesson Quiz

Analyzing Lines of Fit

1. The calculator screen shows the linear regression for the data in the table. What type of correlation does the correlation coefficient indicate?

x	1	3	4	5	6	8	9
y	17	12	12	10	8	3	1

Ⓐ a strong positive correlation

Ⓑ a weak positive correlation

Ⓒ a strong negative correlation

Ⓓ a weak negative correlation

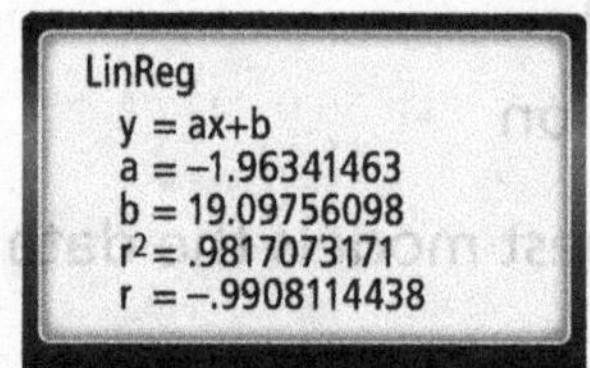

2. Write the equation for the line of best fit for the data in Item 1. Round values to the nearest whole number.

3. Make a residual plot for the model in Item 1. Is the model a *good fit* or a *bad fit* for the data? Explain.

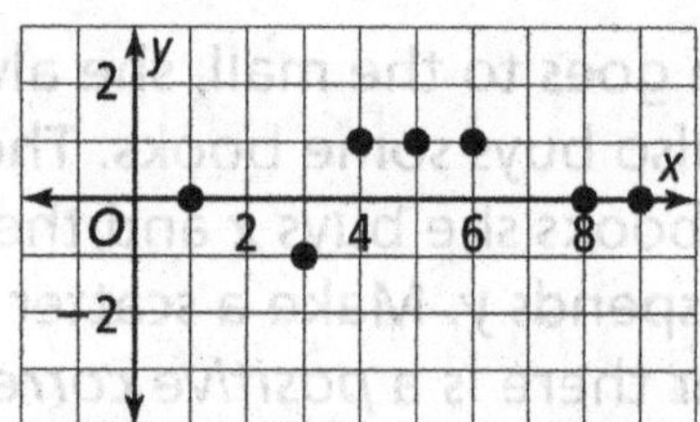

4. Use the equation you wrote in Item 2 to predict the value of y when $x = 10$. Is your prediction an example of *extrapolation* or *interpolation*?

5. Each month, Nadeem keeps track of the number of times he visits the library and the number of books he checks out. Is there a correlation if you model his data with a linear equation? Is there a causal relationship?

Visits	3	4	5	6	7	8
Books	12	5	6	8	9	11

Ⓐ There is a positive correlation and no causal relationship.

Ⓑ There is a negative correlation and no causal relationship.

Ⓒ There is a causal relationship but no positive correlation.

Ⓓ There is neither a correlation nor a causal relationship.

Name ____________________

3 Topic Assessment Form A

1. Which relation is a function?

   Ⓐ (1, 0), (3, 0), (1, 1), (3, 1) (1, 3)
   Ⓑ (1, 1), (2, 2), (3, 3), (4, 4), (5, 8)
   Ⓒ (2, 7), (6, 5), (4, 4), (3, 3), (2, 1)
   Ⓓ (9, −3), (9, 3), (4, −2), (4, 2), (0, 0)

2. Identify the domain and range of the relation.

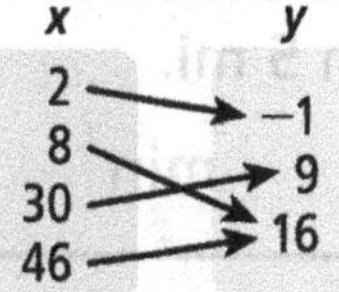

   domain: ____________________

   range: ____________________

3. What is the best description of the relation in Item 2?

   Ⓐ a function that is one-to-one
   Ⓑ a function that is many-to-one
   Ⓒ a function that is one-to-many
   Ⓓ a relation that is not a function

4. Jack works after school. Each day he earns a set amount, plus an hourly wage. Write a linear function *f* Jack can use to determine his pay.

Hours	1	1.5	2	2.5	3
Pay	18	23	28	33	38

5. Which is a reasonable domain for the function in Item 4?

   Ⓐ $0 < x < 6$
   Ⓑ $0 < x < 24$
   Ⓒ $0 < x < 68$
   Ⓓ $0 < x < 248$

6. In Item 4, assume Jack works from 2:30 P.M. to 7:00 P.M. How much would he earn?

   Ⓐ \$33
   Ⓑ \$35.50
   Ⓒ \$45
   Ⓓ \$53

7. Given $f(x) = -x + 6$ and $g(x) = f(x + 3)$, write an equation for function *g*.

8. Given $g(x) = f(x) + k$, identify a value of *k* that transforms *f* into *g*.

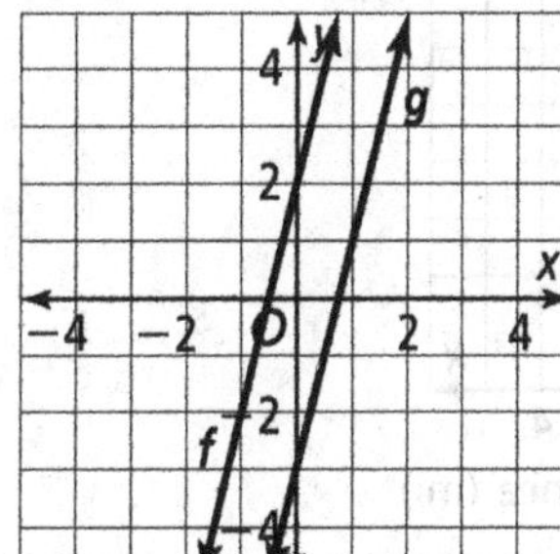

   $k =$ ____________________

9. For any linear function $f(x) = mx + b$, when does $5f(x) = f(5x) + 5$?

   Ⓐ when $b = 0$
   Ⓑ when $b = \frac{5}{4}$
   Ⓒ when $b = 5$
   Ⓓ always

10. Which of the following is an arithmetic sequence?

   Ⓐ −2, −5, −8, −11, −14, −17, ...
   Ⓑ 0, 5, 0, 10, 0, 15, ...
   Ⓒ 2, 4, 8, 16, 32, ...
   Ⓓ 5, 11, 17, 23, 29, 36, ...

11. The cost of having one pizza delivered is $14. Each additional pizza costs $9 more. Write the formulas to represent the situation.

explicit formula: ______________

recursive formula: ______________

12. Each day, Yumiko exercises by first doing sit-ups and then running. Make a scatter plot of the total time she exercises as a function of the distance she runs. Draw a trend line.

Distance (mi)	1.5	2	2.5	3	3.5	4
Time (min)	18	23	28	34	34	40

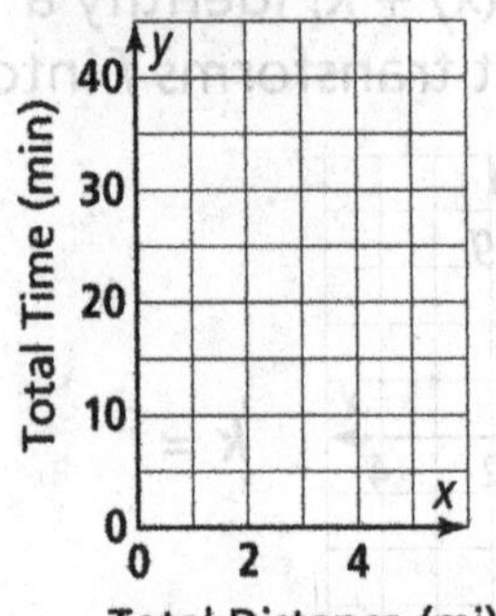

13. What type of correlation does the scatter plot in Item 12 show?

Ⓐ positive

Ⓑ negative

Ⓓ cannot tell

Ⓒ none

14. Which of the following equations is the best trend line for the data in Item 12?

Ⓐ $y = 6x + 12$

Ⓑ $y = 8x + 15$

Ⓒ $y = 6x + 6$

Ⓓ $y = 8x + 8$

15. What does the *y*-intercept of the line in Item 12 represent?

Ⓐ average time spent doing sit-ups

Ⓑ average time spent running

Ⓒ total time spent running

Ⓓ average distance run

16. Compute the residuals for the trend line in Item 14.

x	2	2.5	3	3.5	4
Residual					

17. In Item 12, estimate the time it will take Yumiko to run 5 mi.

estimate: about ______ min

18. Is the estimate in Item 17 an *interpolation* or an *extrapolation*?

19. Which *r*-value suggests a weak positive correlation?

Ⓐ $r = 0.17454$

Ⓑ $r = -0.17454$

Ⓒ $r = 0.98264$

Ⓓ $r = -0.98264$

20. The table shows grade levels and heights of six students. Do the data show a *positive* or a *negative* correlation? Can the data be used to show *causation*?

Grade	1	2	3	4	5	6
Height (in.)	46	48	51	53	56	59

Name ______________________

3 Topic Assessment Form B

1. Which relation is not a function?

Ⓐ (7, 3), (7, 6), (7, 9), (7, 12), (7, 15)

Ⓑ (−4, 6), (0, 6), (7, 6), (4, 6), (−7, 6)

Ⓒ (4, 1), (8, 2), (12, 3), (16, 4), (20, 4)

Ⓓ (1, 3), (3, 5), (5, 7), (7, 9), (9, 1)

2. Identify the domain and range of the relation.

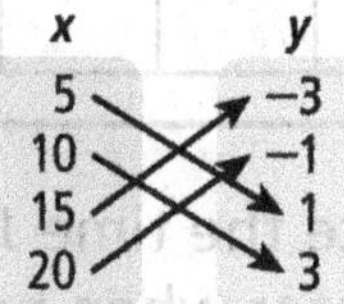

domain: ______

range: ______

3. What is the best description of the function in Item 2?

Ⓐ a function that is one-to-one

Ⓑ a function that is many-to-one

Ⓒ a function that is one-to-many

Ⓓ a relation that is not a function

4. Sasha sells T-shirts. Each day she earns a set amount, plus a commission. Write a linear function f to determine Sasha's pay.

T-shirts	1	2	3	4	5
Total Pay	68	71	74	77	80

$f(x) =$ ______

5. Which is a reasonable domain for the function in Item 4?

Ⓐ $0 < x < 3$ Ⓒ $68 < x < 80$

Ⓑ $0 < x < 50$ Ⓓ all real numbers

6. In Item 4, assume Sasha sells 24 T-shirts in one day. How much would she earn that day?

Ⓐ \$36 Ⓒ \$101

Ⓑ \$72 Ⓓ \$137

7. Given $f(x) = 4x - 6$ and $g(x) = f(2x)$, write an equation for g.

8. Given $g(x) = kf(x)$, identify a value of k that transforms f into g.

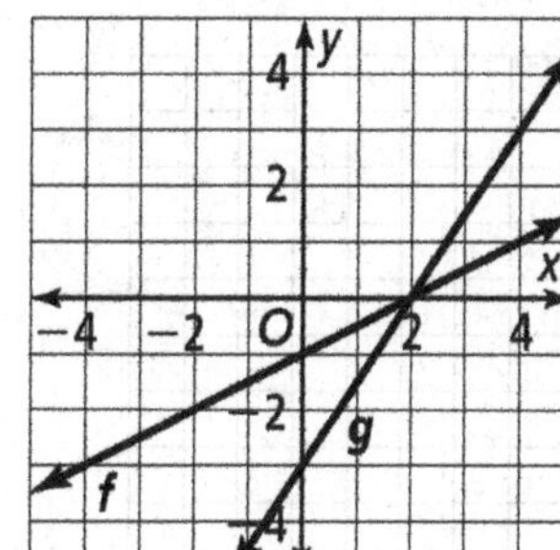

$k =$ ______

9. For $f(x) = -x + 8$, which statement is true?

Ⓐ $f(x + k) = f(x) + k$

Ⓑ $f(x - k) = f(x) - k$

Ⓒ $f(x + k) = f(x) + f(k)$

Ⓓ $f(x - k) = f(x) + k$

10. Which of the following is an arithmetic sequence?

Ⓐ 1, 3, 6, 10, 15, …

Ⓑ −8, −11, −14, −17, −20, …

Ⓒ 48, 24, 12, 6, 3, …

Ⓓ 1, 12, 123, 1234, 12345, …

11. A pizza with one topping costs \$11. Each additional topping costs \$2 more. Write a recursive formula and an explicit formula for the situation.

explicit formula: ______________

recursive formula:

____

12. Each day at the bakery, Jack bakes cakes and helps out at the counter. Make a scatter plot of the hours Jack spends at the counter as a function of the number of cakes he bakes. Draw a trend line.

Cakes	2	3	4	5	6	7
Time (h)	4	4	2.9	1.5	2.5	1.5

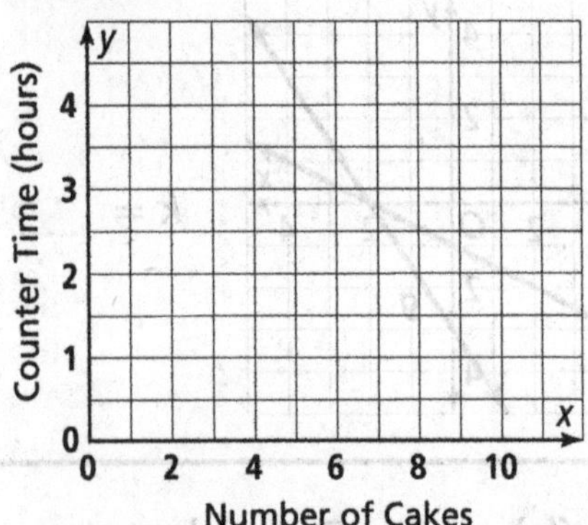

13. What type of correlation does the scatter plot in Item 12 show?

Ⓐ positive correlation

Ⓑ negative correlation

Ⓒ no correlation

Ⓓ cannot be determined

14. Which could be an equation of a trend line for the data in Item 12?

Ⓐ $y = -0.5x + 5$ Ⓒ $y = -0.5x + 3.5$

Ⓑ $y = -0.8x + 8$ Ⓓ $y = -0.8x + 5$

15. What does the *y*-intercept of the line in Item 12 represent?

Ⓐ average time it takes to bake one cake

Ⓑ average number of cakes per hour Jack can bake

Ⓒ total time spent baking cakes

Ⓓ total number of hours Jack works each day

16. Compute the residuals for the trend line in Item 14.

x	2	3	5	6	7
Residual					

17. In Item 12, estimate the time Jack spends at the counter when he bakes 4 cakes.

estimate: about ______ h

18. Is the estimate in Item 17 an *interpolation* or an *extrapolation*?

19. Which *r*-value suggests a strong positive correlation?

Ⓐ $r = 0.1847$

Ⓑ $r = -0.1847$

Ⓒ $r = 0.9974$

Ⓓ $r = -0.9974$

20. The table shows test scores for six students. Do the data show a *positive* or a *negative* correlation? Can the data be used to show *causation*?

History	76	79	83	88	91	92
Math	85	87	89	90	93	93

Name ___

3 Performance Assessment Form A

Radio announcers must time their speeches so that commercials and news updates are the correct length. Do you know how fast you talk? How fast your friends talk? Students wrote tongue twisters like the ones below to use in an experiment. Each tongue twister is made up of a different number of words. For each tongue twister, the students timed how long each person in the experiment took to say it. Then they calculated the average time.

- Cheyenne shares pseudo sonar noise codes. (6 words)
- The sunshade sheltered Sawyer from the sunshine. (7 words)
- Parker picked a plenitude of perfect Paradise pears. (8 words)

1. The results of the students' experiment are shown in the table.

Number of words	Average Time (s)
6	4.0
7	3.3
8	3.6
9	5.6
10	6.6
11	4.1
13	4.6

Part A

According to the data, is the relationship between the number of words n and the number of seconds it takes to say the tongue twister t a function? If so, describe the domain, its constraints, and the type of function (continuous or discrete) given by the domain.

Part B

Make a scatter plot of the data in the table. Use technology to help you draw a line of best fit. What do you observe about the data?

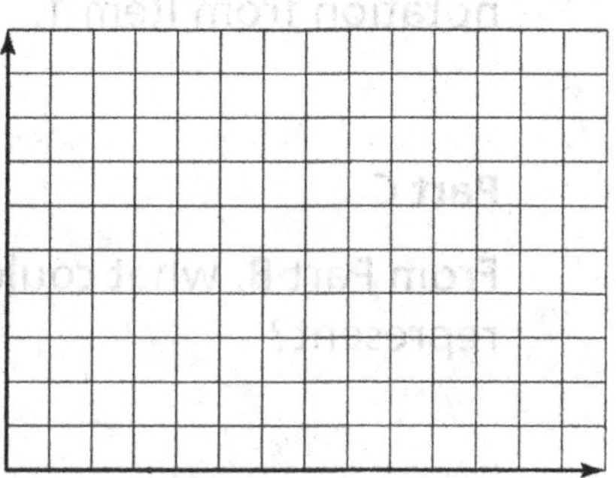

2. From Item 1 Part B, describe the type of association the scatter plot shows. Is there a correlation between the number of words a tongue twister has and the time it takes to say the tongue twister? If so, do you think there is also a causal relationship? If not, what could influence the data? Explain.

3. A teacher decides to use text-to-speech software to read the tongue twisters and time the results. The results of the teacher's experiment are shown in the table.

Number of words	Average Time (s)
6	2.1
7	2.7
8	2.9
9	3.4
10	3.9
11	4.1
13	4.5

Part A

From the two data sets in the table, is there a correlation between the number of words a tongue twister has and the time it takes to say the tongue twister? If so, do you think there is also a causal relationship? Explain.

Part B

Using a graphing calculator, perform a linear regression to calculate the line of best fit for a scatter plot of the data. Write your function using the function notation from Item 1.

Part C

From Part B, what could the slope and the *y*-intercept of the line of best fit represent?

Name ____________________

3 Performance Assessment Form B

Alani receives a collection of coins from her mother as a gift. She wants to start collecting coins. She projects the total number of coins she believes she will own over the next 5 years and graphs the results.

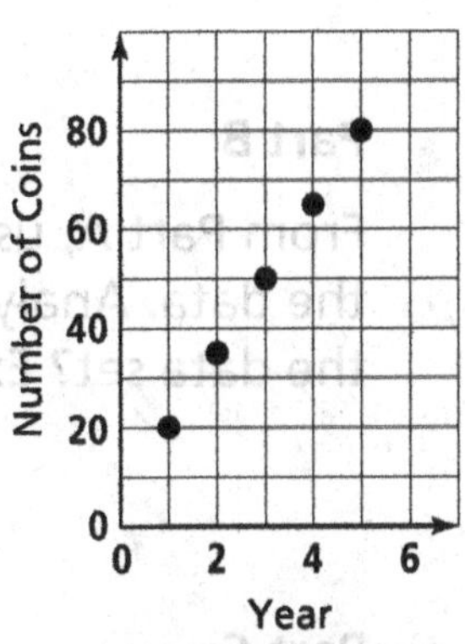

1. The graph shows the relationship between the number of coins Alani believes she will own and the amount of time she thinks it will take to acquire them.

Part A

Complete the table using the data from the graph. What type of sequence do the data represent? What is a recursive formula that represents the total number of coins for the *n*th year if Alani keeps collecting coins at the same rate? What is an explicit formula that represents the situation? Explain.

Year	Number of Coins

Part B

From Part A, how is the explicit formula of the sequence related to a linear function? What is the linear function for the number of coins $f(x)$ as it relates to the number of years x? What is the domain of $f(x)$?

2. The data in the table below shows the actual total number of coins Alani owns over a five-year period.

Year	1	2	3	4	5
Actual Number of Coins	18	29	36	59	62

Part A

What is the equation of the line of best fit for the data? Use a graphing calculator. Round values to the nearest whole number, and write your answer using function notation.

Part B

From Part A, use a graphing calculator to find the correlation coefficient *r* of the data. Analyze the coefficient *r*. How well does the line of best fit describe the data set? Explain.

Part C

Fill out the table of residual values below to compare the actual number of coins in Item 2 to the predicted number of coins from the function model in Part A. Then make a residual plot of the data. How good a fit is the model to its data set?

Year (x)	Actual Number of Coins $f(x)$	Predicted Number of Coins ($\hat{f}(x)$)	Residual ($f(x) - \hat{f}(x)$)
1			
2			
3			
4			
5			

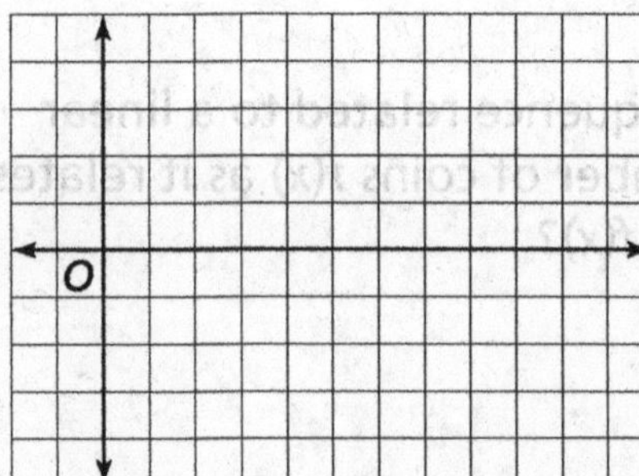

3. From Item 2, Part A, what would be the effect on the graph of the function if Alani's mother initially gave her 15 coins?

Name ___________________________

4 Readiness Assessment

1. Which statement(s) about the line below are true? Select all that apply.

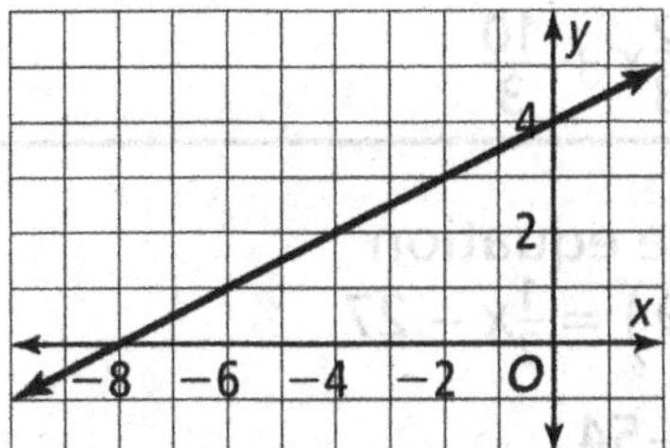

Ⓐ The x-intercept is −8.

Ⓑ The line has a positive slope.

Ⓒ The y-intercept is 4.

Ⓓ The line has a negative slope.

2. Which statement(s) describe the graph of the equation $x = -2$? Select all that apply.

Ⓐ The graph of the line is a horizontal line.

Ⓑ The slope of the line is undefined.

Ⓒ The graph passes through the ordered pair (−2, 3).

Ⓓ The x-intercept of the line is (−2, 0).

3. Which equation represents the graph?

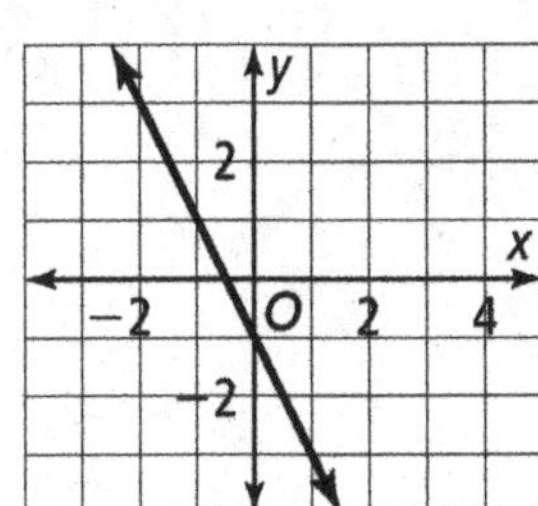

Ⓐ $y = \frac{1}{2}x - 1$ Ⓒ $y = 2x - 1$

Ⓑ $y = -\frac{1}{2}x - 1$ Ⓓ $y = -2x - 1$

4. Which statement describes the graphs of $y = -x + 3$ and $y = -x + 6$?

Ⓐ They intersect at point (3, 6).

Ⓑ They are parallel.

Ⓒ They are perpendicular.

Ⓓ They intersect at point (6, 3).

5. Which equation represents the values in the table?

x	−1	0	1	2
y	−1	3	7	11

Ⓐ $y = 4x + 3$ Ⓒ $y = 3x - 1$

Ⓑ $y = -x - 1$ Ⓓ $y = \frac{1}{4}x - \frac{3}{4}$

6. The table of values represents a linear function. For this function, what is the value of y when $x = 4$?

x	−4	0	4	6
y	3	4	?	5.5

7. What is the equation in slope-intercept form of a line that has a slope of $-\frac{1}{2}$ and a y-intercept of 6?

8. What is the slope of the graph of the equation $4x - 6y = 2$?

Ⓐ −4 Ⓒ $\frac{2}{3}$

Ⓑ −1 Ⓓ $\frac{3}{2}$

9. What is the slope of the line that passes through points (0, 7) and (−3, 0)?

Ⓐ $-\frac{7}{3}$

Ⓑ $\frac{7}{3}$

Ⓒ $-\frac{3}{7}$

Ⓓ $\frac{3}{7}$

---

10. What is the *y*-intercept of the graph of the equation $5x + (-2y) = 8$?

---

11. Which ordered pair(s) are solutions to $3x - y = 1$? Select all that apply.

Ⓐ (−2, −7)

Ⓑ (−1, −4)

Ⓒ (0, 1)

Ⓓ (3, 8)

---

12. Rewrite the equation $6x - 9y = 12$ in terms of *y*.

---

13. Name the property of addition modeled here.

If $a = b$, then $a + c = b + c$.

Ⓐ Addition Property of Equality

Ⓑ Commutative Property of Addition

Ⓒ Associative Property of Addition

Ⓓ None of the above

14. Which of the following equation(s) are equivalent to $y - 4 = \frac{2}{3}(x - 1)$? Select all that apply.

Ⓐ $y = \frac{2}{3}x - \frac{10}{3}$

Ⓑ $y = \frac{2}{3}x + 3\frac{1}{3}$

Ⓒ $y = \frac{2}{3}x + 3$

Ⓓ $y = \frac{2}{3}x + \frac{10}{3}$

---

15. Solve the equation $3\left(\frac{1}{6}x + 9\right) = \frac{1}{2}x - 27$.

Ⓐ $x = -54$

Ⓑ $x = 0$

Ⓒ $x = 54$

Ⓓ no solution

---

16. Solve the equation $3x + \frac{1}{2}(2x + 6) = 6x + 1$.

Ⓐ $x = \frac{2}{5}$

Ⓑ $x = 1$

Ⓒ $x = 2$

Ⓓ $x = \frac{5}{2}$

---

17. Solve the inequality $\frac{1}{3}(x - 6) > 2$.

---

18. Consider the inequality $7 + 4x > x - 2$. Which value(s) of *x* are solutions? Select all that apply.

Ⓐ $x = -3$

Ⓑ $x = 0$

Ⓒ $x = 3$

Ⓓ $x = -6$

Name ______________________________

4-1 Lesson Quiz

Solving Systems of Equations by Graphing

1. What is the solution of the system of equations shown below?

$y = -x + 3$

$y = 4x - 2$

Ⓐ (0, 3) Ⓑ (1, 2) Ⓒ (2, 1) Ⓓ (0, −2)

2. Solve the system of equations below by graphing.

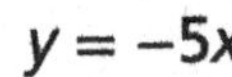

$y = -5x$

$y = x - 6$

Solution: ______________

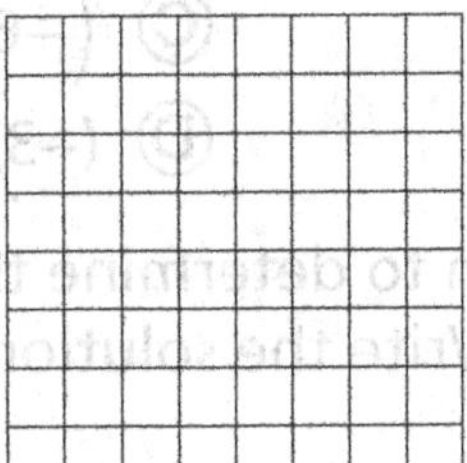

3. Match each graph of a system of equations to the solution of the system.

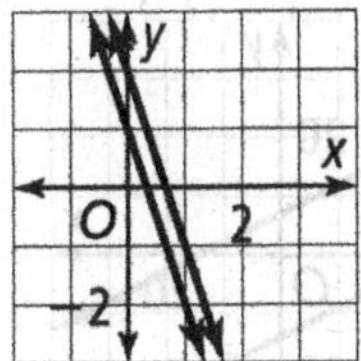

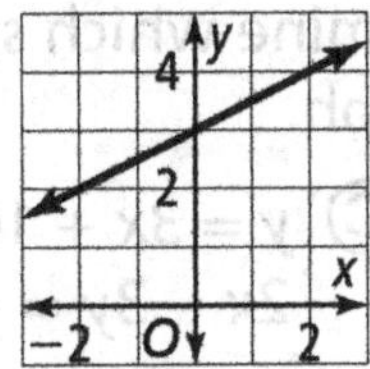

A. infinitely many solutions **B.** no solutions

4. From the graph shown, what is an approximate solution of the system of equations?

$y = -0.5x + 4$

$y = 1 + 2x$

Ⓐ (1.25, 3.4) Ⓒ (3.4, 1.25)

Ⓑ (2.25, 3.4) Ⓓ (3.4, 2.25)

5. Caterer A charges \$15 per person and \$100 to set up tables. Caterer B charges \$20 per person and \$50 to set up tables. Graph a system of equations. For what number of guests will the cost of Caterer A be the same as the cost of Caterer B? What is the cost for that number of guests?

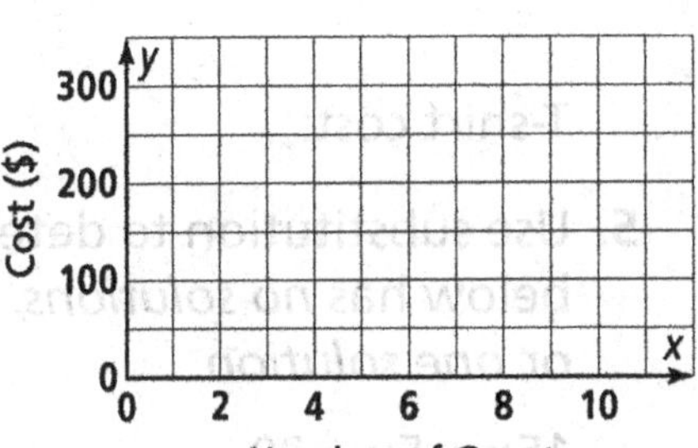

Number of guests: __________ Cost: __________

4-2 Lesson Quiz

Solving Systems of Equations by Substitution

1. Use substitution to determine the solution of the system of equations.

   $y = -2x - 7$

   $2y - x = 1$

   Ⓐ $(-1, 0)$
   Ⓑ $\left(\frac{21}{2}, -28\right)$
   Ⓒ $\left(-6, -\frac{5}{2}\right)$
   Ⓓ $(-3, -1)$

2. Use substitution to determine the solution of the system of equations. Write the solution as an ordered pair.

   $x + 2y = 14$

   $y = 3x - 14$

3. Use substitution to determine which system is represented by the graph.

   Ⓐ $2x + 4y = 28$
   $-2y = x + 28$

   Ⓑ $y = 10x - 15$
   $-9x + 2y = 10$

   Ⓒ $y = 3x + 10$
   $2x - 3y = -6$

   Ⓓ $2y = 2x + 5$
   $3x - 4y = -5$

4. Skyler buys 8 T-Shirts and 5 hats for $220. The next day, he buys 5 T-shirts and 1 hat for $112. How much does each T-shirt and each hat cost? Write a system of equations that can be used to solve the problem. Then solve the problem.

   System of equations: ____________________

   ____

   T-shirt cost: __________ Hat cost: __________

5. Use substitution to determine whether the system below has *no solutions, infinitely many solutions,* or *one solution.*

   $15x + 5y = 20$

   $y = 8 - 3x$

4-3 Lesson Quiz

Solving Systems of Equations by Elimination

1. Solve the system using the elimination method. Write the solution as an ordered pair.

$3x + 2y = 22$

$-x + 4y = 2$

2. Which of the following gives a valid reason for using the given solution method to solve the system of equations shown?

Equation I: $4x - 5y = 4$

Equation II: $2x + 3y = 2$

Ⓐ Elimination; a coefficient in Equation I is an integer multiple of a coefficient in Equation II.

Ⓑ Elimination; a coefficient in Equation II is an integer multiple of a coefficient in Equation I.

Ⓒ Substitution; equation I can be solved for x in one step by dividing both sides by 4.

Ⓓ Substitution; equation II can be solved for x in one step by subtracting $3y$ from both sides.

3. Which of the systems of equations below is equivalent to the system shown?

$4x + 5y = 3$
$2x + 3y = 1$

Ⓐ $4x + 5y = 3$
$-4x - 6y = 2$

Ⓑ $12x + 15y = 9$
$-12x + 18y = 6$

Ⓒ $4x + 5y = 3$
$-4x - 3y = 1$

Ⓓ $12x + 15y = 9$
$-12x - 18y = -6$

4. Steve buys 2 lb of grapefruit and 3 lb of oranges for $7.20. Kennedy buys 4 lb of grapefruit and 2 lb of oranges for $8.80. Let x represent the price per pound for grapefruit, and let y represent the price per pound for oranges. Write a system of equations to model the situation. What is the price per pound for oranges?

System of equations: ______________

____

Price per pound for oranges: ______________

5. As a first step in solving the system shown, Yumiko multiplies both sides of the equation $2x - 3y = 12$ by 6. By what factor should she multiply both sides of the other equation so she can add the equations and eliminate a variable?

$5x + 6y = 18$
$2x - 3y = 12$

Name ____________________

4-4 Lesson Quiz

Linear Inequalities in Two Variables

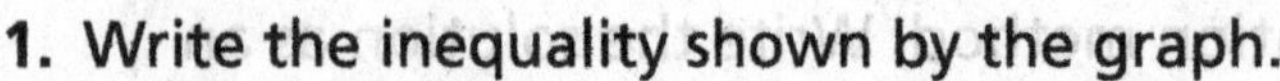

1. Write the inequality shown by the graph.

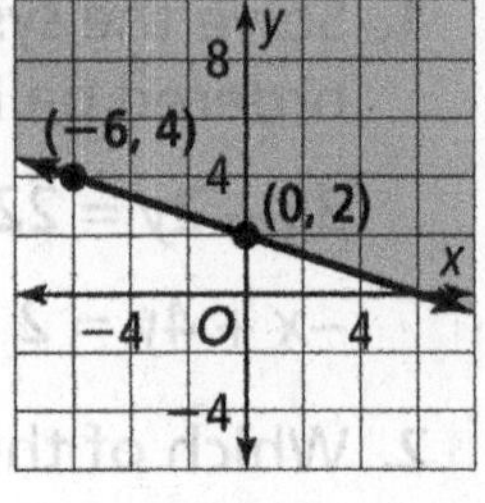

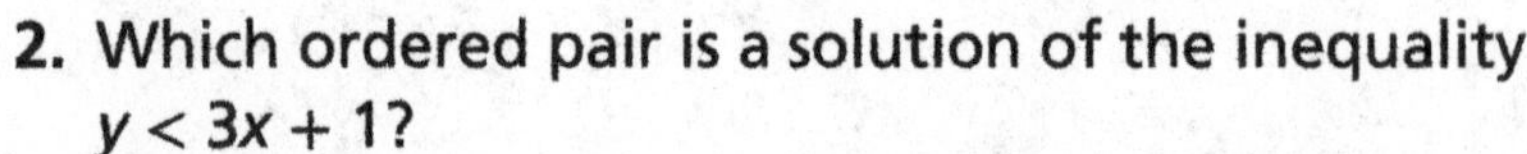

2. Which ordered pair is a solution of the inequality $y < 3x + 1$?

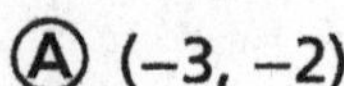

Ⓐ (−3, −2) Ⓒ (1, −3)

Ⓑ (3, 14) Ⓓ (1, 6)

3. Graph the solution of the inequality $-x + y \geq 2$.

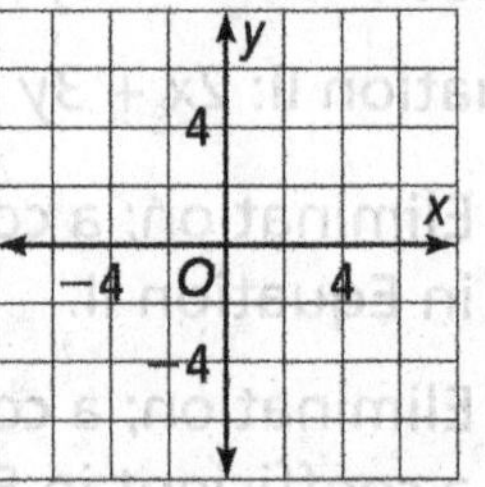

4. Tickets to a play cost $4 in advance and $5 at the door. The theater club president wants to raise at least $400 from the ticket sales. Write and graph an inequality for the number of tickets the theater club needs to sell. If the club sells 40 tickets in advance, what is the least number the club needs to sell at the door to reach the president's goal?

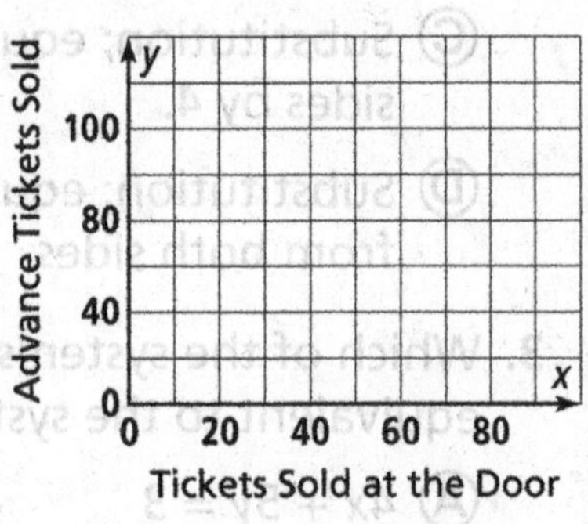

Inequality: ____________________

Least number of tickets sold at door: ____________________

5. Which describes the solution of the inequality $y > -15$?

Ⓐ solid vertical line through (0, −15) with shading to left of line

Ⓑ dashed vertical line through (0, −15) with shading to left of line

Ⓒ solid horizontal line through (0, −15) with shading below line

Ⓓ dashed horizontal line through (0, −15) with shading above line

Name ____________________

4-5 Lesson Quiz

Systems of Linear Inequalities

1. Match each system of inequalities with the graph of the solution.

A. $3x + y \leq 1$
$x - y \leq 3$

B. $4x + 3y \leq 1$
$2x - y \leq 2$

C. $x + y > -3$
$2x + 2y > -2$

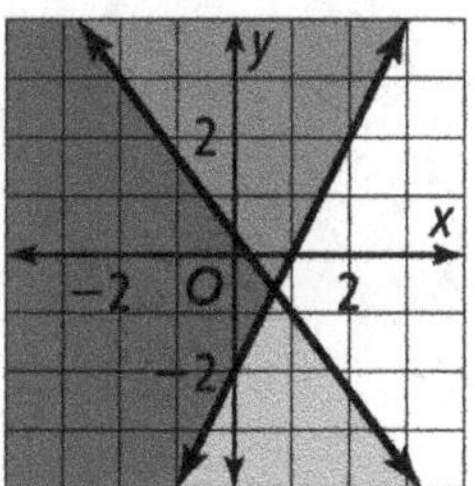

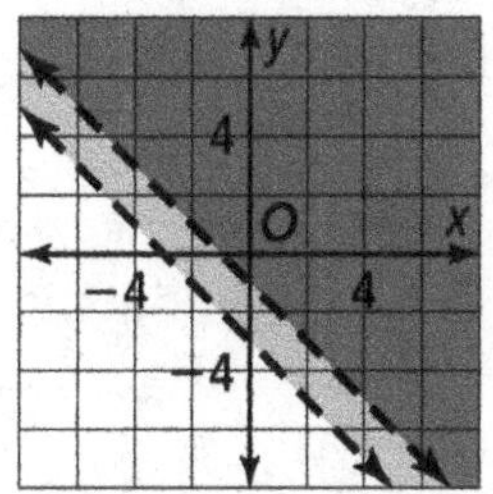

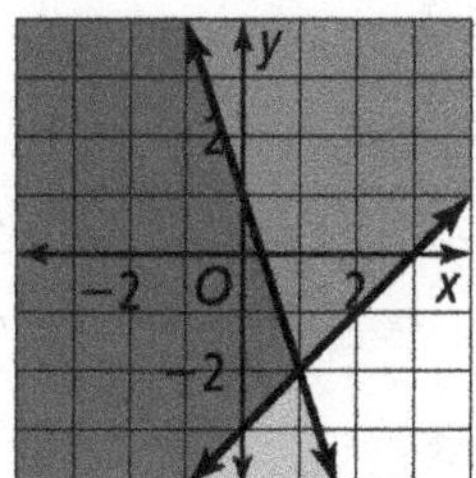

2. Which system of inequalities is shown by the graph?

Ⓐ $-y \geq x + 4$
$-3x + 3y \leq -9$

Ⓑ $-y \leq 3x + 4$
$-3x + 3y \leq -9$

Ⓒ $y \leq -x + 4$
$-4x + 4y \leq 16$

Ⓓ $y \leq -x - 4$
$-x - y \leq -4$

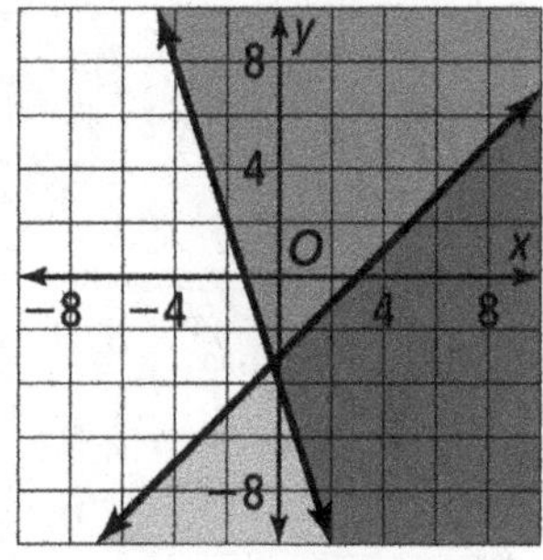

3. Kona wants to bake at most 30 loaves of banana bread and nut bread for a bake sale. Each loaf of banana bread sells for \$2.50, and each loaf of nut bread sells for \$2.75. Kona wants to make at least \$44. Let *x* represent the number of loaves of banana bread and let *y* represent the number of loaves of nut bread Kona can bake. Write a system of inequalities to model the situation.

Bake at most 30 loaves: ____________________

Make at least \$44 in sales: ____________________

4. Graph the system of inequalities you wrote for the situation described in Item 3. In which quadrant(s) are there solutions that make sense for the situation?

Quadrant(s) ________

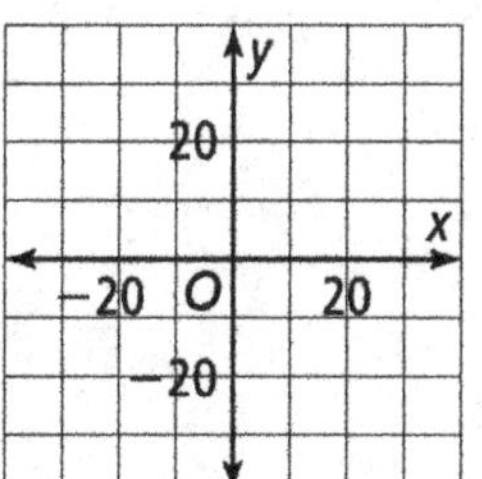

5. Which system of inequalities has no solution?

Ⓐ $y < 2x - 4$
$y > 2x + 1$

Ⓑ $2x + y \geq 3$
$y \geq -2x - 3$

Ⓒ $4x + 4y < 16$
$x > y + 16$

Ⓓ $y < -6x - 24$
$y < 6x + 6$

Name

PearsonRealize.com

4-5 Lesson Quiz

Systems of Linear Inequalities

1. Match each system of inequalities with the graph of the solution.

A. $3x + y \leq 1$
$x - y \leq 3$

B. $4x + 3y \leq 1$
$2x - y \geq 2$

C. $x + y > -3$
$2x + 2y > -2$

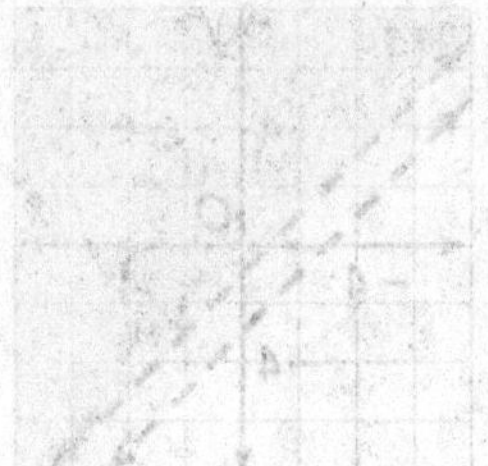

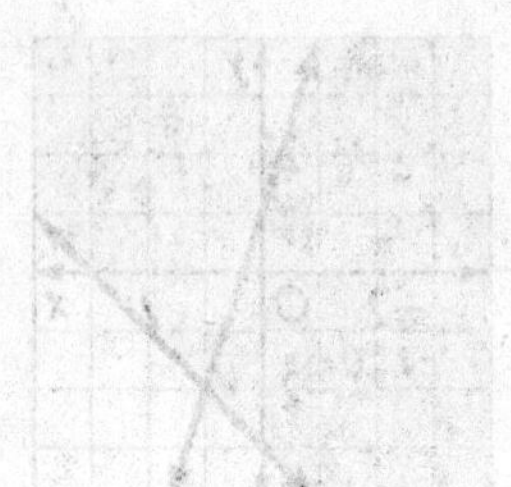

2. Which system of inequalities is shown by the graph?

Ⓐ $-y \geq x + 4$
$-3x + 3y \leq -9$

Ⓑ $-y \leq 3x + 4$
$-3x + 3y \geq -9$

Ⓒ $y \leq -x + 4$
$-4x + 4y \leq 16$

Ⓓ $y \leq -x + 4$
$-x - y \leq -4$

3. Kona wants to bake at most 30 loaves of banana bread and nut bread for a bake sale. Each loaf of banana bread sells for $2.50, and each loaf of nut bread sells for $2.75. Kona wants to make at least $44. Let x represent the number of loaves of banana bread and let y represent the number of loaves of nut bread Kona can bake. Write a system of inequalities to model the situation.

Bake at most 30 loaves:

Make at least $44 in sales:

4. Graph the system of inequalities you wrote for the situation described in Item 3. In which quadrant(s) are there solutions that make sense for the situation?

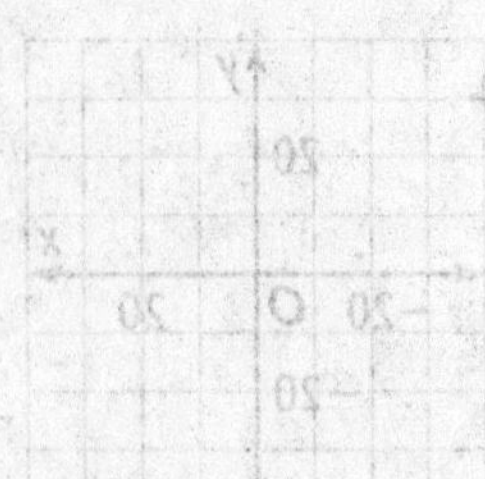

Quadrant(s)

5. Which system of inequalities has no solution?

Ⓐ $y < 2x - 4$
$y > 2x + 1$

Ⓑ $2x + y \geq 3$
$y \geq -2x - 3$

Ⓒ $4x + 4y < 16$
$x > y + 16$

Ⓓ $y < -6x - 24$
$y < 6x + 6$

Name ______________________________

4 Topic Assessment Form A

1. Solve the system by graphing.

$y = \frac{1}{3}x + 2$

$y = -x - 2$

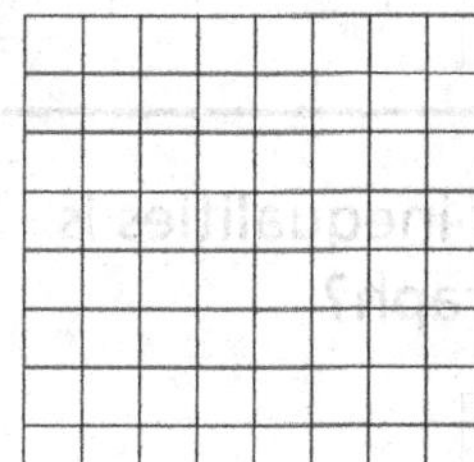

solution: ____________

2. Does the system of equations have *no solution* or *infinitely many solutions*?

$2x + y = 2$

$y = -2x - 1$

3. Estimate the solution of the system of equations.

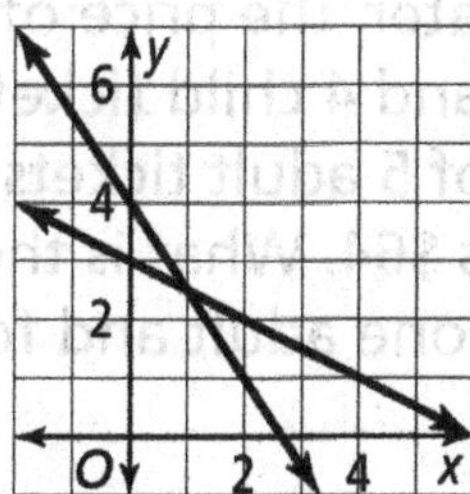

solution: ____________

4. Aaron starts walking at a rate of 3 mi/h on a road toward a store 10 mi away. Zhang leaves the store when Aaron starts walking, and he walks toward Aaron along the same road at 2 mi/h. How many hours will pass before they meet?

Ⓐ 1.5 h　　Ⓒ 2 h

Ⓑ 10 h　　Ⓓ 3 h

5. What is the solution of the system of equations?

$y = \frac{1}{8}x - 1$

$-5x + 4y = -13$

6. What is the solution of the system of equations?

$y = \frac{1}{3}x + 2$

$-x + 3y = 6$

7. Henry sells rings for \$8 each. His expenses are \$1.50 per ring, plus \$91 for supplies. How many rings does he need to sell for his revenue to equal his expenses?

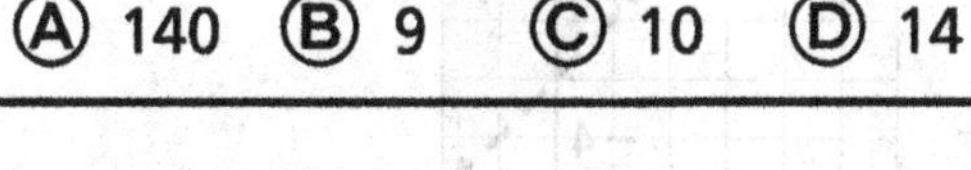

Ⓐ 140　Ⓑ 9　Ⓒ 10　Ⓓ 14

8. What is the solution of the system of equations?

$5x - 4y = -10$

$3x + 2y = 16$

9. Which system has the same solution as the system of equations shown?

$8x + 3y = 5$

$4x + 2y = 3$

Ⓐ $8x + 3y = 5$, $-8x + 4y = 6$　　Ⓒ $16x + 6y = 5$, $12x - 6y = 9$

Ⓑ $8x + 3y = 5$, $-8x - 4y = -6$　　Ⓓ $8x + 3y = 5$, $8x + 4y = 3$

10. What is the solution of the system of equations?

$5x + 2y = 6$

$4x - 8y = 0$

11. The cost of 6 sandwiches and 4 drinks is $53. The cost of 4 sandwiches and 6 drinks is $47. How much does one sandwich cost?

Ⓐ $5.30 Ⓒ $4.50
Ⓑ $3.50 Ⓓ $6.50

---

12. Graph the inequality $y < -2x + 4$.

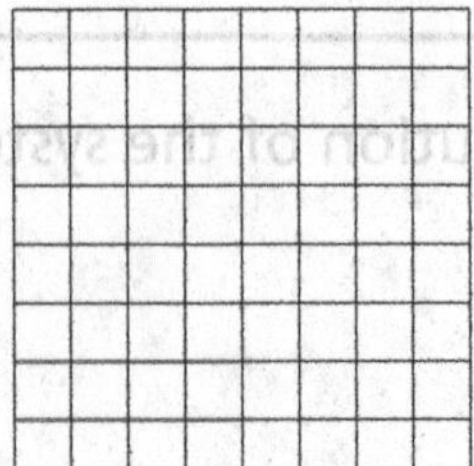

---

13. Which inequality does the graph represent?

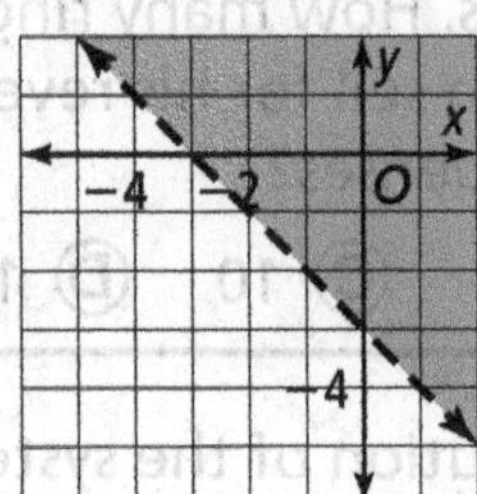

Ⓐ $y < -x - 3$ Ⓒ $y \leq -x - 3$
Ⓑ $y > -x - 3$ Ⓓ $y \geq -x - 3$

---

14. In the graph of an inequality, the area above a solid line through the points (−5, 2) and (3, 2) is shaded. Which inequality does this graph represent?

Ⓐ $y \geq 2$ Ⓒ $y < 2$
Ⓑ $y \leq 2$ Ⓓ $x > 2$

---

15. In the graph of an inequality, the region to the left of a dashed vertical line through the point (−3, 0) is shaded. What inequality does the graph represent?

16. Graph the system of inequalities.

$-x + y \leq -1$

$x + 2y \geq 4$

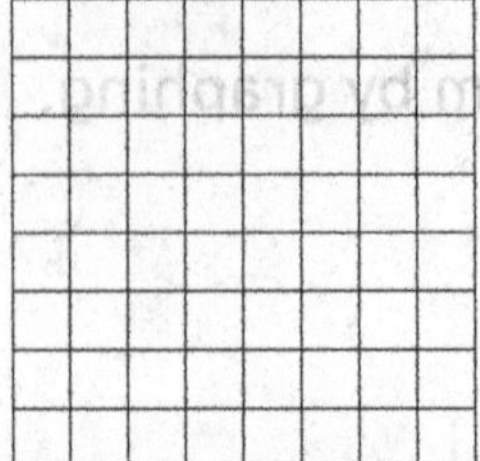

---

17. What system of inequalities is shown in the graph?

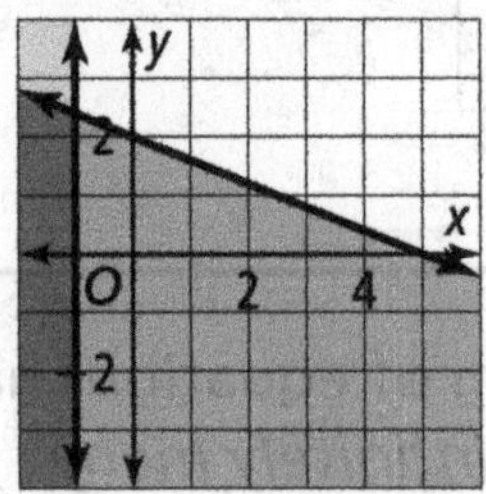

Ⓐ $x < -1$ and $y > 2x + 3$
Ⓑ $x < -1$ and $y > 3x + 2$
Ⓒ $x \leq -1$ and $y \leq -0.4x + 2$
Ⓓ $x \leq -1$ and $y \leq -2x + 2$

---

18. At a movie theater, the price of 2 adult tickets and 4 child tickets is $48. The price of 5 adult tickets and 2 child tickets is $64. What is the ticket price for one adult and for one child?

adult: ________ child: ________

---

19. The owner of the theater in Item 18 wants to make at least $300 when a movie is shown. Let x be the number of adult tickets and y be the number of child tickets sold. Write an inequality to show the number of tickets that need to be sold.

Name ____________________

4 Topic Assessment Form B

1. Solve the system by graphing.

$y = 2x + 2$

$y = x$

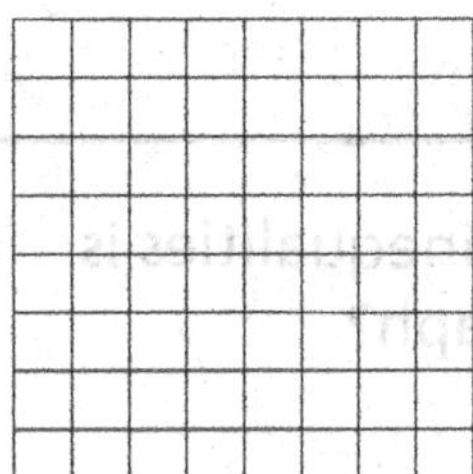

solution: __________

2. Does the system have *no solution* or *infinitely many solutions*?

$y = \frac{2}{3}x + 2$

$-2x + 3y = 6$

3. Estimate the solution of the system of equations.

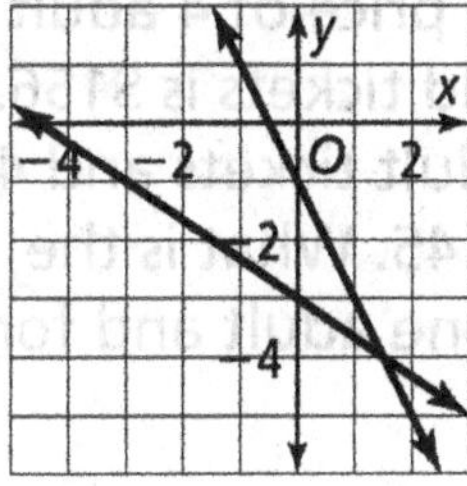

solution: __________

4. Raul bikes 6 mi home from school at a rate of 3 mi/h. Leah leaves school 30 min after Raul and bikes the same route at a rate of 4 mi/h. How many hours does it take Leah to catch up with Raul?

Ⓐ 1.5 h Ⓒ 6 h

Ⓑ 3 h Ⓓ $\frac{2}{3}$ h

5. What is the solution of the system of equations?

$y = \frac{3}{2}x + \frac{5}{4}$

$-2x + 8y = -25$

6. What is the solution of the system of equations?

$2x + 5y = 20$

$y = -\frac{2}{5}x - 1$

7. Luke sells toy cars for $12 each. His expenses are $3.50 per car, plus $34 for tools. How many cars must he sell for his revenue to equal his expenses?

Ⓐ 3 Ⓑ 10 Ⓒ 4 Ⓓ 3.5

8. What is the solution of the system?

$2x + 5y = 14$

$x + 3y = 16$

9. Which system has the same solution as the system of equations shown?

$3x + 2y = -5$

$2x + 3y = 5$

Ⓐ $6x + 4y = -5$, $6x + 9y = 5$ Ⓒ $6x + 4y = -10$, $-6x + 9y = 15$

Ⓑ $9x + 6y = -15$, $4x + 6y = 10$ Ⓓ $6x + 4y = -10$, $6x + 9y = 5$

10. What is the solution of the system?

$5x + 2y = 9$

$4x - 3y = 44$

11. The price of 6 slices of pizza and 4 drinks is \$37. The price of 4 slices of pizza and 6 drinks is \$33. How much does one drink cost?

Ⓐ \$1.75 Ⓒ \$3.50
Ⓑ \$2.50 Ⓓ \$4.50

12. Graph the inequality $y > 3x + 3$.

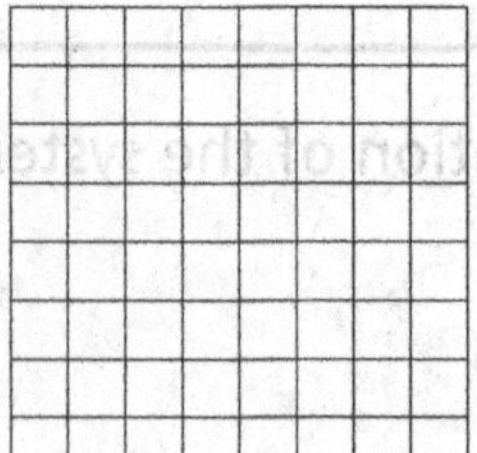

13. Which inequality does the graph represent?

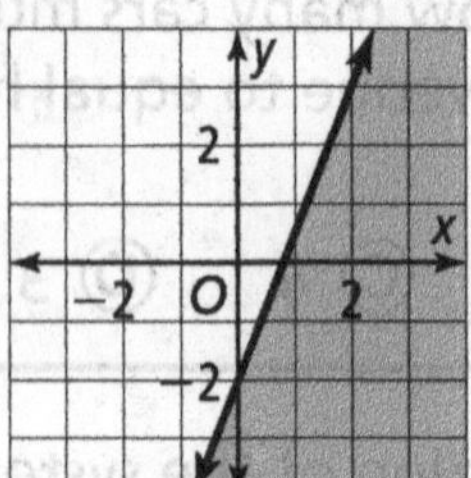

Ⓐ $y < 2.5x - 2$ Ⓒ $y \leq 2.5x - 2$
Ⓑ $y > 2.5x - 2$ Ⓓ $y \geq 2.5x - 2$

14. In the graph of an inequality, the area below a dashed line through the points (−2, −2) and (3, −2) is shaded. Which inequality does the graph represent?

Ⓐ $y \geq -2$ Ⓒ $y < -2$
Ⓑ $y \leq -2$ Ⓓ $x < -2$

15. In the graph of an inequality, the region to the right of a dashed vertical line through the point (−4, 0) is shaded. What inequality does the graph represent?

16. Graph the system of inequalities.

$x - y \leq 1$

$x + 2y < 4$

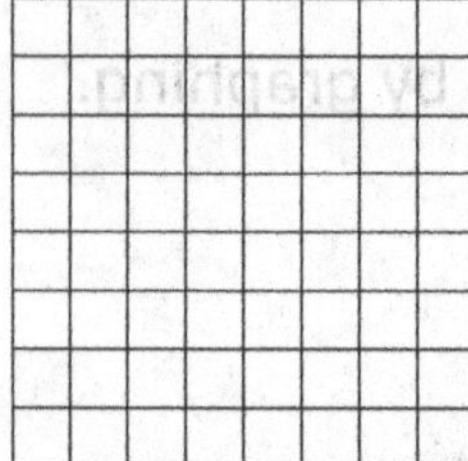

17. What system of inequalities is shown in the graph?

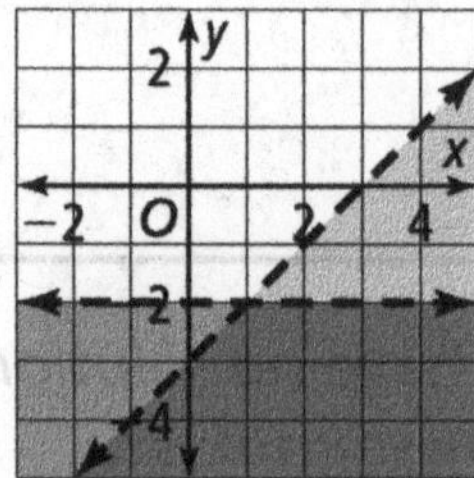

Ⓐ $y < -2$ and $y < x - 3$
Ⓑ $x < -2$ and $y < x - 3$
Ⓒ $y \leq -1$ and $y \leq x - 3$
Ⓓ $y \leq -1$ and $y \leq x - 3$

18. At a theater, the price of 4 adult tickets and 3 child tickets is \$156. The price of 3 adult tickets and 4 child tickets is \$145. What is the ticket price for one adult and for one child?

adult: ______ child: ______

19. The owner of the theater in Item 18 wants to make at least \$400 at each performance. Let x be the number of adult tickets and y be the number of child tickets sold. Write an inequality to show the number of tickets that need to be sold.

Name ________________________________

4 Performance Assessment Form A

Paula is the student council member responsible for planning an outdoor student dinner dance. Plans include hiring a band and buying and serving dinner. She wants to keep the ticket price as low as possible to encourage student attendance while still covering the cost of the band and the food.

1. Band A charges $600 to play for the evening. Band B charges $350 plus $1.25 per student.

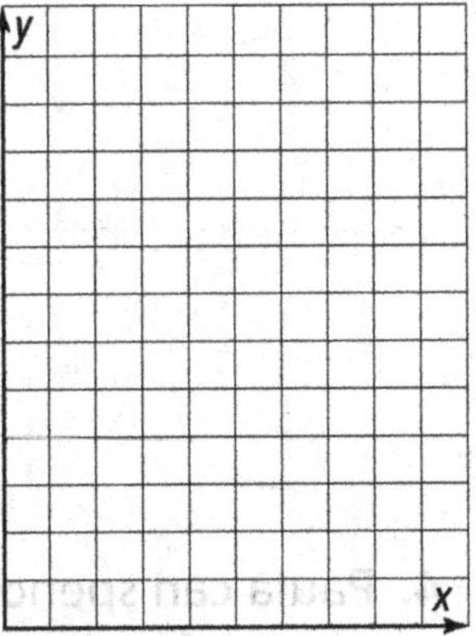

Part A

Write a system of equations to represent the costs of the two bands.

Part B

Graph the system of equations and find the number of students for which the costs for both bands would be equal.

2. A caterer charges a fixed amount for preparing a dinner plus a rate per student served. The total cost is modeled by this equation:

total cost = fixed amount + rate · number of students

Paula knows that the total cost for 100 students will be $750, and the total cost for 150 students will be $1,050. Find the caterer's fixed cost and the rate per student served. Explain.

3. Use the information you found in Items 1 and 2. Assume that 200 students attend the dance. Decide which band Paula should choose and what the cost per ticket should be so that the expenses for the dance are covered. Then repeat your calculations for 300 students. Explain.

4. Paula can spend no more than $500 for a photographer to take specialty photos for the dinner. Aerial photos from a drone cost $25 each, and wide-angle photos cost $50 each.

Part A

Write and graph an inequality that represents the number of each type of photo that Paula can buy.

y

x

Part B

Suppose the photographer takes 11 aerial photos. What is the maximum number of wide-angle photos that Paula can afford? Explain.

4 Performance Assessment Form B

Andrew owns a company that makes two different kinds of hot sauce and sells them to restaurants and stores. Both sauces are made from the same ingredients, but they vary in the number of green peppers and hot chili peppers used.

Sauce I (hot)	Sauce II (very hot)
Yield: 1 pint	Yield: 1 pint
6 green peppers	3 green peppers
4 hot chili peppers	10 hot chili peppers

1. Andrew buys 975 green peppers and 1,250 hot chili peppers. He uses all of those peppers to make the two types of sauce.

Part A

Write a system of equations that shows how Andrew can use the peppers to make *x* pints of Sauce I and *y* pints of Sauce II. Then graph and solve the system. Explain what information is given by the solution of the system.

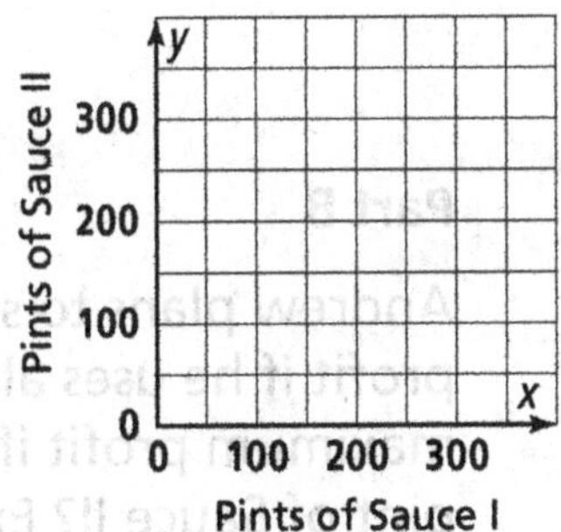

Part B

How many of each type of pepper will Andrew use for each type of sauce? Explain.

2. For a second batch of Sauce 1 and Sauce II, Andrew plans to use 3,180 green peppers and 5,560 hot chili peppers.

Part A

Write a system of equations that shows how Andrew can use the peppers to make x pints of Sauce I and y pints of Sauce II. Identify and describe a method you could use to solve this system. Explain your choice and give the solution.

Part B

Andrew plans to sell his second batch of sauce. He will make a maximum profit if he uses all the peppers and sells all of the sauce he makes. What is his maximum profit if he makes $1.20 profit per pint of Sauce I and $1.00 profit per pint of Sauce II? Explain.

3. For a third batch, Andrew buys 2,400 green peppers and 3,200 hot chili peppers. Based on customer demand, he will decide how many of those peppers he will use to make Sauce I and Sauce II.

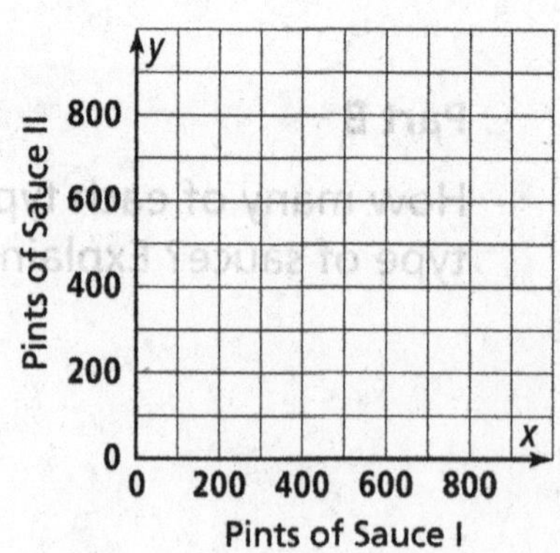

Given that the maximum number of green peppers Andrew can use is 2,400 and the maximum number of chili peppers is 3,200, write and graph a system of inequalities to show the different amounts of each type of sauce that Andrew can make. Explain.

Name ______________________________

Benchmark Test 2

1. If $m\angle NOP = 24°$ and $m\angle NOQ = 110°$, what is $m\angle POQ$?

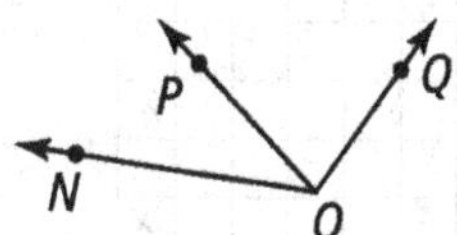

Ⓐ 62°
Ⓑ 86°
Ⓒ 134°
Ⓓ 156°

2. The angle bisector of $\angle ABC$ is $\overrightarrow{BP}$. If $m\angle ABP$ is $6n°$, what is $m\angle ABC$?

____

3. What are the coordinates of the point $\frac{4}{5}$ of the way from D to E?

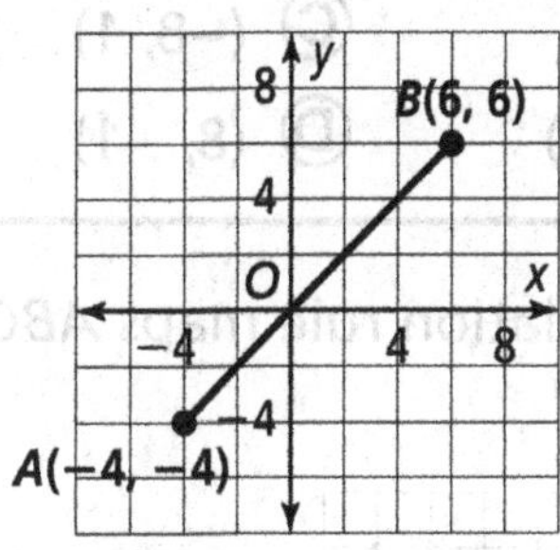

Ⓐ (−2, −2)
Ⓑ (0, 0)
Ⓒ (2, 2)
Ⓓ (4, 4)

4. Which figure is a counterexample for the conditional?

If a quadrilateral has four right angles, then it is a square.

Ⓐ rectangle
Ⓑ kite
Ⓒ parallelogram
Ⓓ rhombus

5. Use the Law of Detachment to make a conclusion.

If a person studies architecture, then that person must take calculus. Caroline is studying architecture.

____

6. What is the value of x?

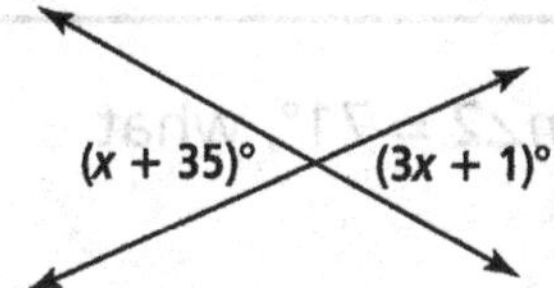

____

7. Martha Washington was the first First Lady of the United States. Prove the conditional statement by proving the contrapositive.

If a person was not the first First Lady of the United States, then that person was not Martha Washington.

Fill in the blanks to write the contrapositive.

If a person __________ Martha Washington, then that person __________ the first First Lady of the United States.

Fill in the blanks to write the contrapositive.

Since Martha Washington was the first First Lady of the United States, the contrapositive is __________.

Since the contrapositive is __________, the __________ __________ must be true.

8. Which pairs of angles are alternate interior angles? Select all that apply.

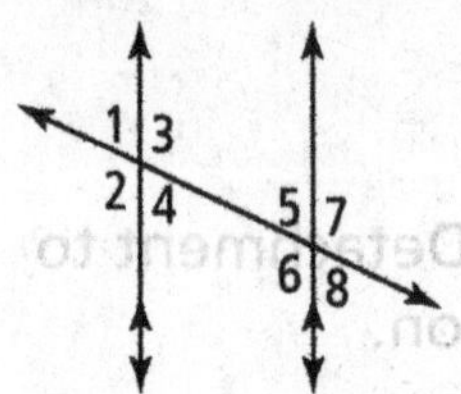

Ⓐ ∠3 and ∠6

Ⓑ ∠3 and ∠8

Ⓒ ∠4 and ∠5

Ⓓ ∠4 and ∠7

Ⓔ ∠1 and ∠8

9. If $a \parallel b$ and $m\angle 2 = 71°$, what is $m\angle 1$?

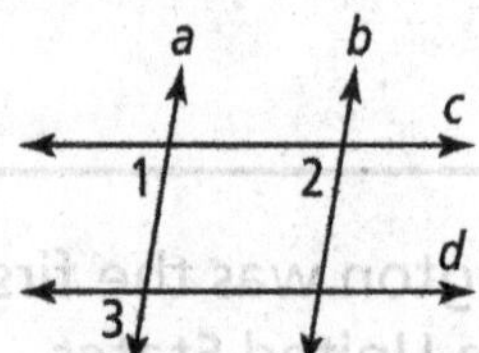

Ⓐ 19°

Ⓑ 71°

Ⓒ 109°

Ⓓ 142°

10. Which equation represents a line that is perpendicular to the line with equation $y = 2x - 8$? Select all that apply.

Ⓐ $y = \frac{1}{2}x + 1$

Ⓑ $y = -\frac{1}{2}x + 1$

Ⓒ $x + 2y = 5$

Ⓓ $-x + 2y = -3$

Ⓔ $-x - 2y = 9$

11. Quadrilateral $ABCD$ has coordinates $A(-2, 0)$, $B(0, 4)$, $C(4, 6)$, and $D(2, 2)$. Graph and label quadrilateral $ABCD$, and then graph and label the image $R_{x\text{-axis}}(ABCD) = A'B'C'D'$.

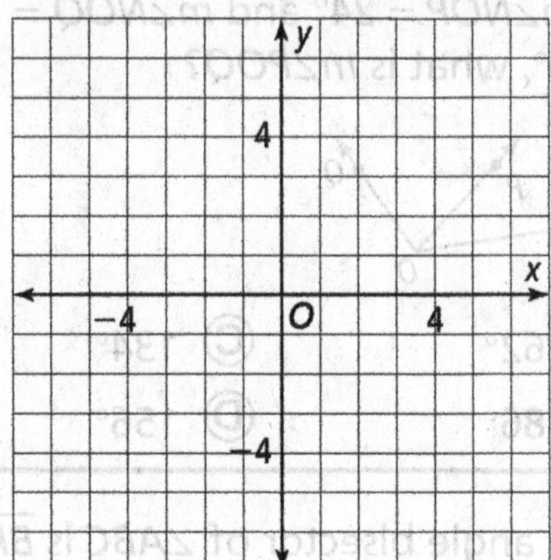

12. If point B has coordinates $(-8, 1)$, what are the coordinates of the point when it is reflected across the y-axis?

Ⓐ (8, 1)

Ⓑ (−8, −1)

Ⓒ (−8, 1)

Ⓓ (8, −1)

13. What translation rule maps $ABCD$ to $A'B'C'D'$?

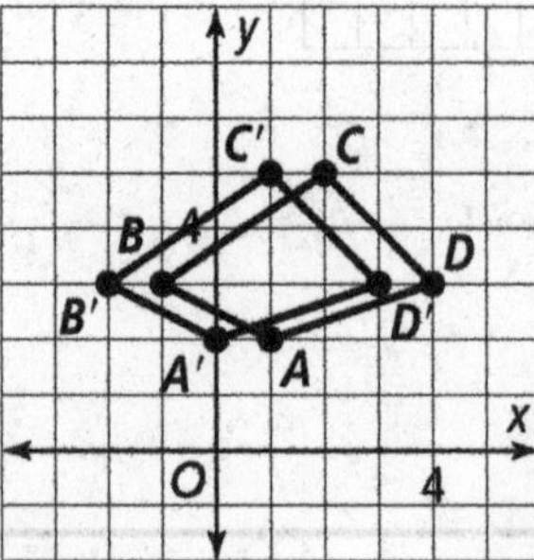

Ⓐ $T_{\langle -1, 0\rangle}$

Ⓑ $T_{\langle 1, 0\rangle}$

Ⓒ $T_{\langle 0, -1\rangle}$

Ⓓ $T_{\langle 0, 1\rangle}$

14. Triangle ABC has vertices $A(1, 3)$, $B(2, 5)$, and $C(5, 3)$. If the coordinates of B' are (p, q), what are the values of p and q after the translation described by the rule $T_{\langle 1, 4\rangle}$?

For Items 15 and 16, use pentagon *ABCDE*.

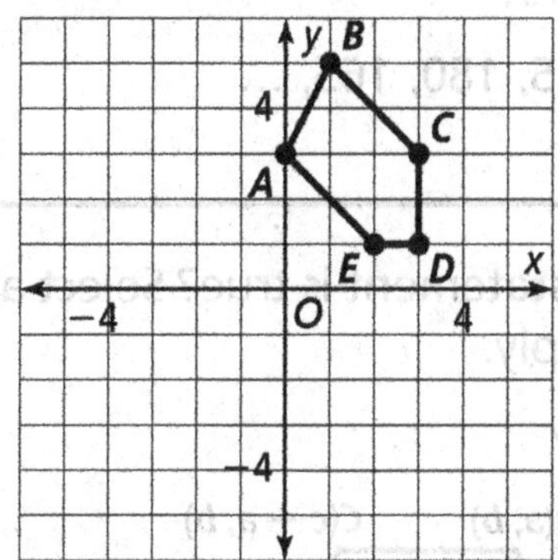

15. What are the coordinates of *B′* after the pentagon is rotated 90° about the origin?

Ⓐ (1, 5)

Ⓑ (−1, 5)

Ⓒ (−5, 1)

Ⓓ (5, 1)

16. What are the coordinates of *E′* after the pentagon is rotated 270° about the origin?

Ⓐ (1, −2)

Ⓑ (1, 2)

Ⓒ (2, −1)

Ⓓ (2, 1)

---

17. Given △*ABC* with coordinates *A*(1, 3), *B*(4, 5), and *C*(5, 2), what are the coordinates of △*A′B′C′* after the glide reflection described by $T_{\langle -1, 1\rangle} \circ R_{y\text{-axis}}$?

---

18. Write a rule for the glide reflection that maps △*ABC* with vertices *A*(−4, −2), *B*(−2, 6), and *C*(4, 4) to △*A′B′C′* with vertices *A′*(−2, −2), *B′*(0, −10), and *C′*(6, −8).

19. How many lines of symmetry does a regular decagon have?

Ⓐ 2

Ⓑ 5

Ⓒ 10

Ⓓ 12

---

20. Which letter has rotational symmetry?

Ⓐ E

Ⓑ B

Ⓒ Z

Ⓓ V

---

21. Triangle *JKL* is reflected across the *y*-axis to create △*J′K′L′*. Are the two figures are congruent? Explain.

---

22. Triangles *ABC* and *DEF* are isosceles triangles. Answer yes or no to the statements about the triangles.

	Yes	No
The base angles of △*ABC* are congruent to the base angles of △*EDF*.	❑	❑
Two sides of △*ABC* are congruent.	❑	❑
Two angles of △*DEF* are congruent.	❑	❑
Two sides of △*ABC* are congruent to two sides of △*EDF*.	❑	❑

For Items 23 and 24, use $\triangle DEF$.

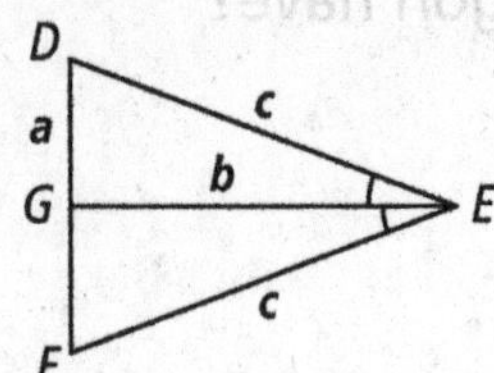

23. What is $m\angle DFE$ if $m\angle DEG = 18°$?

Ⓐ 9°
Ⓑ 18°
Ⓒ 36°
Ⓓ 72°

24. What is the value of b if $a = 9$ and $c = 41$? Round to the nearest whole number.

Ⓐ 32
Ⓑ 40
Ⓒ 42
Ⓓ 50

25. Which criterion can be used to prove the triangles are congruent?

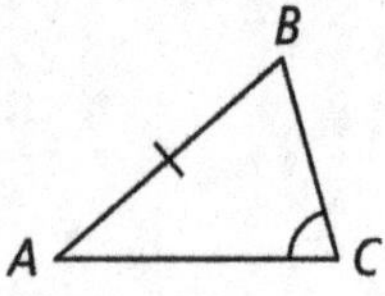

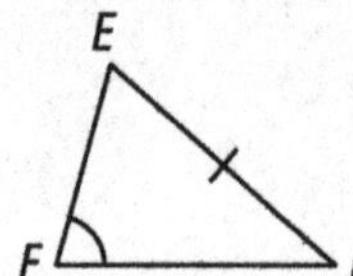

Ⓐ SSS
Ⓑ SAS
Ⓒ SSA
Ⓓ cannot be determined

26. What is the value of x? Explain.

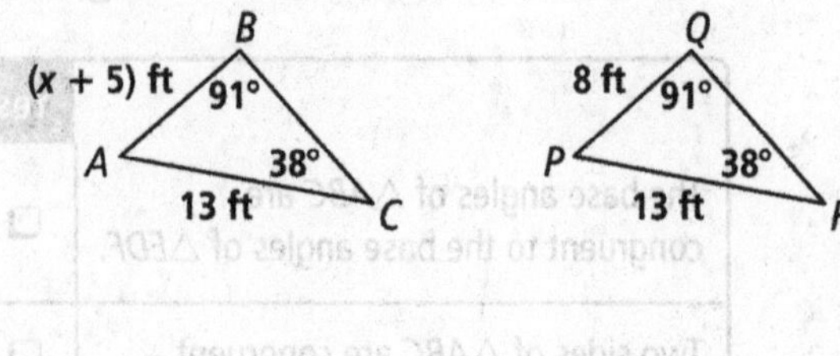

27. For the sequence below, what appear to be the next three numbers?

210, 195, 180, 165, ...

28. Which statement is true? Select all that apply.

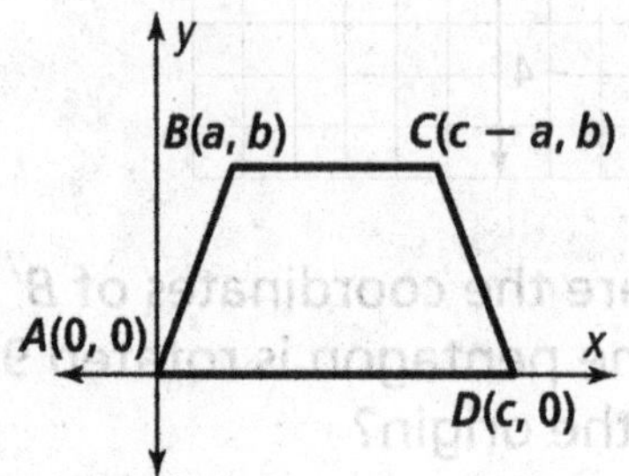

Ⓐ $AB = CD$
Ⓑ $AB = BC$
Ⓒ $AD = BC + 2a$
Ⓓ $\overline{AB} \parallel \overline{CD}$
Ⓔ $\overline{AD} \parallel \overline{BC}$

29. By which theorem can you conclude $\triangle DHF \cong \triangle EHG$?

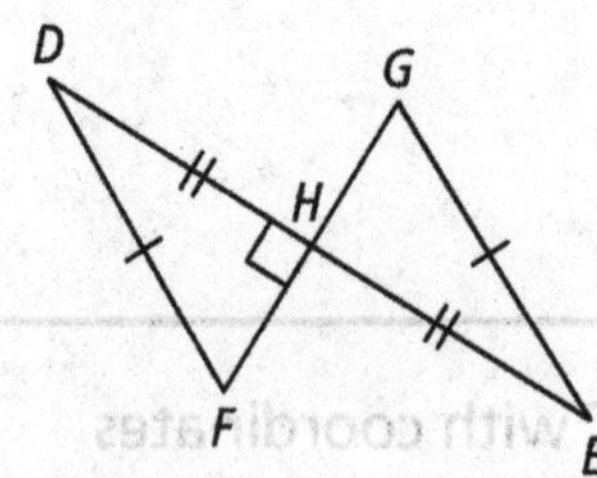

Ⓐ ASA
Ⓑ HL
Ⓒ SAS
Ⓓ SSS

30. Which theorem of triangle congruence shows that $\triangle TUV \cong \triangle WVU$?

U V Y Z X T W

Name ______________________________

5 Readiness Assessment

1. Complete, using >, <, or =.

$3^3 \cdot 3^{-2}$ ■ $3^2 \cdot 3^{-3}$

2. Which of the following expression(s) are equivalent to $\frac{x^2y^3}{xy}$? Select all that apply.

Ⓐ xy^2

Ⓑ $\frac{xy^3}{y}$

Ⓒ $\frac{x^2y^2}{x}$

Ⓓ x^3y^4

3. Which expression is equivalent to $(a^3)^6$?

Ⓐ a^{729}

Ⓑ a^{18}

Ⓒ a^9

Ⓓ a^2

4. Which property can be used to justify the correct choice in Item 3?

Ⓐ Power of a Power Property

Ⓑ Power of a Product Property

Ⓒ Product of Powers Property

Ⓓ Quotient of Powers Property

5. Simplify $\sqrt{2^4}$.

6. Simplify $\sqrt[3]{27}$.

7. Which of the following shows the greatest percent increase?

Ⓐ 50 increased to 75

Ⓑ 500 increased to 700

Ⓒ 5,000 increased to 7,000

Ⓓ 50,000 increased to 74,000

8. The value 2,000 is decreased to 100. What is the percent decrease?

______ decrease

9. Which statement about the data in the table shown is true?

x	−2	−1	0	1
y	−3	−1	1	3

Ⓐ The data do not represent a function.

Ⓑ The data represent a nonlinear function.

Ⓒ The data represent a quadratic function.

Ⓓ The data represent a linear function.

10. Which function represents the data in the table shown?

x	0	2	4	5
y	−2	4	10	13

Ⓐ $y = 3x - 2$

Ⓑ $y = \frac{1}{3}x + \frac{2}{3}$

Ⓒ $y = -3x - 2$

Ⓓ $y = -\frac{1}{3}x + 2$

11. Which function is represented by the graph?

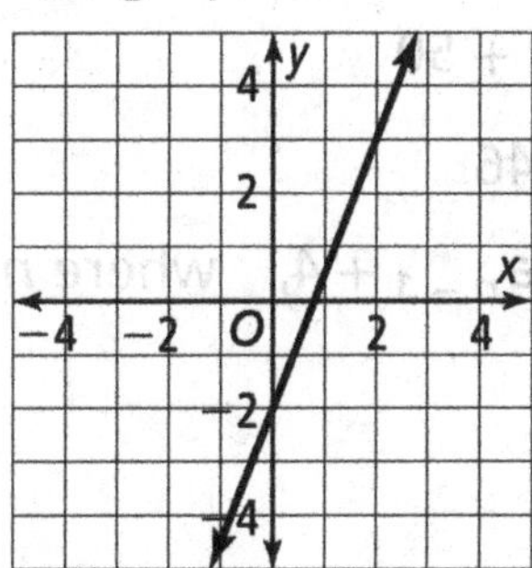

Ⓐ $y = 0.4x - 2$

Ⓑ $y = -0.4x - 2$

Ⓒ $y = 2.5x - 2$

Ⓓ $y = -2.5x - 2$

12. What is the range of the function shown in the graph?

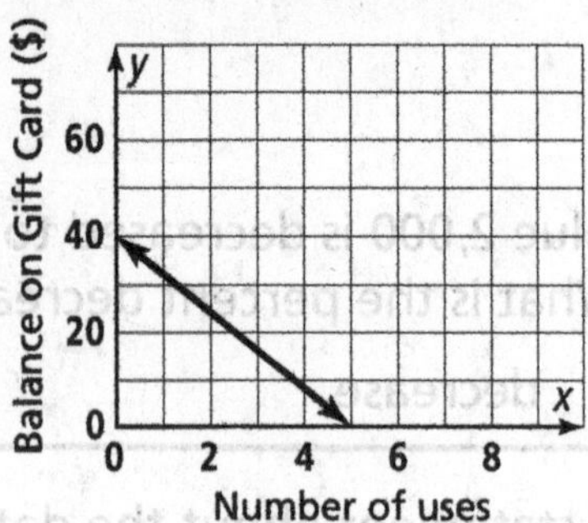

Ⓐ $0 \leq x \leq 40$

Ⓑ $0 \leq y \leq 40$

Ⓒ $0 < x < 40$

Ⓓ $0 < y < 40$

---

13. The first term of an arithmetic sequence is $a_1 = 2$, and the third term is $a_3 = 6$. Which of the following could be formula(s) for the sequence? Select all that apply.

Ⓐ $a_n = 2n$

Ⓑ $a_n = 2n + 2$

Ⓒ $a_n = n + 2$

Ⓓ $a_n = a_{n-1} + 2$

---

14. Which is a recursive formula for the sequence 50, 54, 58, 62, ...?

Ⓐ $a_n = 4n + 46$

Ⓑ $\begin{cases} a_1 = 50 \\ a_n = a_{n-1} + 4, \quad \text{where } n \geq 2 \end{cases}$

Ⓒ $a_n = 4n + 50$

Ⓓ $\begin{cases} a_1 = 46 \\ a_n = a_{n-1} + 4, \quad \text{where } n \geq 2 \end{cases}$

---

15. If $f(x) = -2x - 4$ and $g(x) = -2x + 2$, which statement about the graphs of f and g is true?

Ⓐ g is a translation of f 6 units down.

Ⓑ g is a translation of f 2 units to the right.

Ⓒ g is a translation of f 2 units to the left.

Ⓓ g is a translation of f 6 units up.

---

16. Which of these function(s) have a graph that is a translation of the graph of $f(x) = x$? Select all that apply.

Ⓐ $g(x) = 2x$ Ⓒ $j(x) = x - 2$

Ⓑ $h(x) = x + 1$ Ⓓ $k(x) = \frac{1}{2}x$

---

17. Which statement describes how the y-intercept of the graph of $f(x) = |2x - 1|$ compares to the y-intercept of the graph of $g(x) = |2x - 5|$?

Ⓐ The y-intercept of g is 4 units above the y-intercept of f.

Ⓑ The y-intercept of g is 4 units below the y-intercept of f.

Ⓒ The y-intercept of g is 4 units to the right of the y-intercept of f.

Ⓓ The y-intercept of g is 4 units to the left of the y-intercept of f.

---

18. The graph of function g is a translation 3 units to the right of the function $f(x) = |x| + 4$. Write an equation for function g.

Name ______________________________

5-1 Lesson Quiz

Rational Exponents and Properties of Exponents

1. How can you write $\sqrt[5]{n^4}$ using rational exponents?

   Ⓐ $n^{\frac{4}{5}}$

   Ⓑ $n^{\frac{5}{4}}$

   Ⓒ n^{20}

   Ⓓ $\frac{n^4}{n^5}$

2. The formula $A = 6V^{\frac{2}{3}}$ relates the surface area A, in square units, of a cube to the volume V, in cubic units. What is the volume, in cubic inches, of a cube with surface area 486 in.^{2}?

3. The solution of $(10^{\frac{x}{6}})(10^{\frac{x}{8}}) = 10^{10}$ is

   $x =$ ________.

4. What is the solution of $9^{x-8} = 3^{4x-12}$?

   Ⓐ $-\frac{2}{3}$

   Ⓑ $\frac{4}{3}$

   Ⓒ 2

   Ⓓ −2

5. The diagram below shows a hexagon-shaped tile used for flooring. Each hexagon tile has an area of $18\sqrt{3}$ in.^{2}. Solve for x. Then find the exact length of each side of the hexagon. (*Hint:* Six equilateral triangles make one hexagon.)

   $x =$ ______; side length = ______ in.

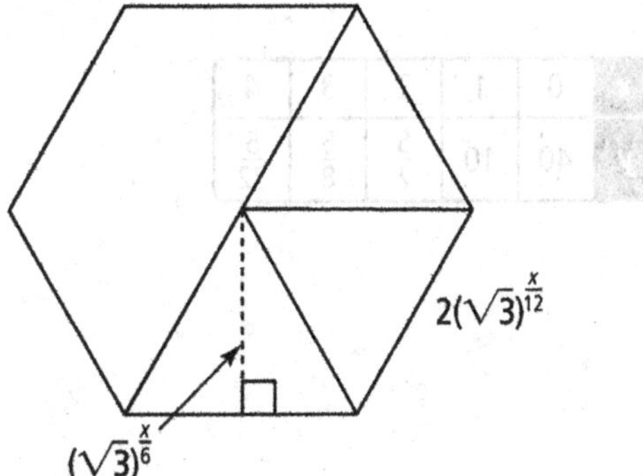

Name ______________________

5-2 Lesson Quiz

Exponential Functions

1. Determine which function(s) are exponential. Select all that apply.

Ⓐ

x	0	1	2	3	4
y	0	1	4	9	16

Ⓑ

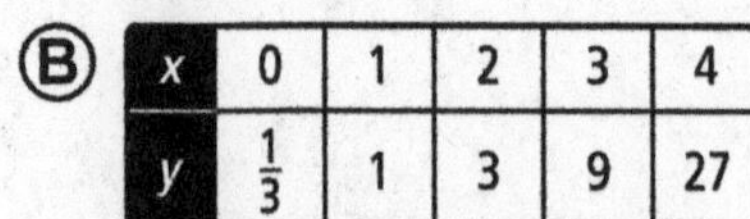

x	0	1	2	3	4
y	$\frac{1}{3}$	1	3	9	27

Ⓒ

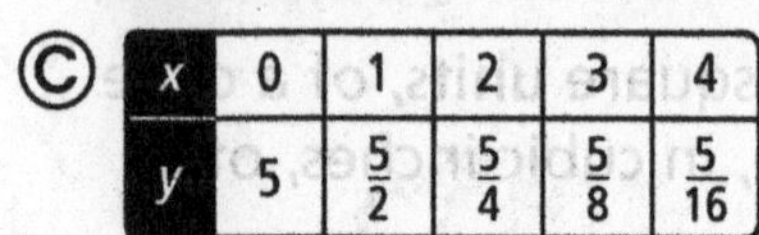

x	0	1	2	3	4
y	5	$\frac{5}{2}$	$\frac{5}{4}$	$\frac{5}{8}$	$\frac{5}{16}$

Ⓓ

x	0	1	2	3	4
y	4.5	4	3.5	3	2.5

2. What are the key features of $f(x) = 8^x$?

y-intercept: ________ asymptote: ________ range: ________

3. Graph $f(x) = 3^x$.

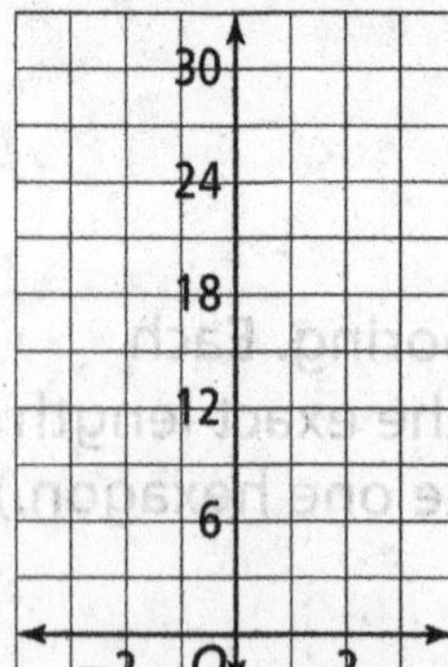

4. What is the rule that defines the function represented by the table?

x	0	1	2	3	4
y	40	10	$\frac{5}{2}$	$\frac{5}{8}$	$\frac{5}{32}$

Ⓐ $f(x) = \frac{1}{4}(40)^x$

Ⓑ $f(x) = \frac{1}{2}(40)^x$

Ⓒ $f(x) = 40\left(\frac{1}{4}\right)^x$

Ⓓ $f(x) = 4\left(\frac{1}{3}\right)^x$

5. An exponential function repeatedly multiplies an initial amount by the same positive number called the ________________.

Name ____________________

5-3 Lesson Quiz

Exponential Growth and Decay

1. A wildlife biologist determines that there are approximately 200 deer in a region of a national park. The population grows at a rate of 7% per year. What is an exponential function that models the expected population?

   Ⓐ $f(x) = 200(0.07)^x$
   Ⓑ $f(x) = 200(1.07)^x$
   Ⓒ $f(x) = 1.07(200)^x$
   Ⓓ $f(x) = 7(200)^x$

2. Compare Accounts A and B. Account ______ will be worth more after 10 years. It will have a value of $__________.

Account A	Account B
principal: $16,000	principal: $16,000
annual interest: 3%	annual interest: 3%
compounded quarterly	compounded monthly
number of years: 10	number of years: 10

3. A business purchases a computer system for $3,000. The value of the system decreases at a rate of 15% per year. Write an exponential function to model this situation. Then determine how much the computer will be worth after 4 years.

   function: $f(x) =$ ______________ value after 4 years: __________

4. There are approximately 3,000 bass in a lake. The population grows at a rate of 2% per year. From Year 1 to Year 4, the average rate of change of the population was about ______ bass per year. From Year 5 to Year 8, the average rate of change of the population was about ______ bass per year. The rate of change increased by about ____ bass per year.

5. Which graph represents functions *f* and *g*?

   f: initial value of 200 decreasing at a rate of 4%

   g: initial value of 40 increasing at a rate of 8%

Ⓐ
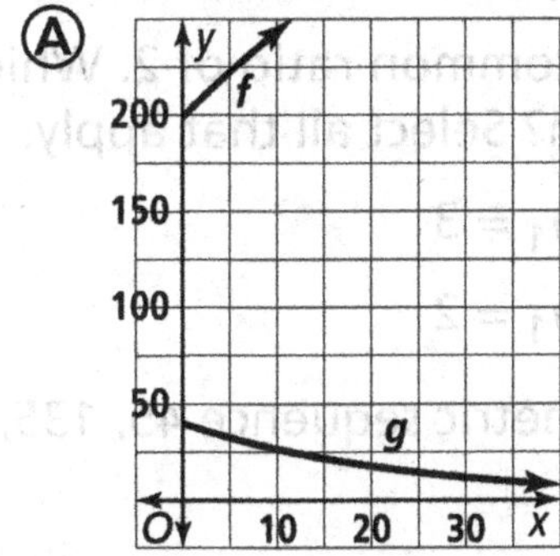

Ⓒ
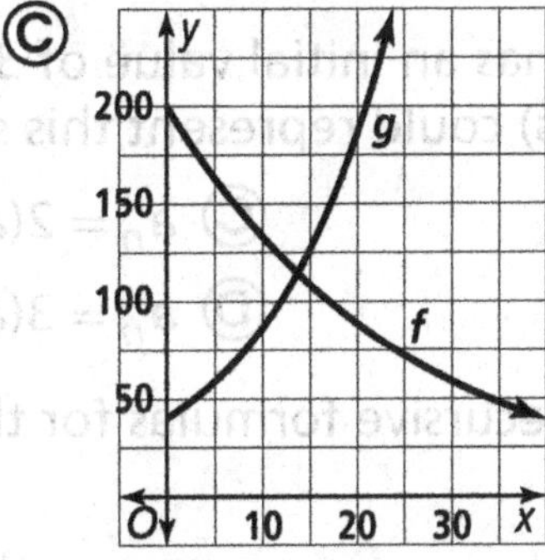

Ⓑ
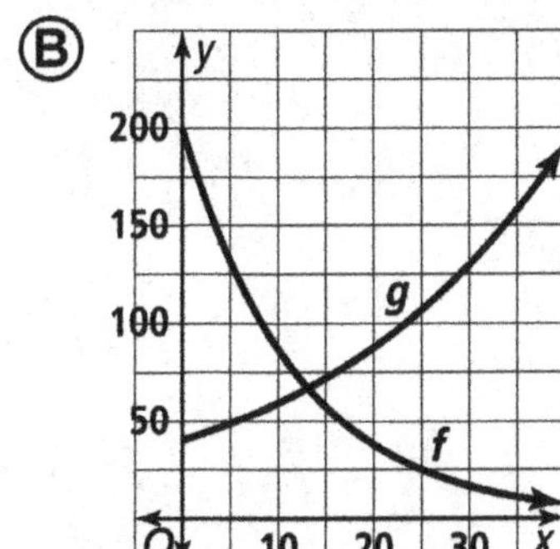

Ⓓ
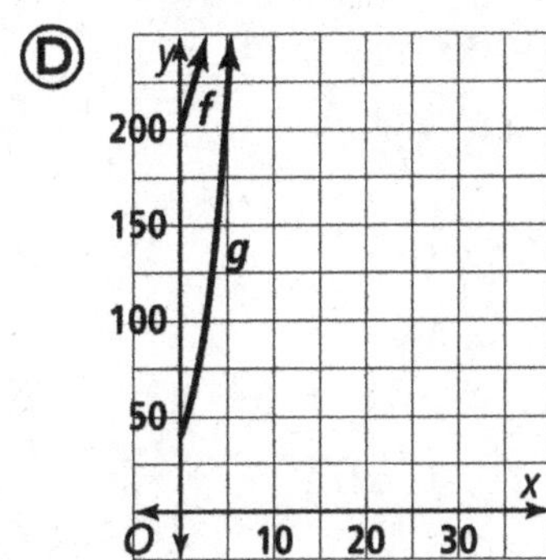

5-4 Lesson Quiz

Geometric Sequences

1. Match the geometric sequence at the left with its explicit and recursive formulas at the right.

5, 20, 80, 320,...	$a_n = 5(3)^{n-1}$; $a_n = 3(a_{n-1})$; $a_1 = 5$
$5, \frac{5}{3}, \frac{5}{9}, \frac{5}{27}, \ldots$	$a_n = 5(20)^{n-1}$; $a_n = 20(a_{n-1})$; $a_1 = 5$
5, 15, 45, 135, ...	$a_n = 5(4)^{n-1}$; $a_n = 4(a_{n-1})$; $a_1 = 5$
5, 100, 2,000, 40,000...	$a_n = 5\left(\frac{1}{3}\right)^{n-1}$; $a_n = \frac{1}{3}(a_{n-1})$; $a_1 = 5$

2. Timothy makes reduced copies of a photograph that has an actual length of 8 in. Each time he presses the reduce button on the copier, the copy is reduced by 12%. What formula shows the pattern for the size of each copy of the photograph as it is reduced? What is the length of the photograph's copy if Timothy presses the reduce button 5 times? Round to the nearest tenth.

Ⓐ $a_n = 8(0.88)^{n-1}$; 4.8 in.

Ⓑ $a_n = 8(0.88)^n$; 4.2 in.

Ⓒ $a_n = 8(0.12)^{n-1}$; 1.9 in.

Ⓓ $a_n = 8(1.12)^n$; 7.1 in.

3. Write a function to model the geometric sequence in the table.

n	1	2	3	4	5
a_n	75	15	3	$\frac{3}{5}$	$\frac{3}{25}$

4. A geometric sequence has an initial value of 3 and a common ratio of 2. Which function(s) or formula(s) could represent this situation? Select all that apply.

Ⓐ $f(n) = 3(2)^{n-1}$

Ⓑ $f(n) = 2(3)^{n-1}$

Ⓒ $a_n = 2(a_{n-1})$; $a_1 = 3$

Ⓓ $a_n = 3(a_{n-1})$; $a_1 = 2$

5. Write the explicit and recursive formulas for the geometric sequence 45, 135, 405, 1215, 3645, ...

Name ______________________________

5-5 Lesson Quiz

Transformations of Exponential Functions

1. Match each graph of f and its transformation, g.

$f(x) = 0.5^x$	$f(x) = 0.5^x$	$f(x) = 2^x$	$f(x) = 2^x$
$g(x) = f(x + k)$	$g(x) = f(x) + k$	$g(x) = f(x) + k$	$g(x) = f(x + k)$
for $k = -2$	for $k = 2$	for $k = 2$	for $k = 2$

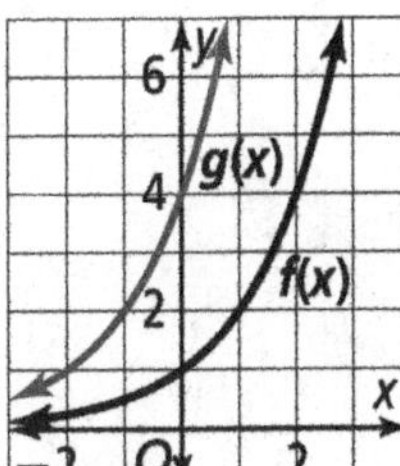

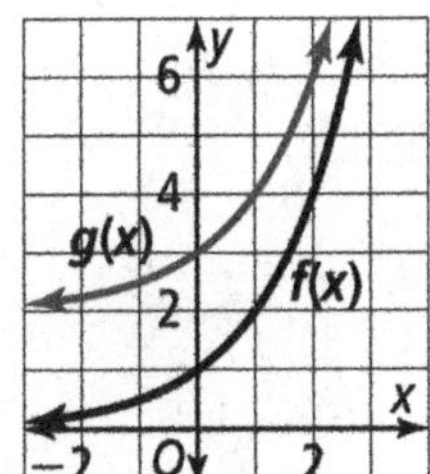

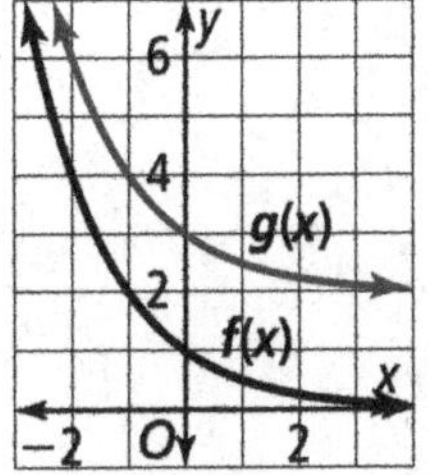

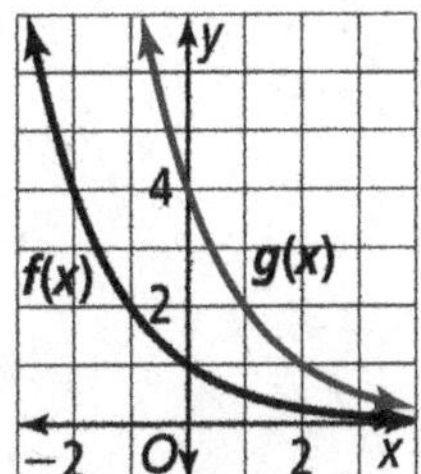

2. How does the graph of $g(x) = 4^x + 5$ compare to the function represented by the table at the right?

x	−2	−1	0	1	2
$h(x)$	$\frac{17}{16}$	$\frac{5}{4}$	2	5	17

Ⓐ The graph of g is a translation $\frac{49}{16}$ units up from the graph of h.

Ⓑ The graph of g is a translation $\frac{49}{16}$ units down from the graph of h.

Ⓒ The graph of g is a translation 4 units up from the graph of h.

Ⓓ The graph of g is a translation 4 units down from the graph of h.

3. Compare the graph of $f(x) = 6^x$ and the graph of $g(x) = 6^x - 12$. The graph of g is a __________ translation of the graph of f _____ units __________.

4. How does the graph of $g(x) = 5^{x-3}$ compare to the graph of $f(x) = 5^x$?

Ⓐ The graph of g is a translation 3 units down from the graph of f.

Ⓑ The graph of g is a translation 3 units up from the graph of f.

Ⓒ The graph of g is a translation 3 units left from the graph of f.

Ⓓ The graph of g is a translation 3 units right from the graph of f.

5. The horizontal asymptote of $f(x) = 0.8^x$ is $y = 0$. What is the horizontal asymptote of $h(x) = 0.8^x - 10$?

Name

PearsonRealize.com

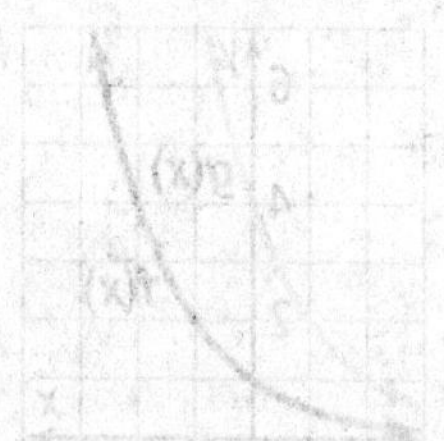
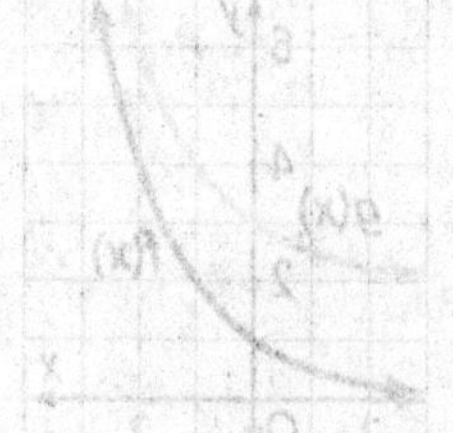
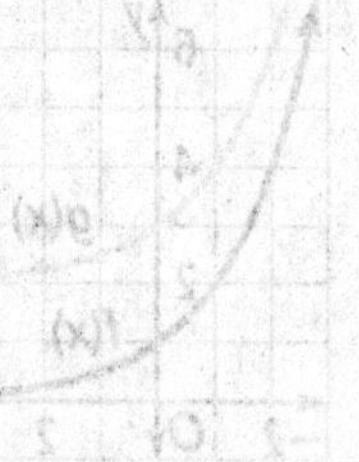
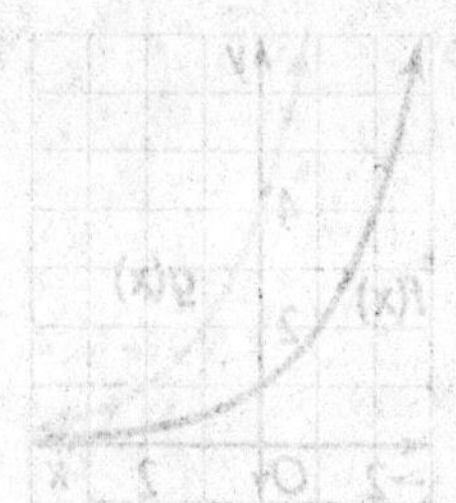

Name ______________________________

5 Topic Assessment Form A

1. Write $\sqrt[4]{5}$ using rational exponents.

Ⓐ $5^{\frac{1}{4}}$ Ⓒ 5^4

Ⓑ $4^{\frac{1}{5}}$ Ⓓ 4^5

2. Solve the equation $(3^{\frac{x}{2}})(3^{\frac{x}{4}}) = 3^6$.

3. Solve the equation $\left(\frac{1}{3}\right)^{x+1} = \left(\frac{1}{9}\right)^{x+3}$.

Ⓐ $x = 5$

Ⓑ $x = -\frac{7}{3}$

Ⓒ $x = -5$

Ⓓ the equation has no solution

4. The diagram shows two squares constructed on the sides of a rectangle. What is the area of Square C?

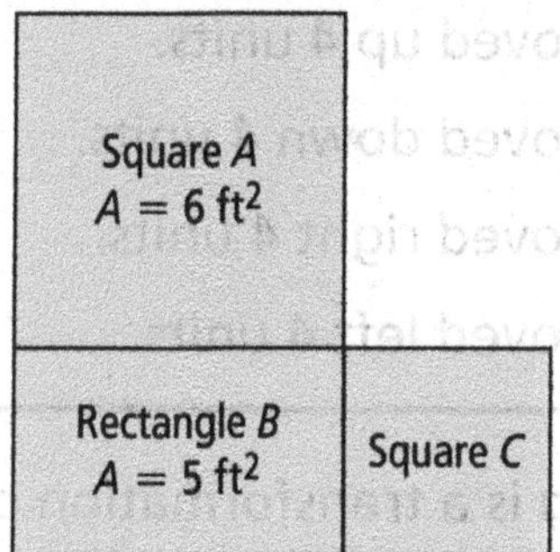

5. Solve the equation $\frac{(3^x)^{\frac{1}{2}}}{3^{\frac{1}{2}}} = 3$.

Ⓐ $x = 3$ Ⓒ $x = \frac{49}{4}$

Ⓑ $x = -1$ Ⓓ $x = 1$

6. Identify the key features of the exponential function $f(x) = 5^x$ and its graph.

The domain is ______________.
The range is ______________.
The asymptote is ______________.
The y-intercept is ______________.

7. Graph $f(x) = 3^x$.

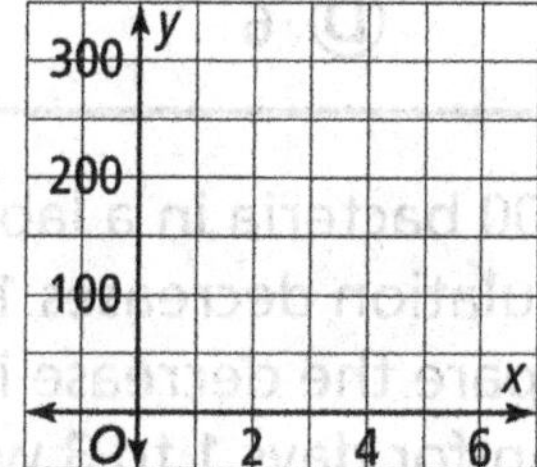

8. Write an exponential function for the set of points.

x	0	1	2	3	4
$f(x)$	27	9	3	1	$\frac{1}{3}$

9. Luis has saved \$6. He doubles the amount he saves each week. Does this represent an exponential function? Complete:

This ______________ represent an exponential function, because his savings increase by a constant ______________.

10. The population of a town is 12,000, and it grows at a rate of 5% per year. What will the population be in 4 years?

Ⓐ about 12,600 Ⓒ about 14,586

Ⓑ about 14,420 Ⓓ about 56,401

11. Leo invests $2,000 at an interest rate of 4%, compounded quarterly. How much is the investment worth at the end of 3 years?

Ⓐ $2,249.73 Ⓒ $1,124.86

Ⓑ $2,253.65 Ⓓ $2,080.00

12. The population of a town is 20,000. It decreases at a rate of 9% per year. In about how many years will the population be fewer than 13,000?

Ⓐ 3 Ⓒ 5

Ⓑ 4 Ⓓ 6

13. There are 1,200 bacteria in a lab dish. The population decreases 10% per day. Compare the decrease in the population for days 1 to 3 with the decrease for days 4 to 6.

Complete the sentence with "more quickly," "less quickly," or "at the same rate." The population decreases ______________ from day 1 to day 3 than from day 4 to day 6.

14. Is the sequence 18, 9, $\frac{9}{2}, \frac{9}{4}, \frac{9}{8}, \ldots$ a geometric sequence?

Complete: The sequence has a common ______________, so it ______________ a geometric sequence.

15. What are the explicit and recursive formulas for the sequence 10, 15, 22.5, 33.75, ...?

explicit: ______________

recursive: ______________

____

16. The explicit formula for a geometric sequence is $a_n = 125\left(\frac{1}{5}\right)^{n-1}$. What is a recursive formula for the sequence?

17. The recursive formula for a geometric sequence is $a_n = 2a_{n-1}$ with an initial value of $a_1 = \frac{1}{8}$. What is the explicit formula for the sequence?

18. How does the graph of the function $g(x) = 2^x - 3$ differ from the graph of $f(x) = 2^x$?

Ⓐ It is moved up 3 units.

Ⓑ It is moved down 3 units.

Ⓒ It is moved right 3 units.

Ⓓ It is moved left 3 units.

19. How does the graph of the function $g(x) = 2^{x-4}$ differ from the graph of $f(x) = 2^x$?

Ⓐ It is moved up 4 units.

Ⓑ It is moved down 4 units.

Ⓒ It is moved right 4 units.

Ⓓ It is moved left 4 units.

20. Function g is a transformation of $f(x) = 2^x$. Compare the graphs of the functions. Select all that apply.

x	0	1	2	3	4
$g(x)$	$\frac{1}{2}$	1	2	4	8

Ⓐ They have the same domain.

Ⓑ They have the same range.

Ⓒ They have the same y-intercept.

Ⓓ They have the same asymptote.

Name ______________________

5 Topic Assessment Form B

1. Write $\sqrt[3]{10}$ using rational exponents.

Ⓐ 3^{10} Ⓒ $3^{\frac{1}{10}}$
Ⓑ 10^3 Ⓓ $10^{\frac{1}{3}}$

2. Solve the equation $(5^{\frac{x}{3}})(5^{\frac{x}{5}}) = 5^4$.

3. Solve the equation $\left(\frac{1}{49}\right)^{x+2} = (7)^{x-3}$.

Ⓐ $x = -7$
Ⓑ $x = -\frac{1}{3}$
Ⓒ $x = \frac{1}{3}$
Ⓓ the equation has no solution

4. The diagram shows two squares constructed on the sides of a rectangle. What is the area of Square *C*?

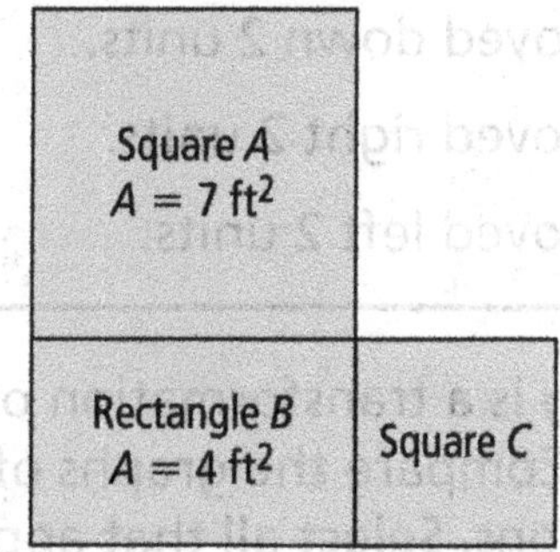

5. Solve the equation $\frac{(10^x)^{\frac{2}{3}}}{10^{\frac{1}{3}}} = 10$.

Ⓐ $x = 0$ Ⓒ $x = \frac{2}{3}$
Ⓑ $x = \frac{1}{2}$ Ⓓ $x = 2$

6. Identify the key features of the exponential function $f(x) = 10^x$ and its graph.

The domain is __________.
The range is __________.
The asymptote is __________.
The *y*-intercept is __________.

7. Graph $f(x) = 6^x$.

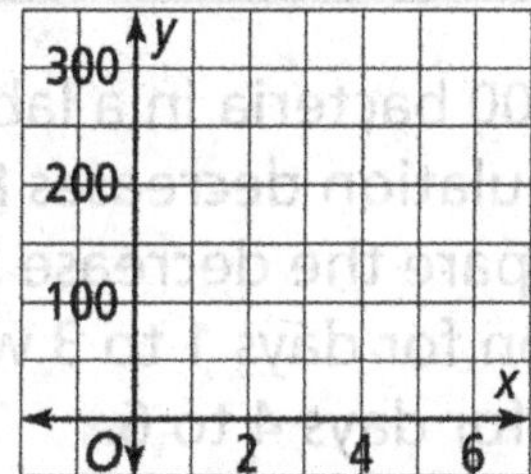

8. Write an exponential function for the set of points.

x	0	1	2	3	4
f(*x*)	6	12	24	48	96

9. Ines has saved $5. She doubles the amount she saves each week. Does this represent an exponential function?

Complete: This ________ represent an exponential function, because her savings increase by a constant ________.

10. The population of a town is 14,000, and it grows at a rate of 4% per year. What will the population be in 6 years?

Ⓐ about 87,360 Ⓒ about 17,714
Ⓑ about 17,360 Ⓓ about 14,560

11. Tia invests $2,500 at an interest rate of 4%, compounded quarterly. How much is the investment worth at the end of 5 years?

Ⓐ $2,600.00 Ⓒ $3,041.63

Ⓑ $3,000.00 Ⓓ $3,050.48

12. The population of a town is 18,000. It decreases at a rate of 8% per year. In about how many years will the population be fewer than 11,000?

Ⓐ 6 Ⓒ 4

Ⓑ 5 Ⓓ 3

13. There are 4,200 bacteria in a lab dish. The population decreases 8% per day. Compare the decrease in the population for days 1 to 3 with the decrease for days 4 to 6.

Complete the sentence with "more quickly," "less quickly," or "at the same rate." The population decreases ________________ from day 4 to day 6 than from day 1 to day 3.

14. Is the sequence 10, 15, 22.5, 33.75, ... a geometric sequence?

Complete: The sequence has a common ________, so it ____ a geometric sequence.

15. What are the explicit and recursive formulas for the sequence 540, 180, 60, 20, ...?

explicit: ________________

recursive: ________________

16. The explicit formula for a geometric sequence is $a_n = 6(3)^{n-1}$. What is the recursive formula for the sequence?

17. The recursive formula for a geometric sequence is $a_n = \frac{1}{5} a_{n-1}$ with an initial value of $a_1 = 125$. What is the explicit formula for the sequence?

18. How does the graph of the function $g(x) = 2^x + 6$ differ from the graph of $f(x) = 2^x$?

Ⓐ It is moved up 6 units.

Ⓑ It is moved down 6 units.

Ⓒ It is moved right 6 units.

Ⓓ It is moved left 6 units.

19. How does the graph of the function $g(x) = 3^{x+2}$ differ from the graph of $f(x) = 3^x$?

Ⓐ It is moved up 2 units.

Ⓑ It is moved down 2 units.

Ⓒ It is moved right 2 units.

Ⓓ It is moved left 2 units.

20. Function g is a transformation of $f(x) = 2^x$. Compare the graphs of the functions. Select all that apply.

x	0	1	2	3	4
$g(x)$	5	6	8	12	20

Ⓐ They have the same domain.

Ⓑ They have the same range.

Ⓒ They have the same y-intercept.

Ⓓ They have the same asymptote.

5 Performance Assessment Form A

Botanists conduct field research to develop recovery plans for endangered species. They use linear and exponential models and graphs to interpret the resulting data.

1. Seth tracks the average number of a plant species found in a forest area. He uses volunteers to help search for the species. The number n of plants found increases by r percent for each volunteer added to the search. Seth found I plants before adding any volunteers.

Part A

Write an exponential growth function that relates the number n of plants found to the number x of volunteers Seth has. What is an appropriate domain of the function? Explain.

Part B

Seth found 50 plants before adding volunteers to the search, and the rate of increase is 12% per volunteer. For $0 \leq x \leq 5$, determine the following:

- The function n models the situation. Graph the function. What are the appropriate domain and y-intercept?

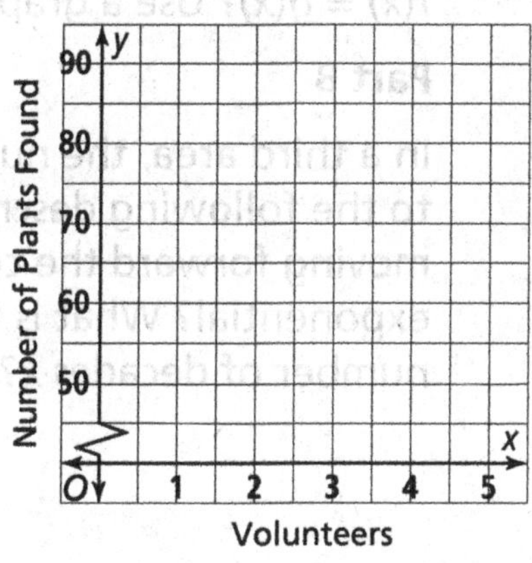

- What is the average rate of change from 0 to 5 volunteers?

Part C

Seth has a different team of volunteers search another region for the plant species. He has already found 30 plants himself, and the number of plants found increases by 16% for each new volunteer added to the search. Find a function that relates the number p of plants found to the number x of volunteers in the search. Determine the average rate of change from 0 to 5 volunteers. Then compare that value to the average rate of change you found in Part B.

2. In one part of the world, the number of a certain species of forest wildflowers is expected to grow according to the function *f* graphed below. In another area of the world, the same species is expected to grow according to the the function *g* represented by the data in the table. The values for *x* in each function represent time, in decades.

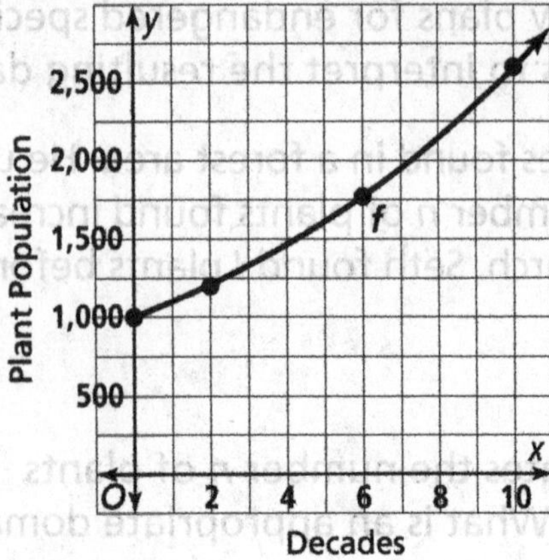

Decades, x	Population, $g(x)$
0	750
2	991
4	1,312
6	1,734
8	2,294
10	3,035

Part A

Which function has the greater initial value? Which has the greater growth rate? If you graphed g, what would be the approximate value of x that makes $f(x) = g(x)$? Use a graphing calculator.

Part B

In a third area, the number of flowering plants is expected to grow according to the following description: "The initial count is 1,500, and for each decade moving forward the count will increase by 200." Will this model be linear or exponential? What is the model that relates the number of plants h to the number of decades x? How does this model compare with the models in Part A?

Part C

Some studies find that the yearly growth rate of a certain wildflower can be modeled by the equation $y = 1{,}000(1.08)^x$. Use the properties of exponents to show an equivalent equation that represents the monthly growth of the wildflowers. Show your work.

5 Performance Assessment Form B

The population of African elephants has been decreasing at an alarming rate for the past century. In the late 1800s, there were several million African elephants. In the 1990s, that number dropped to only about half a million. The goal of conservationists is to collect and analyze scientific data to work toward a better future for the species.

1. The population decline of African elephants can be modeled by an exponential function f, where $f(x)$ is the elephant population in millions and x is the number of years since 1900. If the elephant population was 12 million in 1900 and declined by 3% per year, write the function f that relates the elephant population to the number of years since 1900. If the population decline continues, estimate the population in 2020. Explain.

2. An international student conservation group submits the report shown. Use your answer from Item 1 as the initial population projected in 2020.

African Elephant Population Goals

- The population decline terminates in 2020.
- After 2020, the population starts to increase by a constant ratio of 1.05 each year (a growth rate of 5%).
- The goal is to restore the population to 2 million elephants.

Part A

The potential population increase of African elephants can be modeled by a function g, where $g(x)$ is the elephant population in millions and x is the number of years since 2020. Is g an exponential or a linear function? Write the function g that relates the elephant population to the number of years since 2020. Explain.

Part B

Analyze the meaning of *g* from Part A in terms of the population per year (in millions). Then determine the number of years it will take after 2020 to reach a population of 2 million elephants. Use a graphing calculator to help. Explain.

Part C

The conservation group graphs the function from Part A. A new study suggests that even when the population stops declining in 2020, the population will likely remain constant for 4 years before starting to increase by 5% as stated in the report. How will that affect the graph?

3. The data in the table show the costs for conservationists to monitor the population of elephants.

Year	1	2	3	4
Cost ($)	100,000	106,000	112,360	119,102

Part A

The data can be modeled by a geometric sequence. Write the explicit and recursive formulas for that geometric sequence. How would an exponential function *f* that models the data compare with the explicit formula? Explain.

Part B

Use *f* from Part A and the properties of rational exponents to find a new function, *m*, that represents the costs of population monitoring on a monthly basis.

Name 

Mid-Year Assessment

1. Solve for x.

$6x - 4(3x - 5) = 2$

Ⓐ $x = \frac{11}{3}$

Ⓑ $x = 3$

Ⓒ $x = -3$

Ⓓ $x = -\frac{11}{3}$

2. How many solutions are there to the following equation?

$5(x - 3) - 3x = 8x - 15 - 6x$

Ⓐ no solution

Ⓑ exactly one solution

Ⓒ exactly two solutions

Ⓓ infinitely many solutions

3. Solve the compound inequality $6 - x > 15$ or $2x - 9 \geq 3$.

Ⓐ $x > 9$ or $x \leq 6$

Ⓑ $x < 9$ or $x \geq -6$

Ⓒ $x > -9$ or $x \leq -6$

Ⓓ $x < -9$ or $x \geq 6$

4. Solve the absolute value equation.

$|x - 2| - 7 = -3$

5. What is the graph of $y = \frac{1}{2}x - 1$?

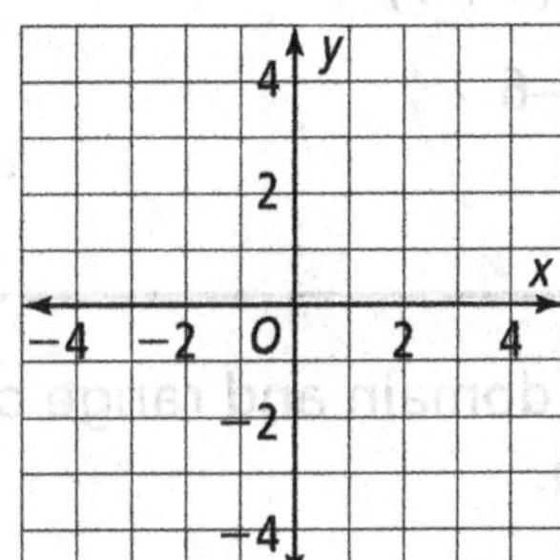

6. Which is an equation of the line through (−8, −4) and (4, 5)?

Ⓐ $y = \frac{3}{4}x + 2$

Ⓑ $y = -\frac{3}{4}x - 2$

Ⓒ $y = \frac{4}{3}x + \frac{31}{3}$

Ⓓ $y = -\frac{4}{3}x - \frac{1}{3}$

7. What is an equation in point-slope form of the line that passes through the point (6, −2) and has a slope of 3?

8. What are the x- and y-intercepts of the graph of $5x - 4y = 20$?

x-intercept: ____________

y-intercept: ____________

9. Which lines are perpendicular to the graph of $3x + 6y = 5$? Select all that apply.

Ⓐ $3x + 6y = 10$

Ⓑ $y = 2x - 1$

Ⓒ $y - 4 = 2(x + 7)$

Ⓓ $x - 2y = -6$

10. Identify the domain and range of the function.

x	y
7	9
9	9
12	10
21	9

domain: ____________

range: ____________

11. Emaan charges a fixed amount for a bracelet, with an additional charge for each charm a customer adds to the bracelet. Write a linear function *f* that Emaan can use to find the price of a bracelet.

Charms	5	10	20	30
Cost ($)	110	180	320	460

Ⓐ $f(x) = 2x + 100$

Ⓑ $f(x) = 14x + 40$

Ⓒ $f(x) = 6x + 80$

Ⓓ $f(x) = 12x + 60$

12. Given that $g(x) = f(x) + k$, identify the value of *k* for the functions *f* and *g* shown on the graph.

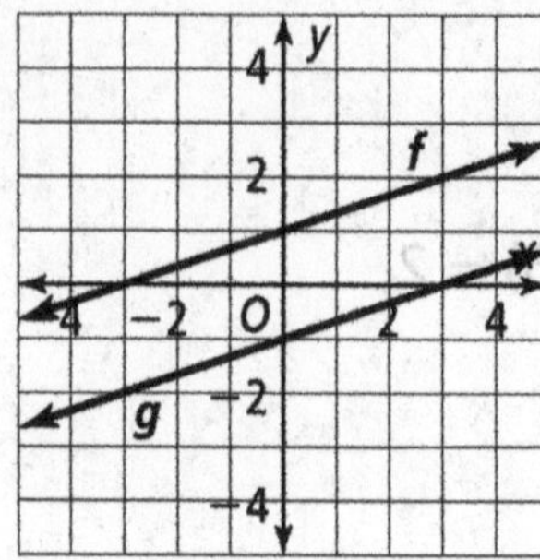

$k =$ ____________

13. Which of the following is an arithmetic sequence that could be modeled by an explicit formula expressed as a linear function?

Ⓐ −1, −8, −27, −64, −125, ...

Ⓑ −5, −2, 3, 10, 19, ...

Ⓒ −5, −1, 3, 7, 11, ...

Ⓓ $\frac{1}{2}, \frac{1}{4}, \frac{1}{8}, \frac{1}{16}, \frac{1}{32}, \ldots$

14. What is the solution of the system of equations?

$4x + 2y = -1$
$3x + 4y = 3$

15. How many solutions does the system of equations have?

$y = \frac{1}{5}x - \frac{2}{5}$
$x - 5y = 2$

16. Which of the following could be the equation of a trend line for the data shown in the scatter plot?

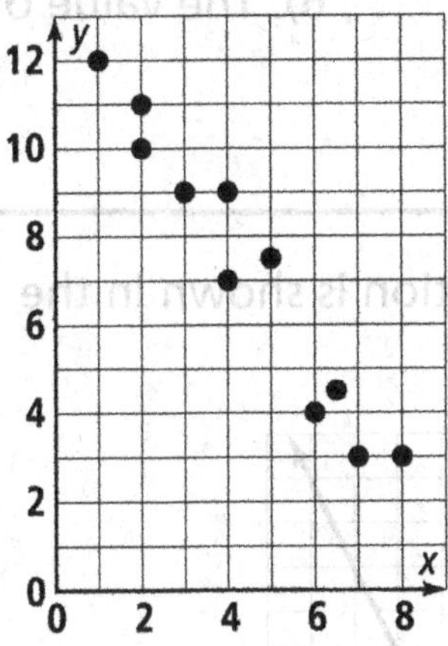

Ⓐ $y = -1.4x + 13$

Ⓑ $y = -14x + 13$

Ⓒ $y = 1.4x + 1$

Ⓓ $y = -7x$

17. What type of correlation does the scatter plot in Item 17 show?

Ⓐ positive

Ⓑ negative

Ⓒ none

Ⓓ cannot determine

18. Write $\sqrt[3]{9}$ using rational exponents.

Ⓐ $3^{\frac{1}{9}}$

Ⓑ 3

Ⓒ $3^{\frac{2}{3}}$

Ⓓ 3^9

19. Solve the equation for *x*.

$(5^{\frac{x}{6}})(5^{\frac{x}{2}}) = 5^{16}$

______

20. Given the sequence $24, 12, 6, 3, \frac{3}{2}, \ldots$, complete the following: consecutive terms of the sequence have a common ______, so it is a ______ sequence. A function *f* that returns the *n*th term of the sequence for an input *n* is ______.

21. What are the explicit and recursive formulas for the following geometric sequence?

8, 10, 12.5, 15.625, ...

explicit: ______

recursive: ______

22. The recursive formula for a geometric sequence is $a_n = 7a_{n-1}$ with an initial value of $a_1 = \frac{1}{7}$. What is an explicit formula for the sequence?

Ⓐ $a_n = \frac{1}{7}(1)^{n-7}$

Ⓑ $a_n = 7\left(\frac{1}{7}\right)^{n-1}$

Ⓒ $a_n = \frac{1}{7}(7)^{n-1}$

Ⓓ $a_n = 7(7)^{n-1}$

23. How does the graph of the function $g(x) = 5^x + 1$ differ from the graph of $f(x) = 5^x$?

Ⓐ It is translated right 1 unit.

Ⓑ It is translated left 1 unit.

Ⓒ It is translated up 1 unit.

Ⓓ It is translated down 1 unit.

24. Compare the graph of $f(x) = 2^x$ and the graph of the exponential function g described in the table. Select all that apply.

x	0	1	2	3	4
$g(x)$	$\frac{1}{8}$	$\frac{1}{4}$	$\frac{1}{2}$	1	2

Ⓐ They have the same domain.

Ⓑ They have the same range.

Ⓒ They have the same asymptote.

Ⓓ They have the same y-intercept.

25. Which inequality does the graph represent?

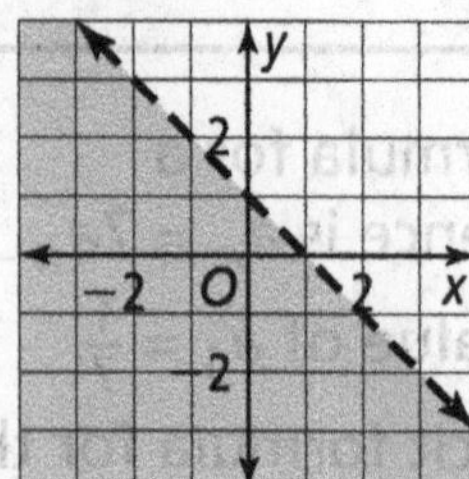

Ⓐ $y < -x - 1$

Ⓑ $y < -x + 1$

Ⓒ $y < x - 1$

Ⓓ $y < x + 1$

26. The graph of an absolute value function $f(x) = a|x|$ includes the point (1, 6). Another point on the graph is (______, 6). The value of a is ______.

27. Which function is shown in the graph?

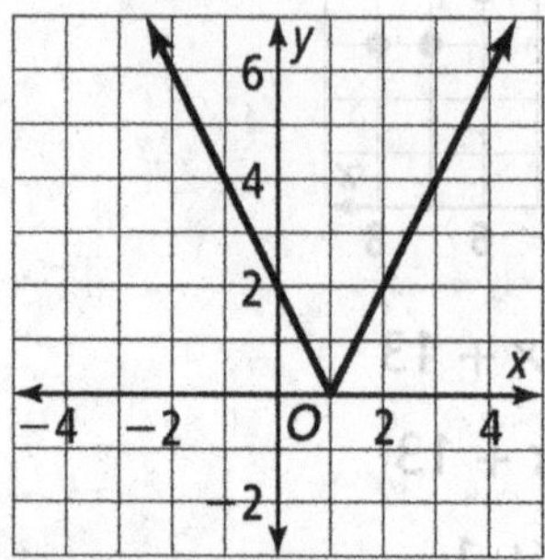

Ⓐ $f(x) = 2|x - 1|$

Ⓑ $f(x) = 2|x + 1|$

Ⓒ $f(x) = -2|x - 1|$

Ⓓ $f(x) = -2|x + 1|$

28. The two-way frequency table shows results of a survey.

Movie Preference

	Action	Comedy	Totals
Grade 11	12	8	20
Grade 12	14	16	30
Totals	26	24	50

What percentage of the students in the survey are eleventh graders?

Ⓐ 16%

Ⓑ 20%

Ⓒ 24%

Ⓓ 40%

29. What is the solution of the system of equations?

$3x - 2y = -9$

$4x + 3y = 22$

30. Which relation is a function?

Ⓐ (8, −4), (8, 4), (6, −3), (6, 3), (0, 0)

Ⓑ (4, 7), (8, 5), (6, 4), (5, 3), (4, 2)

Ⓒ (0, 0), (1, 1), (2, 2), (3, 3), (4, 7)

Ⓓ (0, 0), (1, 0), (1, 1), (2, 1), (1, 2)

31. What is the value of x in this equation?

$7x - 2(3x - 1) = 4$

Ⓐ 2 Ⓒ 4

Ⓑ 3 Ⓓ 5

32. Write the formula for the volume of a rectangular box, $V = lwh$, in terms of h. Then find the height h of a box for which $V = 96\text{ cm}^3$, $l = 8$ cm, and $w = 2$ cm.

formula: ____________________

height: ____________________

33. Damian works after school. Each day he earns a set amount, plus an hourly wage, as shown in the table. Write a linear function f that Damian can use to determine his pay.

Hours	1	1.5	2	2.5	3
Pay	22	28	34	40	46

34. Graph the inequality $y > \frac{2}{3}x - 1$.

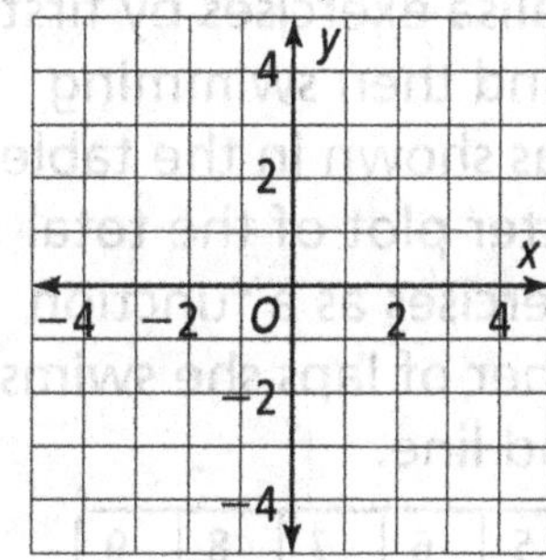

35. In the graph of an inequality, the region below a dashed horizontal line through the point (4, 1) is shaded. What inequality does the graph represent?

Ⓐ $x < 4$

Ⓑ $y < 1$

Ⓒ $y > 1$

Ⓓ $x > 4$

36. For a fundraiser, a group plans to sell granola bars and bottles of water. Ten granola bars and twelve bottles of water cost $23. Five granola bars and four bottles of water cost $10. The group wants the income from the fundraiser to be at least $150. Write an inequality to show the numbers of granola bars x and bottles of water y that the group needs to sell.

37. Each day, Talisa exercises by first stretching and then swimming some laps, as shown in the table. Make a scatter plot of the total time she exercises as a function of the number of laps she swims. Draw a trend line.

Laps	5	6	7	8	9
Total Time	25	28	29	30	32

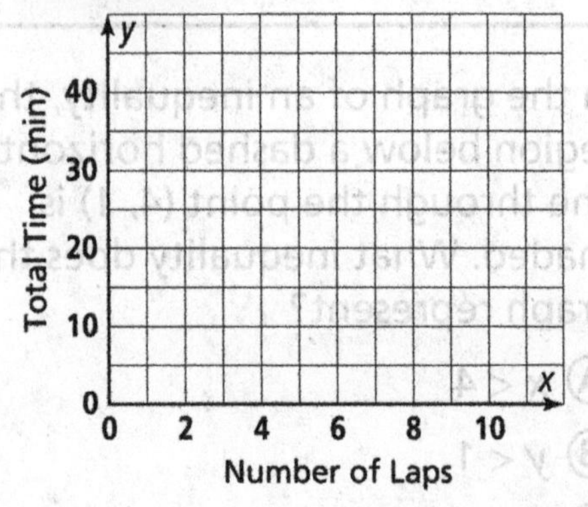

38. Which could be an equation of a trend line for the data in Item 37?

Ⓐ $y = \frac{1}{2}x + 15$

Ⓑ $y = 2x + 15$

Ⓒ $y = \frac{1}{2}x + 25$

Ⓓ $y = 2x + 25$

39. Complete the table of residuals for the trend line in Item 38.

x	5	6	7	8	9
Residual					

40. Which r-value suggests a strong negative correlation?

Ⓐ $r = 0.1859$

Ⓑ $r = -0.1859$

Ⓒ $r = 0.9874$

Ⓓ $r = -0.9874$

Name ______________________________

6 Readiness Assessment

1. How would you define a pair of parallel lines?

Ⓐ Parallel lines intersect at right angles.

Ⓑ Parallel lines intersect to form both acute and obtuse angles.

Ⓒ Parallel lines never intersect.

Ⓓ None of the above

2. How would you define a pair of perpendicular lines?

Ⓐ Perpendicular lines intersect at right angles.

Ⓑ Perpendicular lines intersect to form both acute and obtuse angles.

Ⓒ Perpendicular lines never intersect.

Ⓓ None of the above

3. What is the measure of $\angle XYZ$?

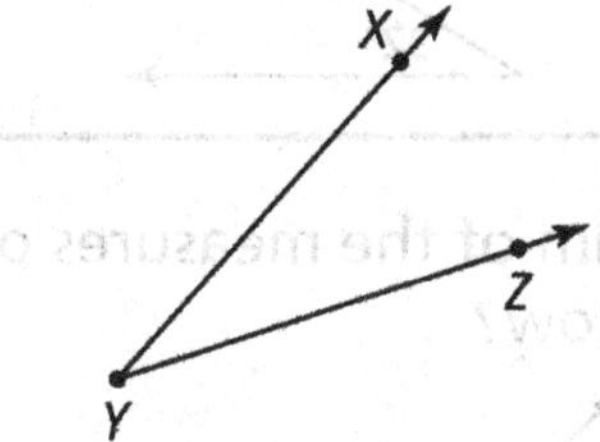

Ⓐ 120 Ⓒ 180

Ⓑ 90 Ⓓ 30

4. What is the name of the angle formed by $\overrightarrow{BA}$ and $\overrightarrow{BC}$?

Ⓐ $\angle BAC$ Ⓒ $\angle ACB$

Ⓑ $\angle ABC$ Ⓓ $\angle CAB$

5. In $\triangle ABC$, what is the measure of side c in centimeters?

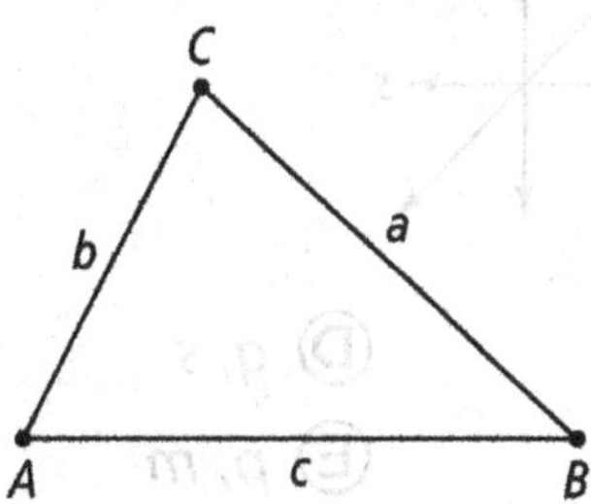

6. What is the midpoint between 2 and 10?

7. What is the distance between 4 and 17?

8. In $\triangle ABC$, if $m\angle CAD = 29°$, what is $m\angle DAB$?

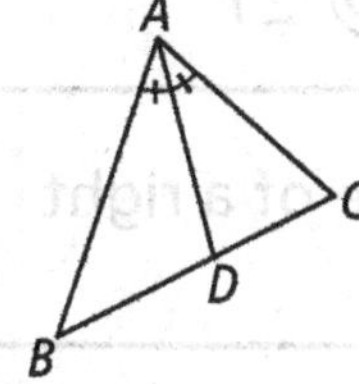

9. In the figure, which two lines appear to be parallel?

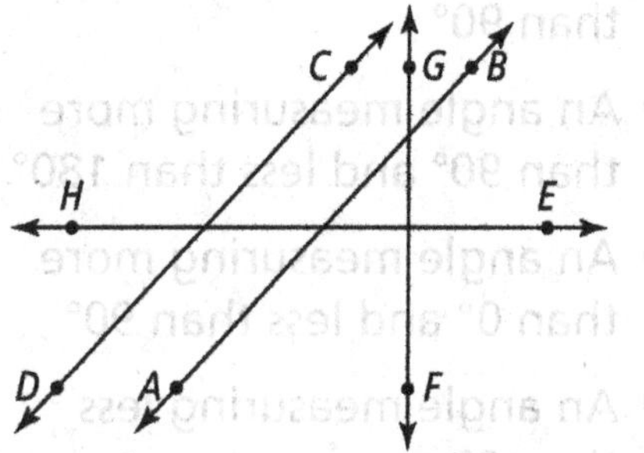

Ⓐ $\overleftrightarrow{AB}$ and $\overleftrightarrow{GF}$ Ⓒ $\overleftrightarrow{AB}$ and $\overleftrightarrow{CD}$

Ⓑ $\overleftrightarrow{HE}$ and $\overleftrightarrow{GF}$ Ⓓ $\overleftrightarrow{HE}$ and $\overleftrightarrow{CD}$

10. Identify all pairs of lines that appear to be perpendicular. Select all that apply.

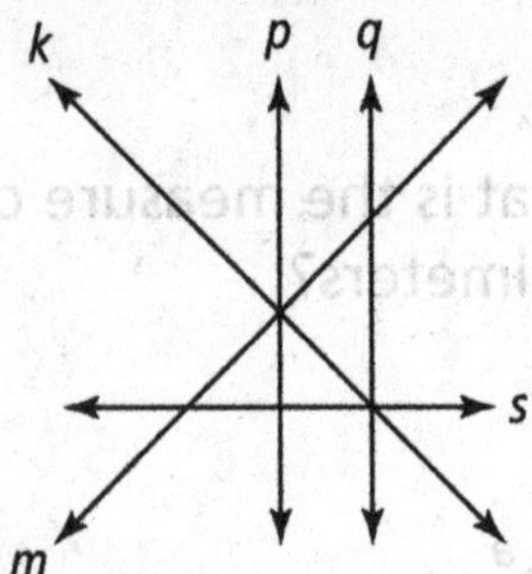

Ⓐ k, m
Ⓑ k, s
Ⓒ p, s
Ⓓ q, s
Ⓔ p, m
Ⓕ q, k

11. What is the vertex of the angle below?

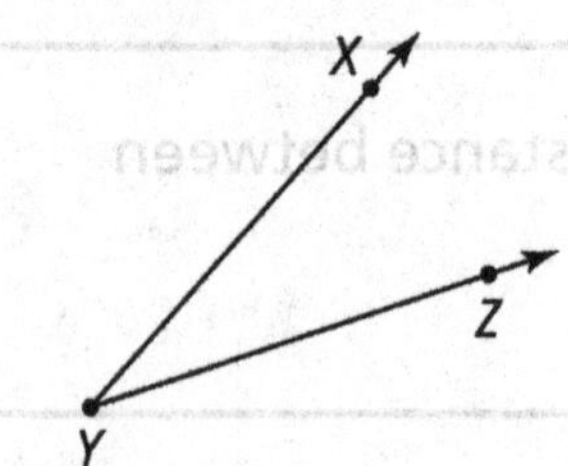

Ⓐ X
Ⓑ Y
Ⓒ Z
Ⓓ ∠Y

12. What is the measure of a right angle?

13. What is the best description of an acute angle?

Ⓐ An angle measuring more than 90°
Ⓑ An angle measuring more than 90° and less than 180°
Ⓒ An angle measuring more than 0° and less than 90°
Ⓓ An angle measuring less than 0°

14. In $\triangle ABC$, what is the length of $\overline{BC}$?

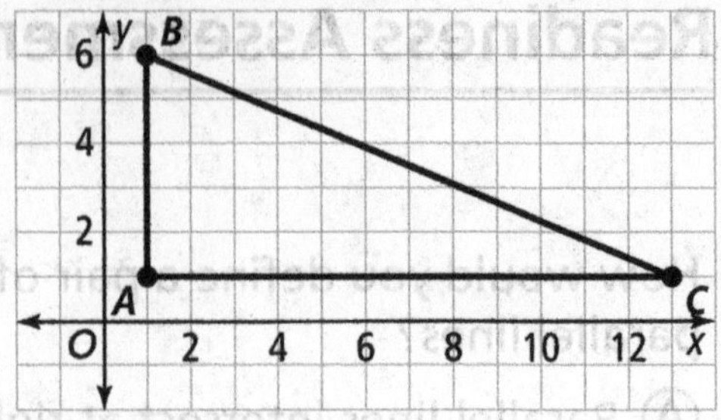

Ⓐ 169
Ⓑ 13
Ⓒ 17
Ⓓ 15

15. Is $2^2 + 3^2 = 4^2$ a true statement? Explain.

Ⓐ Yes; $7 + 9 = 16$
Ⓑ No; $4 + 9 \neq 16$
Ⓒ Yes; $4 + 9 = 13$
Ⓓ No; $7 + 9 \neq 16$

16. What is the sum of the measures of the angles below?

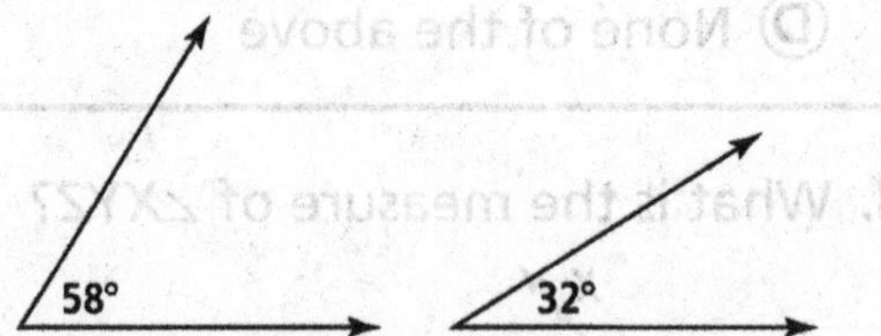

17. What is the sum of the measures of the angles below?

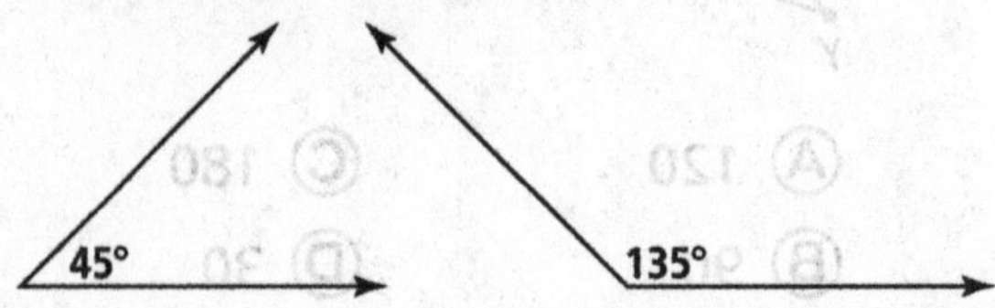

Name ______________________________

6-1 Lesson Quiz

Measuring Segments and Angles

1. Which of the following statements are true? Select all that apply.

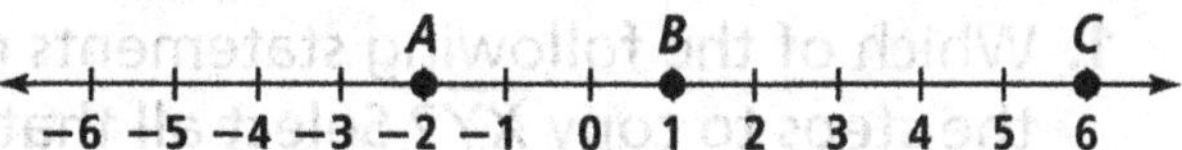

Ⓐ The length of $\overline{AB}$ is −3.

Ⓑ $d(B, C) = BC = |6 - 1|$

Ⓒ $AB + AC = BC$

Ⓓ $AB + BC = AC$

2. Which of the following statements are true? Select all that apply.

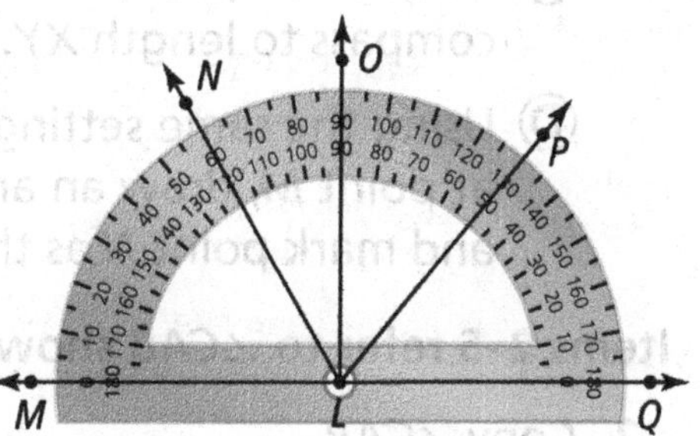

Ⓐ $m\angle MLN = 120$

Ⓑ $m\angle QLP = 50$

Ⓒ $m\angle NLO + m\angle OLP = m\angle NLP$

Ⓓ $m\angle QLP + m\angle PLO = m\angle MLN + m\angle NLO$

3. Points *A*, *B*, and *C* are collinear, and *B* lies between *A* and *C*. If $AC = 48$, $AB = 2x + 2$, and $BC = 3x + 6$, what is *BC*?

4. Point *P* is the interior of $\angle OZQ$. If $m\angle OZQ = 125$ and $m\angle OZP = 62$, what is $m\angle PZQ$?

5. In the figure shown, $AB = 8$ and $AD = 5$. What is *BC*?

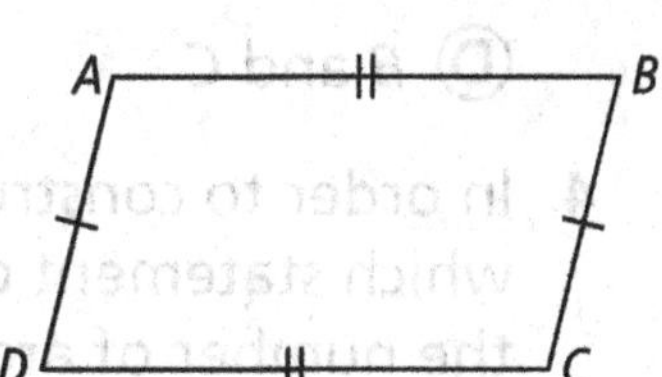

6-2 Lesson Quiz

Basic Constructions

1. Which of the following statements describe the steps to copy $\overline{XY}$? Select all that apply.

   Ⓐ Use a ruler to draw line ℓ and label point M.

   Ⓑ Use a straightedge to draw line ℓ and label point M.

   Ⓒ Place a compass point at X and open the compass to length XY.

   Ⓓ Using the same setting, place the compass at point M, draw an arc through line ℓ, and mark point N as the intersection.

Items 2–5 refer to ∠*CAB* shown.

2. Copy $\angle CAB$.

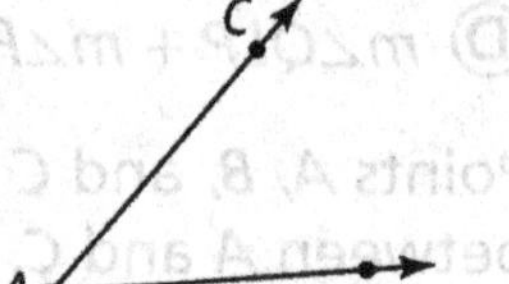

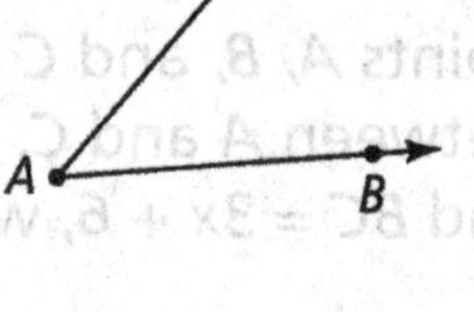

3. In order to construct the interior point of $\angle CAB$ for the angle bisector, where should you place the compass point?

   Ⓐ A

   Ⓑ B

   Ⓒ C

   Ⓓ B and C

4. In order to construct the perpendicular bisector of $\overline{AB}$, which statement describes the compass settings and the number of arc intersections needed?

   Ⓐ less than half the length of $\overline{AB}$; 1

   Ⓑ less than half the length of $\overline{AB}$; 2

   Ⓒ more than half the length of $\overline{AB}$; 1

   Ⓓ more than half the length of $\overline{AB}$; 2

5. Construct the intersection of the perpendicular bisector of $\overline{AB}$ and the angle bisector of $\angle CAB$.

Name ______________________

6-3 Lesson Quiz

Midpoint and Distance

Items 1–3 refer to the graph shown.

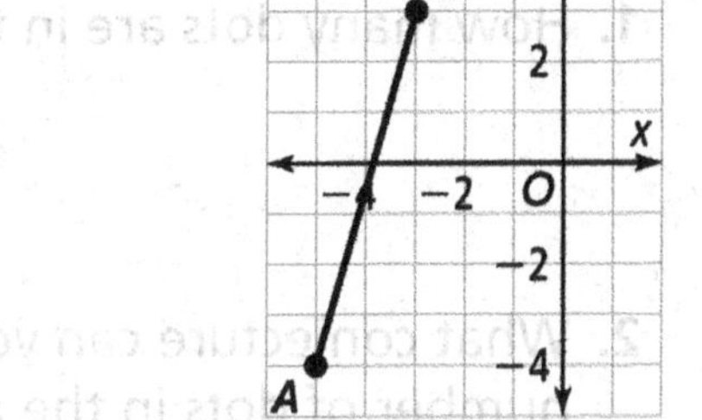

1. What is the midpoint of $\overline{AB}$?

2. What is the length of $\overline{AB}$? Round your answer to the nearest hundredth.

3. What are the coordinates of the point $\frac{3}{4}$ of the way from A to B?

4. Which of the following represent the distance formula? Select all that apply.

Ⓐ $d = \sqrt{(x_1 - x_2)^2 + (y_1 - y_2)^2}$

Ⓑ $d = \sqrt{(x_2 - x_1)^2 + (y_2 - y_1)^2}$

Ⓒ $d = \sqrt{(x_2 + x_1)^2 + (y_2 + y_1)^2}$

Ⓓ $d = \sqrt{|x_2 - x_1|^2 + |y_2 - y_1|^2}$

5. What is an expression for the distance between the origin and a point $P(x, y)$?

Ⓐ $d = 0$

Ⓑ $d = \sqrt{x^2 + y^2}$

Ⓒ $d = \sqrt{x^2 - y^2}$

Ⓓ $d = \sqrt{y^2 - x^2}$

6-4 Lesson Quiz

Inductive Reasoning

Items 1 and 2 refer to diagram shown.

1. How many dots are in the next pattern?

2. What conjecture can you make about the number of dots in the *n*th pattern?

Ⓐ $\frac{n^2}{2}$

Ⓑ $\frac{n(n+1)}{2}$

Ⓒ $\frac{n(n-1)}{2}$

Ⓓ $\frac{(n-1)(n+1)}{2}$

3. Which number is a counterexample to the following statement? *All numbers that are divisible by 2 are divisible by 4.*

Ⓐ 0

Ⓑ 12

Ⓒ 28

Ⓓ 42

4. Determine whether each conjecture is true for all integers.

If n^2 is odd, then n is odd.	Yes	No
If m and n are odd, then mn is even.	Yes	No

5. Based on the data in the table, how many members would you expect in the band in 2018?

Year	Number of Band Members
2014	40
2015	46
2016	54
2017	64

Name ______________________________

6-5 Lesson Quiz

Conditional Statements

1. Identify the hypothesis and conclusion of the following statement: *A rectangle must have four congruent angles.*

   A polygon is a rectangle.

   The polygon has four congruent angles.

2. What is the truth value of the following statement?

   If a number is divisible by 3, then it is odd.

3. Which statement is the converse of the following conditional? *If it is raining, then the ground is wet.*

   Ⓐ If it is not raining, then the ground is not wet.
   Ⓑ If the ground is not wet, then it is not raining.
   Ⓒ If the ground is wet, then it is not raining.
   Ⓓ If the ground is wet, then it is raining.

4. Identify the biconditional for the following statement. *If M is the midpoint of* $\overline{AB}$, *then* $\overline{AM} \cong \overline{MB}$.

   Ⓐ *M* is the midpoint of $\overline{AB}$ only if $\overline{AM} \cong \overline{MB}$.
   Ⓑ $\overline{AM} \cong \overline{MB}$ only if *M* is the midpoint of $\overline{AB}$.
   Ⓒ *M* is the midpoint of $\overline{AB}$ if and only if $\overline{AM} \cong \overline{MB}$.
   Ⓓ If $\overline{AM} \cong \overline{MB}$, then *M is the midpoint of* $\overline{AB}$.

5. Identify the conditionals and truth values implied by the following biconditional. Select all that apply.

   Two lines are parallel if and only if they do not intersect.

   Ⓐ If two lines are parallel, then they do not intersect; T.
   Ⓑ If two lines are not parallel, then they intersect; F.
   Ⓒ If two lines do not intersect, then they are parallel; T.
   Ⓓ If two lines do not intersect, then they are parallel; F.

6-6 Lesson Quiz

Deductive Reasoning

Assume all given information to be true.

1. If $m\angle A$ is less than 90°, then $\angle A$ is an acute angle. $m\angle A = 75°$. What can you logically conclude using the Law of Detachment?

Ⓐ $\angle A$ is acute.

Ⓑ $\angle A$ is right.

Ⓒ $\angle A$ is obtuse.

Ⓓ Not enough information

2. What conclusion can you draw from the following statements using the Law of Syllogism?

- If a figure is a square, then it has four sides.
- If a figure has four sides, then it is not a triangle.

Ⓐ If a figure is not a triangle, then it is a square.

Ⓑ If a figure has four sides, then it is a square.

Ⓒ If a figure is a square, then it is not a triangle.

Ⓓ If a figure is not a triangle, then it has four sides.

3. Can you determine whether the conclusion is true from the given information? Circle *Yes* or *No*.

Given: If *A*, *B*, *C*, and *D* are collinear, then they lie in the same plane.
A, *B*, *C*, and *D* are collinear.

Conclusion: *A*, *B*, *C*, and *D* lie in the same plane. Yes No

Given: If *A*, *B*, *C*, and *D* lie in the same plane, then they are collinear.
A, *B*, *C*, and *D* lie in the same plane.

Conclusion: *A*, *B*, *C*, and *D* are collinear. Yes No

4. In the Law of Syllogism, suppose $p \rightarrow q$ and $q \rightarrow r$ are true. If the truth value of p is T, what is the truth value of r?

5. If *C* lies between *A* and *B* on $\overline{AB}$, then $AC + CB = AB$. What can you logically conclude about $\overline{AB}$?

5.5 5.2
A C B

Name ______________________________

6-7 Lesson Quiz

Writing Proofs

Items 1 and 2 refer to the figure shown.

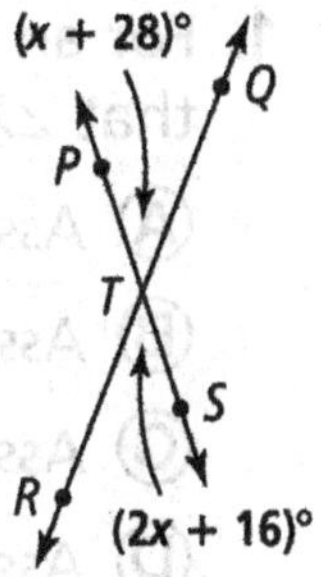

1. What is $m\angle PTQ$?

Ⓐ 12

Ⓑ 40

Ⓒ 50

Ⓓ 140

2. What is $m\angle PTR$?

Ⓐ 12

Ⓑ 40

Ⓒ 50

Ⓓ 140

Items 3–5 refer to the figure shown.

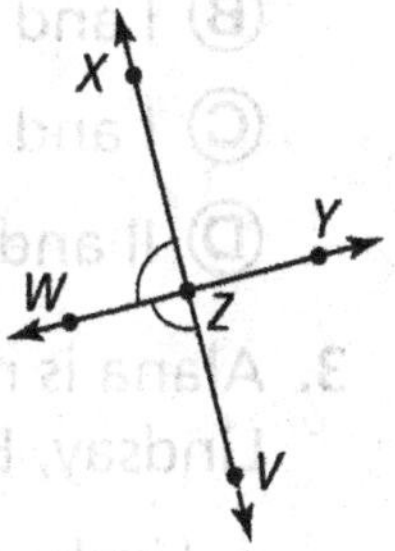

3. Supply the missing reasons in the proof.

4. Supply the missing statements in the proof.

Statement	Reason
1) $\angle WZX \cong \angle WZV$	1) Given
2) $\angle WZX$ and $\angle WZV$ are a linear pair.	2)
3) $m\angle WZX + m\angle WZV = 180$	3)
4)	4) Supplementary congruent angles are right angles.
5)	5) Def. of ⊥ lines

5. What new theorems were used in the above proof?

Name ______________________________

6-8 Lesson Quiz

Indirect Proof

1. For an indirect proof, what is the first step to prove that $\angle X$ is a right angle?

   Ⓐ Assume that $\angle X$ is an acute angle.

   Ⓑ Assume that $\angle X$ is an obtuse angle.

   Ⓒ Assume that $\angle X$ is not a right angle.

   Ⓓ Assume that $\angle X$ is a right angle.

2. Which two statements contradict each other?

   I. $\angle 1$ and $\angle 2$ are complementary angles.

   II. $m\angle 2 = 65$

   III. $m\angle 1 + m\angle 2 + m\angle 3 = 90$; $m\angle 3 \neq 0$

   Ⓐ No statements contradict each other.

   Ⓑ I and II

   Ⓒ I and III

   Ⓓ II and III

3. Alana is riding a Ferris wheel with Brianna and either Lindsay, Emily, or Janelle.

   - Lindsay is at the movies.
   - Emily does not like caramel apples.
   - Janelle is afraid of heights and won't go on rides over 15 feet high.

   Who is the third person riding the Ferris wheel?

4. If a conditional statement is true, what statement must also be true?

5. When writing an indirect proof, what statement will be contradicted?

Name ______________________________

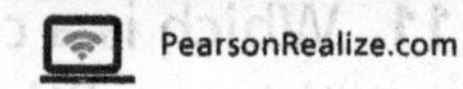

6 Topic Assessment Form A

1. If $DM = 25$, what is the value of r?

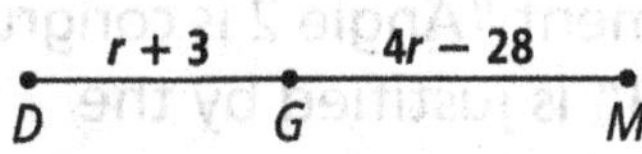

Ⓐ 12

Ⓑ 13

Ⓒ 14

Ⓓ 15

Items 2–3. Points P, Q, and S are collinear.

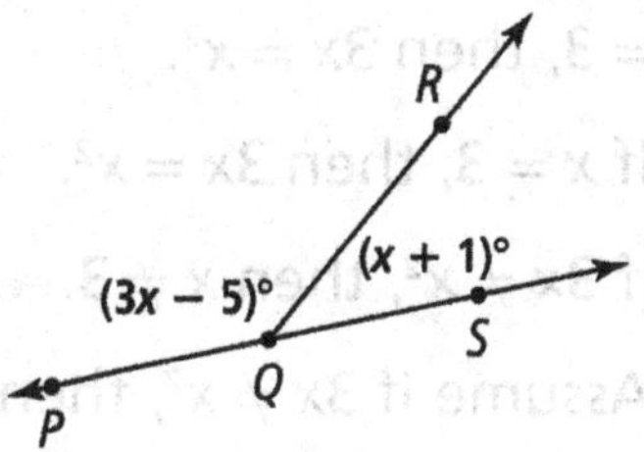

2. What is $m\angle PQR$?

3. If a ray QT bisects $\angle RQS$, what will be the measure of one of the resulting angles?

4. Points L, M, and N are collinear. You are given $LM = 13$ and $LN = 20$. What is a possible value of MN?

Ⓐ 6 Ⓒ 8

Ⓑ 7 Ⓓ 9

5. Ray BD bisects $\angle ABC$ so that $m\angle DBC = (x + 6)$ and $m\angle ABD = (2x - 12)$. What is x?

Ⓐ 12 Ⓒ 16

Ⓑ 14 Ⓓ 18

6. What is the distance between points $F(2, 9)$ and $G(4, 14)$? Round to the nearest whole number.

Items 7–8. Use the number line below.

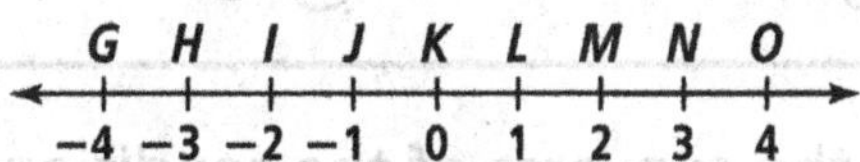

7. What is $KN + IK$?

8. What is the coordinate of the midpoint of $\overline{GO}$?

Items 9–11. Use the following conditional:

If a number is an integer, then it is either positive or negative.

9. Which is the hypothesis of the conditional?

Ⓐ A number is an integer.

Ⓑ A number is either positive or negative.

Ⓒ A number is both positive and negative.

Ⓓ A number is not an integer.

10. Which is the conclusion of the conditional?

Ⓐ A number is an integer.

Ⓑ A number is either positive or negative.

Ⓒ A number is both positive and negative.

Ⓓ A number is not an integer.

11. Which is a counterexample for the conditional?

Ⓐ 0
Ⓑ 1
Ⓒ |1|
Ⓓ 2

12. What is the length of a segment with endpoints at (−3, 4) and (4, 4)?

Ⓐ 1
Ⓑ 4
Ⓒ 7
Ⓓ 8

13. Is the converse of the conditional below true?

If a polygon is a triangle, then it has exactly three sides.

14. Which statements below are true? Select all that apply.

Ⓐ If $p \rightarrow q$ and q are true, then p is true.

Ⓑ If $p \rightarrow q$ and p are true, then q is true.

Ⓒ If $p \rightarrow q$ and $q \rightarrow r$ are true, then $p \rightarrow r$ is true.

Ⓓ If $p \rightarrow q$ and r are true, then $q \rightarrow r$ is true.

15. Use the Law of Detachment to make a conclusion.

If a person wants to get a car, that person must buy car insurance. Jayla wants to get a car.

Ⓐ Jayla has car insurance.

Ⓑ Jayla has her driver's license.

Ⓒ Jayla must get her driver's license.

Ⓓ Jayla must buy car insurance.

Items 16–18. Use the diagram shown.

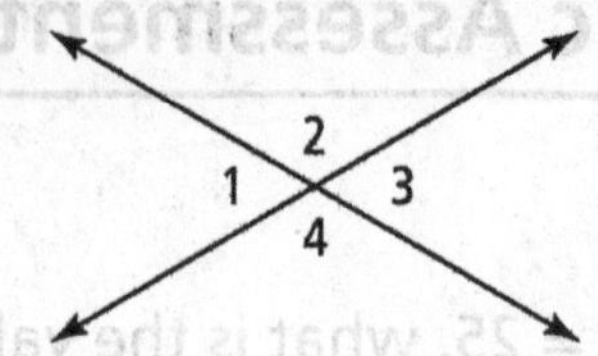

16. The statement "Angle 2 is congruent to angle 4" is justified by the ________________.

17. If $m\angle 1$ equals $(4x + 2)$ and $m\angle 2$ equals 110, what is the value of x?

Ⓐ 14
Ⓑ 15
Ⓒ 16
Ⓓ 17

18. Which could be the first step of an indirect proof of the conditional below? Select all that apply.

If $x = 3$, then $3x = x^2$.

Ⓐ If $x = 3$, then $3x = x^2$.

Ⓑ If $3x \neq x^2$, then $x \neq 3$.

Ⓒ Assume if $3x \neq x^2$, then $x \neq 3$.

Ⓓ Assume if $x \neq 3$, then $3x \neq x^2$.

Items 19–20. Neil Armstrong was the first person to walk on the moon.

If a person was the first to walk on the moon, then that person was Neil Armstrong.

19. If a person ________ Neil Armstrong, then that person ________ the first person to walk on the moon.

20. Since Neil Armstrong was the first person to walk on the moon, the contrapositive is ________.

Since the contrapositive is ________, the ________ must be true.

Name

6 Topic Assessment Form B

1. If $DM = 35$, what is the value of r?

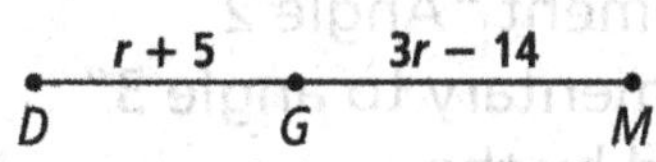

Ⓐ 11

Ⓑ 12

Ⓒ 13

Ⓓ 14

Items 2–3. Points P, Q, and S are collinear.

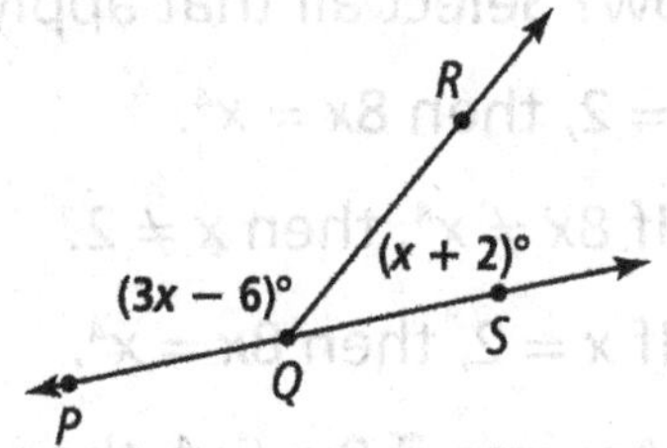

2. What is $m\angle PQR$?

3. If a ray QT bisects $\angle RQS$, what will be the measure of one of the resulting angles?

4. Points L, M, and N are collinear. You are given $LM = 18$ and $LN = 27$. What is a possible value of MN?

Ⓐ 6 Ⓒ 8

Ⓑ 7 Ⓓ 9

5. Ray BD bisects $\angle ABC$ so that $m\angle DBC = (x + 8)°$ and $m\angle ABD = (2x - 15)°$. What is x?

Ⓐ 16 Ⓒ 23

Ⓑ 21 Ⓓ 28

6. What is the distance between points $F(2, 11)$ and $G(5, 16)$? Round to the nearest whole number.

Items 7–8. Use the number line below.

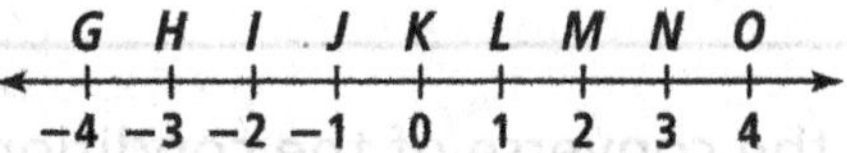

7. What is $KM + IK$?

8. What is the coordinate of the midpoint of $\overline{GK}$?

Items 9–11. Use the following conditional:

If a number is positive, then it is a whole number and an integer.

9. Which is the conclusion of the conditional?

Ⓐ A number is an integer.

Ⓑ A number is either a whole number or an integer.

Ⓒ A number is a both a whole number and an integer.

Ⓓ A number is positive.

10. Which is the hypothesis of the conditional?

Ⓐ A number is an integer.

Ⓑ A number is both a whole number and an integer.

Ⓒ A number is either a whole number or an integer.

Ⓓ A number is positive.

11. Which is a counterexample for the conditional?

Ⓐ −1
Ⓑ 0
Ⓒ $\frac{1}{2}$
Ⓓ 1

12. What is the length of a segment with endpoints at (−4, 6) and (3, 6)?

Ⓐ 1
Ⓑ 5
Ⓒ 7
Ⓓ 9

13. Is the converse of the conditional below true?

If a polygon is a hexagon, then it has exactly six sides.

14. Which statements below are true? Select all that apply.

Ⓐ If $p \to q$ and p are true, then q is true.

Ⓑ If $p \to q$ and q are true, then p is true.

Ⓒ If $p \to q$ and $q \to r$ are true, then $p \to r$ is true.

Ⓓ If $p \to q$ and r are true, then $q \to r$ is true.

15. Use the Law of Detachment to make a conclusion.

If a person parks a car in town, that person must pay the meter. Aidan parks his car in town.

Ⓐ Aidan pays the meter.

Ⓑ Aidan must pay the meter.

Ⓒ Aidan has his driver's license.

Ⓓ Aidan parks in front of the meter.

Items 16–18. Use the diagram shown.

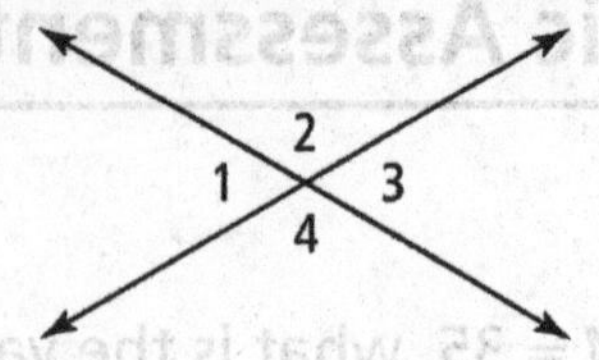

16. The statement "Angle 2 is supplementary to angle 3" is justified by the ________________.

17. If $m\angle 1$ equals $(4x + 2)°$ and $m\angle 4$ equals 110°, what is the value of x?

Ⓐ 17
Ⓑ 28
Ⓒ 30
Ⓓ 32

18. Which could be the first step of an indirect proof of the conditional below? Select all that apply.

If $x = 2$, then $8x = x^4$.

Ⓐ If $8x \neq x^4$, then $x \neq 2$.

Ⓑ If $x = 2$, then $8x = x^4$.

Ⓒ Assume if $8x \neq x^4$, then $x \neq 2$.

Ⓓ Assume if $x \neq 2$, then $8x \neq x^4$.

Items 19–20. Marie Curie discovered radium. Prove the conditional by proving the contrapositive.

If a person discovered radium, then that person was Marie Curie.

19. If a person ________ Marie Curie, then that person ________ discover radium.

20. Since Marie Curie discovered radium, the contrapositive is ________.

Since the contrapositive is ________, the ________ must be true.

6 Performance Assessment Form A

Raheem is making a miniature replica of the De Young Museum. From a brochure, he has a drawing of the garden and first floor.

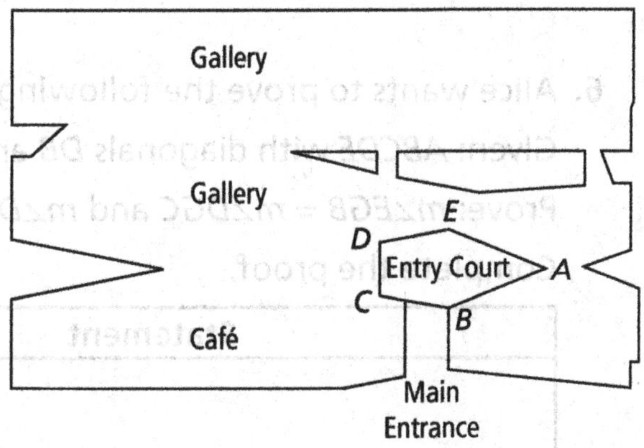

1. Measure the angles and side lengths of the Entry Court. Describe the shape of the Entry Court. What sides and angles are equivalent?

2. Alice plotted the entry court on graph paper. Find the midpoint of side CD. Construct the angle bisector of $\angle A$. Does the angle bisector pass through the midpoint?

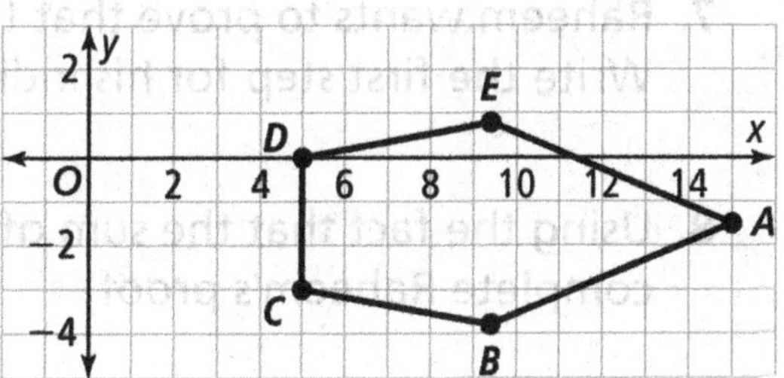

3. Construct a line perpendicular to the angle bisector through point E. Does the perpendicular line pass through point B? Is the midpoint of BE on the perpendicular line? Explain.

4. Raheem said, "In pentagon $ABCDE$, if the angle bisector of $\angle A$ passes through the midpoint of side CD, then $AB = AE$, $BC = ED$, $m\angle B = m\angle E$, and $m\angle C = m\angle D$." Is that true? Explain.

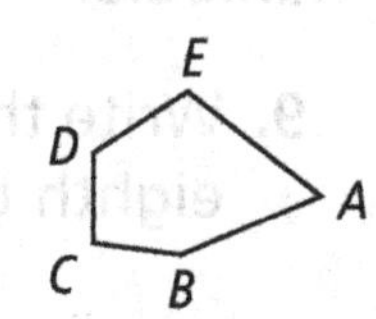

5. Alice writes, "In a pentagon *ABCDE*, if $AB = AE$, $BC = ED$, $m\angle B = m\angle E$, and $m\angle C = m\angle D$, the angle bisector of $\angle A$ passes through the midpoint of side *CD*. The Entry Court polygon *ABCDE* has $AB = AE$, $BC = ED$, $m\angle B = m\angle E$, and $m\angle C = m\angle D$. Therefore, the angle bisector of $\angle A$ passes through the midpoint of side *CD*." What law of deductive reasoning is she using?

6. Alice wants to prove the following:

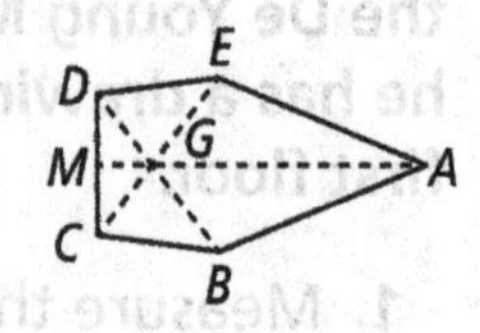

Given: *ABCDE* with diagonals *DB* and *EC* and intersection point *G*

Prove: $m\angle EGB = m\angle DGC$ and $m\angle DGE = m\angle BGC$

Complete the proof.

Statement	Reason

7. Raheem wants to prove that the sum of the angles of *ABCDE* is equal to 540°. Write the first step for his indirect proof.

8. Using the fact that the sum of the angles in a quadrilateral is equal to 360°, complete Raheem's proof.

At each vertex of the entry court, Diborah wants to display a sculpture. The sculptures are of triangular numbers.

9. Write the first seven terms of the sequence. Explain how you find the eighth term.

10. Write a conjecture about the number of dots in the *n*th term.

Name ______________________________

6 Performance Assessment Form B

G'ahan goes to Long Beach for the Grand Prix race every year. He has a map of the race track from last year.

1. Measure the angles and side lengths of *ABCDE* to estimate the measures on the track. Describe the shape of the polygon *ABCDE*. Which sides and angles are congruent?

2. Louis plotted the track on graph paper. Find the midpoint of side *CD*. Construct the angle bisector of angle *A*. Does the angle bisector pass through the midpoint?

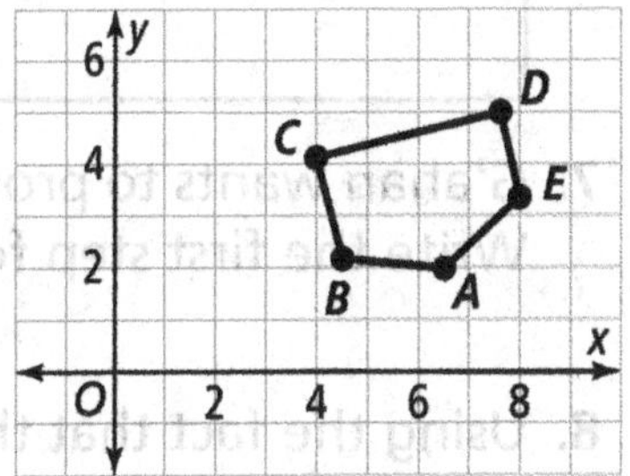

3. Construct a line perpendicular to the angle bisector through point *E*. Does the perpendicular line pass through point *B*? Is the midpoint of *BE* on the perpendicular line? Explain.

4. G'ahan said, "In pentagon *ABCDE*, since the angle bisector of angle *A* does not pass through the midpoint of side *CD*, no sides or angles have equal measures." Is that true? Explain.

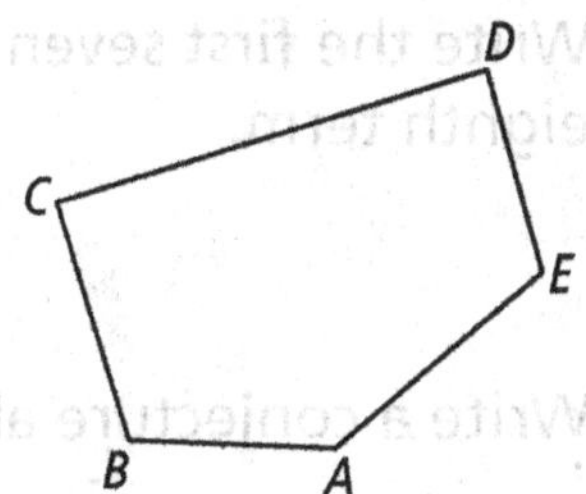

5. Zoe writes, "In pentagon *ABCDE*, if $AB = DE$, $BC \neq ED$, $m\angle B \neq m\angle E$, and $m\angle C = m\angle D$, the angle bisector of angle *A* does not pass through the midpoint of side *CD*. The track polygon *ABCDE* has $AB = DE$, $BC \neq ED$, $m\angle B \neq m\angle E$, and $m\angle C = m\angle D$. Therefore, the angle bisector of angle *A* does not pass through the midpoint of side *CD*." What law of deductive reasoning is she using?

6. Zoe wants to prove the following:

   Given: *ABCDE* with diagonals *DA* and *EB* and intersection point *G*

   Prove: $m\angle DGE = m\angle AGB$ and $m\angle BGD = m\angle EGA$

   Complete the proof.

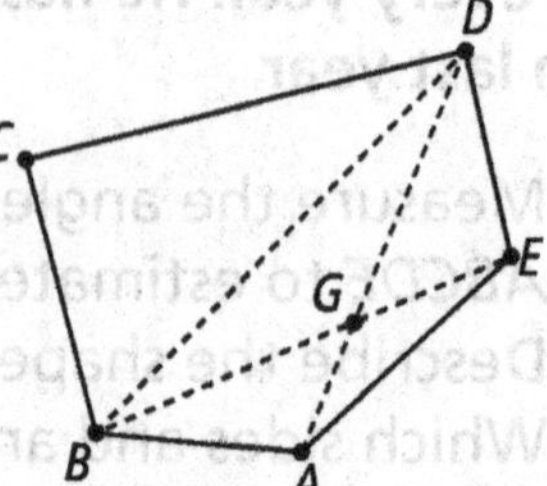

Statement	Reason

7. G'ahan wants to prove that the sum of the angles of *ABDE* is equal to 360°. Write the first step for his indirect proof.

8. Using the fact that the sum of the angles in a triangle is equal to 180°, prove that the sum of the angles in *ABCDE* is 540°.

Neveah wants to display a hexagonal number at each intersection along the raceway.

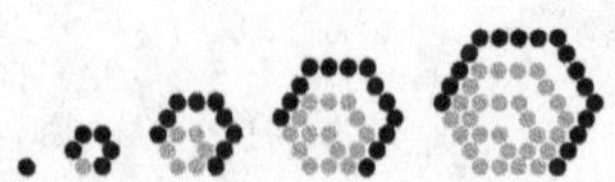

9. Write the first seven terms of the sequence. Explain how to find the eighth term.

10. Write a conjecture about the number of dots in the *n*th term.

Name ______________________________

7 Readiness Assessment

1. If $DG = 10$, what is the value of x?

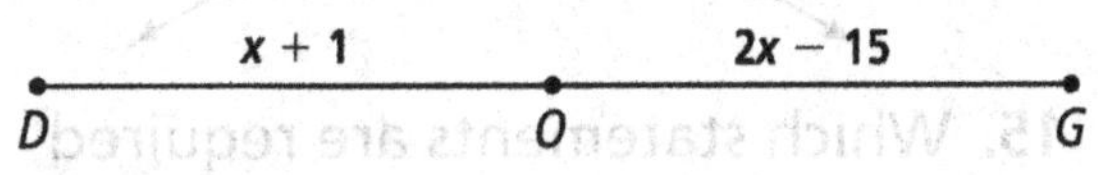

Ⓐ 12 Ⓑ 8 Ⓒ $-\frac{4}{3}$ Ⓓ 14

Use the figure for Items 2 and 3. Points *P*, *Q*, and *S* are collinear.

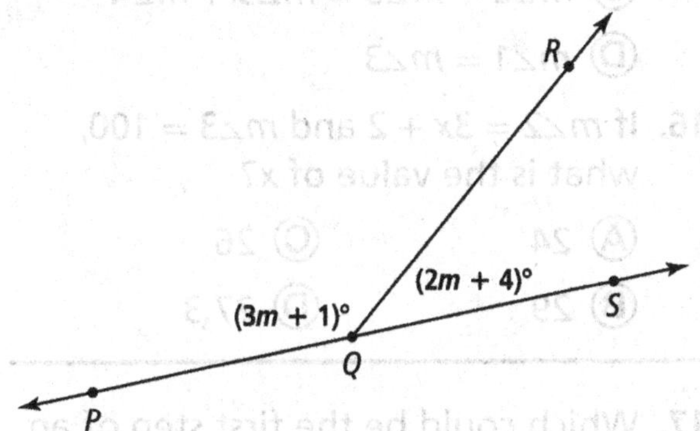

2. What is $m\angle SQR$?

3. If $\overrightarrow{QT}$ bisects $\angle PQR$, what is the measure of $\angle PQT$?

4. Points *C*, *D*, and *E* are collinear. You are given $CD = 18$ and $CE = 27$. What is a possible measure of *DE*?

Ⓐ 6 Ⓑ 7 Ⓒ 8 Ⓓ 9

5. $\overrightarrow{BD}$ bisects $\angle ABC$ so that $m\angle DBC = (x + 2)°$ and $m\angle ABD = (2x - 5)°$. What is x?

Ⓐ 2 Ⓑ 7 Ⓒ 6 Ⓓ 8

6. What is the distance between points $H(6, 11)$ and $N(1, -1)$?

Items 7–8. Use the number line.

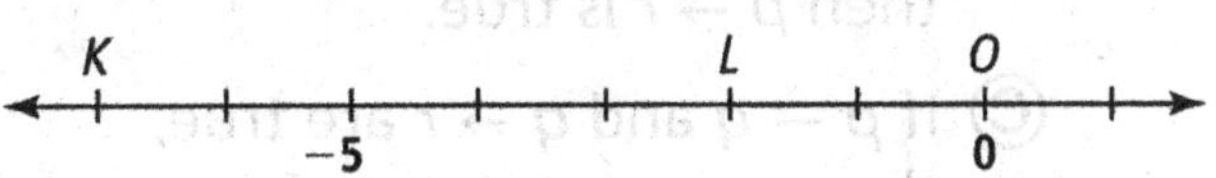

7. What is the distance $KL + KO$?

8. What is the coordinate of the midpoint of $\overline{KL}$?

Items 9–11. Use the following conditional: If a number is odd, then it has a remainder of 1 when divided by 2.

9. Which is the hypothesis of the conditional?

Ⓐ A number is not odd.

Ⓑ A number has a remainder of 1 when divided by 2.

Ⓒ A number is odd when it has a remainder of 1.

Ⓓ A number is odd.

10. Which is the conclusion of the conditional?

Ⓐ A number is not odd.

Ⓑ A number has a remainder of 1 when divided by 2.

Ⓒ A number is odd when it has a remainder of 1.

Ⓓ A number is odd.

11. Write the converse. Is it true?

12. Which statements below are true? Select all that apply.

Ⓐ If $p \rightarrow q$ and r are true, then $q \rightarrow r$ is true.

Ⓑ If $p \rightarrow q$ and $q \rightarrow r$ are true, then $p \rightarrow r$ is true.

Ⓒ If $p \rightarrow q$ and $q \rightarrow r$ are true, then $r \rightarrow p$ is true.

Ⓓ If $p \rightarrow q$ and p are true, then q is true.

For Items 13 and 14, use the Law of Detachment and the Law of Syllogism to make a conclusion.

13. If I miss my bus, then I'll be late to school. I missed my bus.

Ⓐ I get a ride.

Ⓑ I am late to school.

Ⓒ I am not late to school.

Ⓓ I do not go to school.

14. If I go to the movie, then I will eat popcorn. If I eat popcorn, then I will enjoy the movie.

Ⓐ I will enjoy the movie if I eat popcorn.

Ⓑ If I am eating popcorn, then I am enjoying the movie.

Ⓒ I enjoy the movie.

Ⓓ If I go to the movie, then I will enjoy the movie.

Items 15–16. Use the diagram shown.

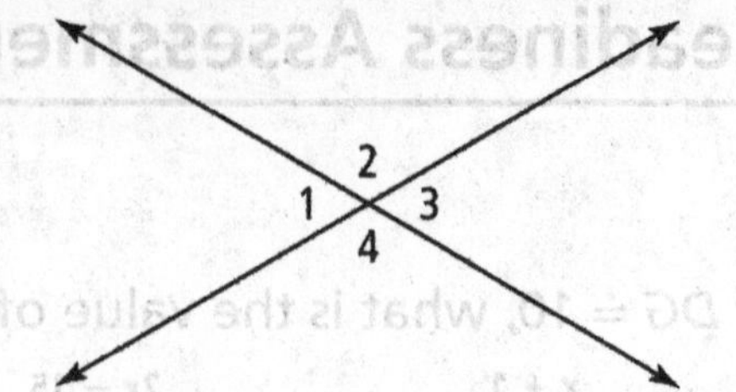

15. Which statements are required to prove $\angle 2 \cong \angle 4$? Select all that apply.

Ⓐ $m\angle 2 + m\angle 3 = 180$

Ⓑ $m\angle 3 + m\angle 4 = 180$

Ⓒ $m\angle 2 + m\angle 3 = m\angle 3 + m\angle 4$

Ⓓ $m\angle 1 = m\angle 3$

16. If $m\angle 2 = 3x + 2$ and $m\angle 3 = 100$, what is the value of x?

Ⓐ 24 Ⓒ 26

Ⓑ 29 Ⓓ 27.3

---

17. Which could be the first step of an indirect proof of the conditional below? Select all that apply.

If $x^2 = 25$, then $5^2 = 25$ and $x = 5$.

Ⓐ Assume $x = 5$ is true.

Ⓑ Assume $5^2 = 25$ is true.

Ⓒ Assume $x^2 \neq 25$ is true.

Ⓓ Assume $5^2 \neq 25$ and $x \neq 5$ are true.

Name ______________________________

7-1 Lesson Quiz

Properties of Parallel Lines

Use the figure shown for Items 1 and 2.

1. Which of the following statements are true? Select all that apply.

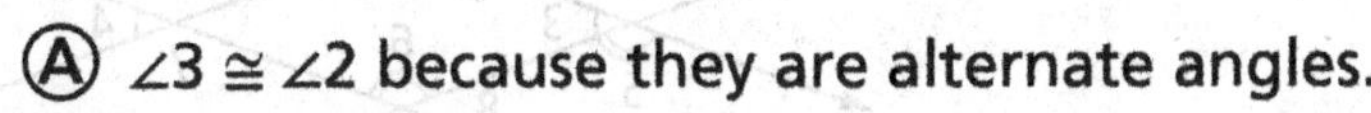

   Ⓐ $\angle 3 \cong \angle 2$ because they are alternate angles.

   Ⓑ $m\angle 1 + m\angle 3 = 180°$ because they form a straight angle.

   Ⓒ $\angle 3 \cong \angle 6$ because they are alternate interior angles.

   Ⓓ $\angle 1$ and $\angle 6$ are supplementary because $\angle 3 \cong \angle 6$ and $m\angle 1 + m\angle 3 = 180°$.

2. If $m\angle 7 = 55°$, which of the following statements are true? Select all that apply.

   Ⓐ $m\angle 6 = 55°$

   Ⓑ $m\angle 5 = 135°$

   Ⓒ $m\angle 1 + m\angle 4 = 250°$

   Ⓓ $m\angle 1 + m\angle 6 = m\angle 7 + m\angle 4$

Use the figure shown for Items 3 and 4.

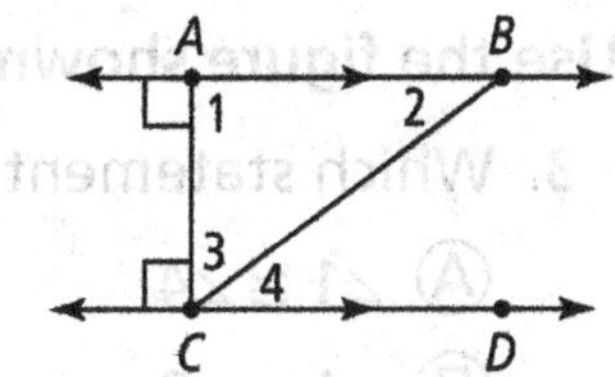

3. What is $m\angle 2 + m\angle 3$?

4. If $m\angle 4 = 35°$, find $m\angle 2$ and $m\angle 3$.

5. In the figure shown, $t \parallel x$ and $k \parallel w$. If $m\angle 3 = 20°$, list all the angles that are 20° and all the angles that are 160°.

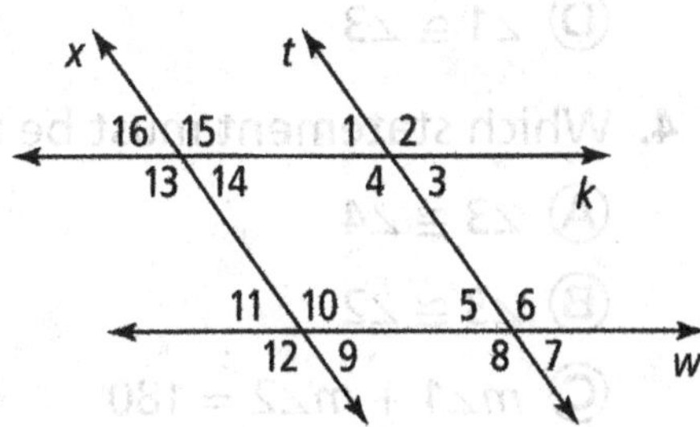

Name ______________________________

7-2 Lesson Quiz

Proving Lines Parallel

1. Which of the following statements are true? Select all that apply.

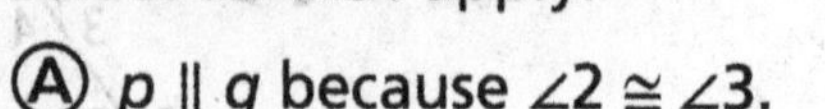

Ⓐ $p \parallel q$ because $\angle 2 \cong \angle 3$.

Ⓑ $p \parallel q$ because $\angle 5 \cong \angle 7$.

Ⓒ $r \parallel s$ because $\angle 2 \cong \angle 4$.

Ⓓ $r \parallel s$ because $\angle 5 \cong \angle 6$.

2. If $m\angle 1 = m\angle 2$, which of the following statements are true? Select all that apply.

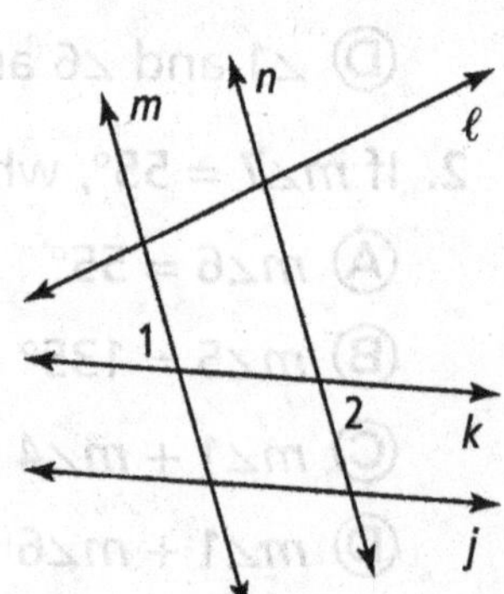

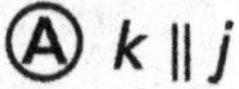

Ⓐ $k \parallel j$

Ⓑ $n \parallel m$

Ⓒ $\ell \parallel k$

Ⓓ $\ell \parallel m$

Use the figure shown for Items 3 and 4.

3. Which statement must be true to prove $\ell \parallel m$?

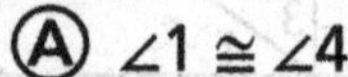

Ⓐ $\angle 1 \cong \angle 4$

Ⓑ $\angle 1 \cong \angle 2$

Ⓒ $m\angle 2 + m\angle 3 = 180°$

Ⓓ $\angle 1 \cong \angle 3$

4. Which statement must be true to prove $\ell \parallel m$?

Ⓐ $\angle 3 \cong \angle 4$

Ⓑ $\angle 3 \cong \angle 2$

Ⓒ $m\angle 1 + m\angle 2 = 180°$

Ⓓ $\angle 1 \cong \angle 2$

5. If $\angle 1 \cong \angle 2$, which lines are parallel?

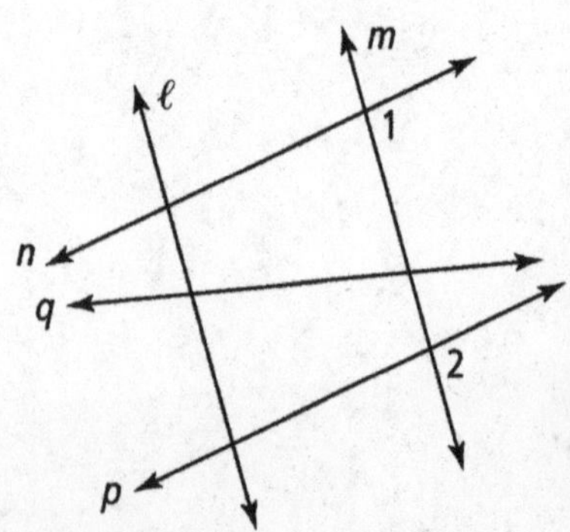

Name ______________________

7-3 Lesson Quiz

Parallel Lines and Triangles

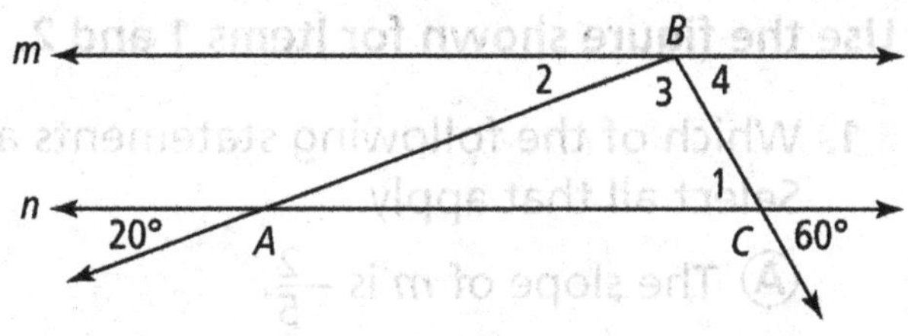

1. If $n \parallel m$, which of the following statements are true? Select all that apply.

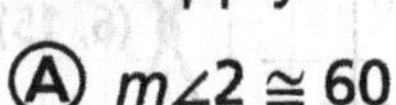

Ⓐ $m\angle 2 \cong 60$

Ⓑ $m\angle 3 = 100$

Ⓒ $m\angle 2 + m\angle 4 = 80$

Ⓓ $m\angle 2 + m\angle 3 = 80$

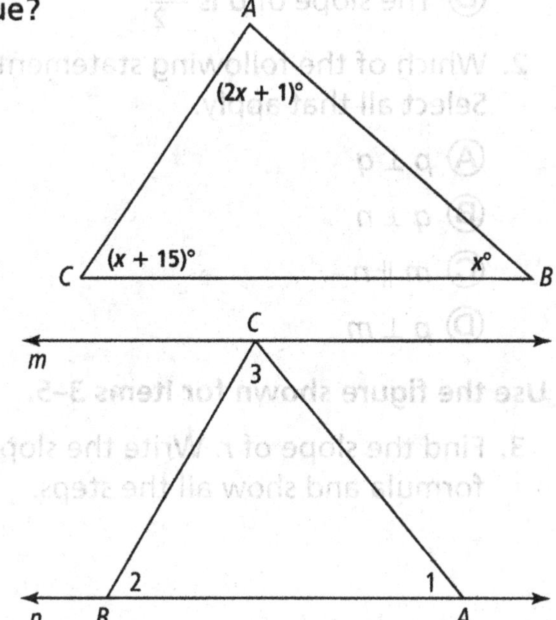

2. Which of the following statements are true? Select all that apply.

Ⓐ $(4x + 16) = 180$

Ⓑ $x = 49$

Ⓒ $m\angle A = 99$

Ⓓ From smallest to largest: $\angle B$, $\angle C$, $\angle A$

3. Which statement must be true to prove $m\angle 1 + m\angle 2 + m\angle 3 = 180$?

Ⓐ $m \parallel n$

Ⓑ $m\angle 1 + m\angle 2 = 180 - m\angle 3$

Ⓒ $m\angle 1 + m\angle 2 = 90$

Ⓓ $m\angle 1 + m\angle 2 + m\angle 3 = 180$

Use the figure shown for Items 4 and 5.

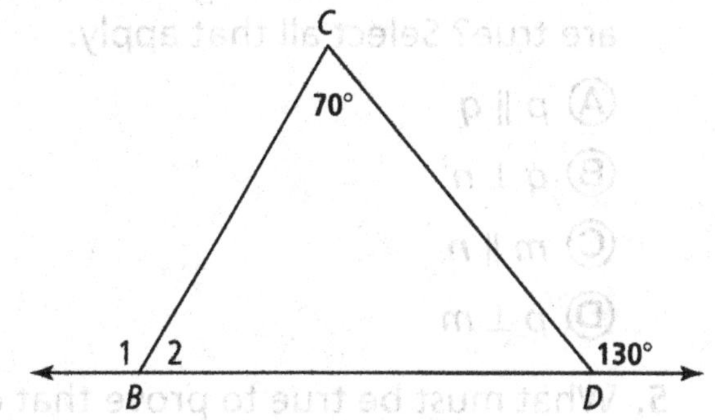

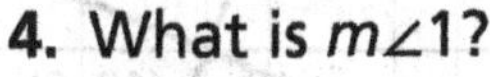

4. What is $m\angle 1$?

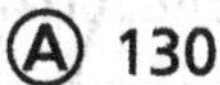

Ⓐ 130

Ⓑ 70

Ⓒ 60

Ⓓ 120

5. What kind of triangle is BCD?

Name ______________________

7-4 Lesson Quiz

Slopes of Parallel and Perpendicular Lines

Use the figure shown for Items 1 and 2.

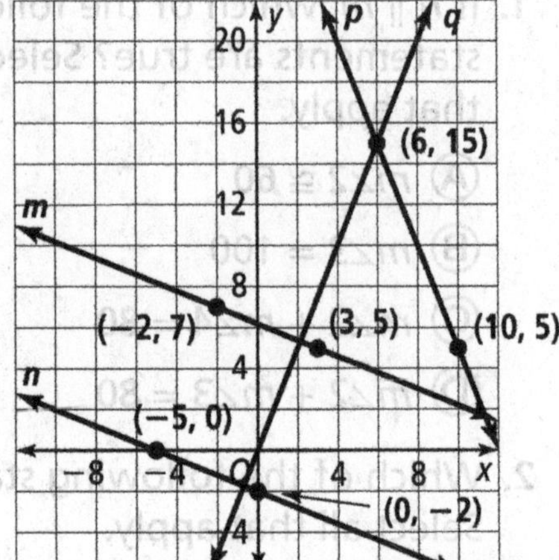

1. Which of the following statements are true? Select all that apply.

   Ⓐ The slope of m is $-\frac{2}{5}$.

   Ⓑ The slope of q is $-\frac{5}{2}$.

   Ⓒ The slope of n is $\frac{2}{5}$.

   Ⓓ The slope of p is $-\frac{5}{2}$.

2. Which of the following statements are true? Select all that apply.

   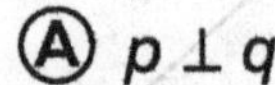

   Ⓐ $p \perp q$

   Ⓑ $q \perp n$

   Ⓒ $m \parallel n$

   Ⓓ $p \perp m$

Use the figure shown for Items 3–5.

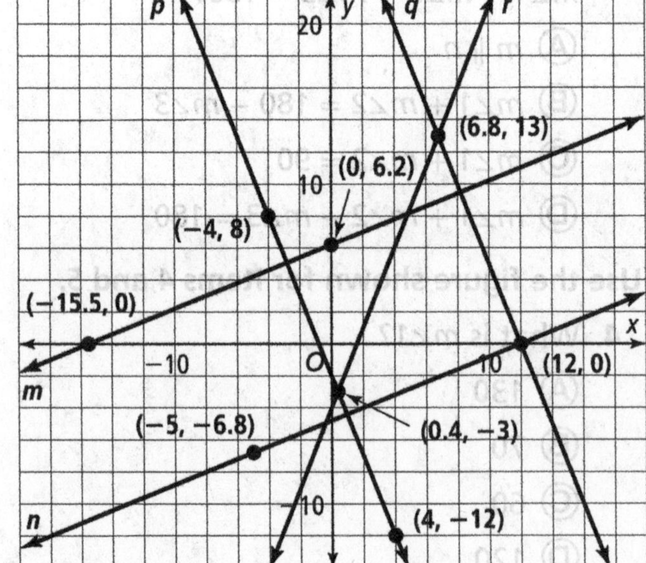

3. Find the slope of r. Write the slope formula and show all the steps.

4. Which of the following statements are true? Select all that apply.

   Ⓐ $p \parallel q$

   Ⓑ $q \perp n$

   Ⓒ $m \parallel n$

   Ⓓ $p \perp m$

5. What must be true to prove that $q \perp n$?

Name ______________________________

enVision Integrated MATHEMATICS I

PearsonRealize.com

7 Topic Assessment Form A

1. What type of lines are coplanar and do not intersect?

Ⓐ parallel
Ⓑ perpendicular
Ⓒ segments
Ⓓ transversal

Items 2–5. Lines ℓ and m are intersected by transversal t. $\ell \parallel m$

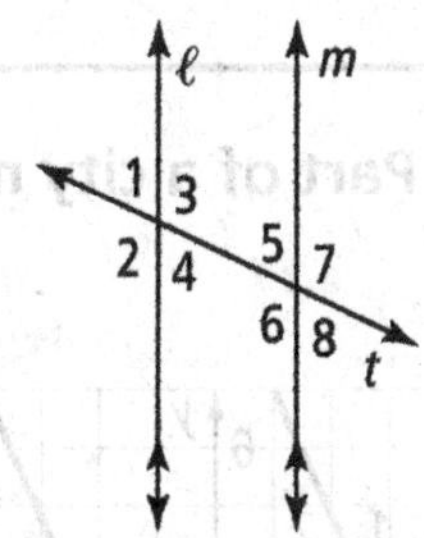

2. Which of the following angles are supplementary to $\angle 1$? Select all that apply.

Ⓐ $\angle 5$
Ⓑ $\angle 6$
Ⓒ $\angle 7$
Ⓓ $\angle 8$

3. Which of the following angles are congruent to $\angle 5$? Select all that apply.

Ⓐ $\angle 1$
Ⓑ $\angle 2$
Ⓒ $\angle 3$
Ⓓ $\angle 4$

4. By which postulate or theorem is $\angle 3 \cong \angle 6$?

Ⓐ Alternate Exterior Angles Theorem
Ⓑ Alternate Interior Angles Theorem
Ⓒ Corresponding Angles Theorem
Ⓓ Same-Side Interior Angles Postulate

5. If $m\angle 2 = 112$, what is $m\angle 7$?

6. Write two equations relating the measure of $\angle 4$ to the measures of $\angle 1$, $\angle 2$, and $\angle 3$.

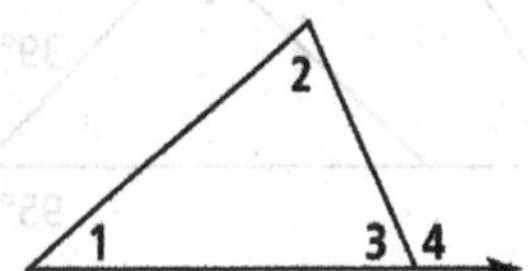

Items 7–9. A triangle is shown.

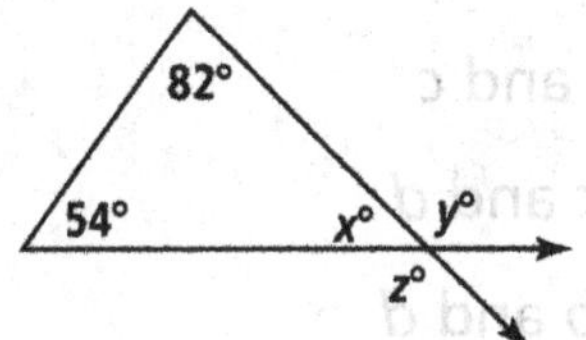

7. What is x?

Ⓐ 28
Ⓑ 44
Ⓒ 136
Ⓓ 224

8. What is y?

9. Which of the following statements are true? Select all that apply.

Ⓐ $x = y$
Ⓑ $x + y = 180$
Ⓒ $y = z$
Ⓓ $x + z = 180$

10. In $\triangle ABC$, $m\angle A = 75$ and $m\angle C = 20$. What is $m\angle B$?

Ⓐ 55
Ⓑ 85
Ⓒ 95
Ⓓ 265

Items 11–15. Lines *a*, *b*, *c*, and *d* intersect as shown.

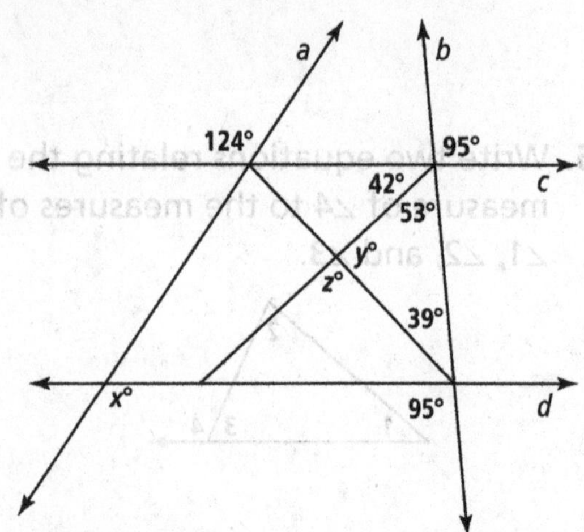

11. Which pair of lines are parallel?

Ⓐ *a* and *b*

Ⓑ *a* and *c*

Ⓒ *c* and *d*

Ⓓ *b* and *d*

12. What is *x*?

13. What is *y*?

Ⓐ 42

Ⓑ 85

Ⓒ 88

Ⓓ 95

14. What is *z*?

Ⓐ 88

Ⓑ 92

Ⓒ 95

Ⓓ 124

15. If the slope of line *c* is given, the slope of which other line is known?

16. What is the equation of a line that is parallel to the line $y = 2x + 7$ and passes through the point (–2, 4)?

Ⓐ $y = -\frac{1}{2}x + 3$

Ⓑ $y = 2x + 4$

Ⓒ $y = -\frac{1}{2}x - 2$

Ⓓ $y = 2x + 8$

17. What is the slope of a line perpendicular to the line $y = \frac{1}{4}x - 1$?

Items 18–20. Part of a city map is shown.

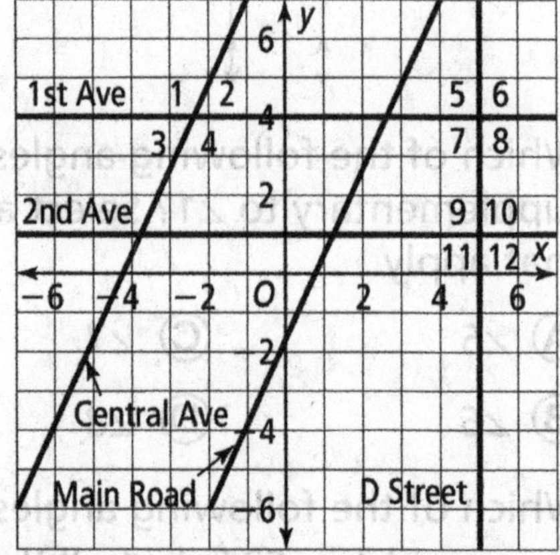

18. Which street is parallel to 1st Ave?

Ⓐ 2nd Ave

Ⓑ Main Road

Ⓒ Central Ave

Ⓓ D Street

19. A city planner wants to build a road perpendicular to D Street. What is the slope of the new road?

20. If $m\angle 5 = x$, which angles also have a measure of *x*? Select all that apply.

Ⓐ ∠1

Ⓑ ∠4

Ⓒ ∠9

Ⓓ ∠12

Name ______________________________

7 Topic Assessment Form B

1. Which statement is true about parallel lines?

   Ⓐ They are coplanar and intersect.

   Ⓑ They are not coplanar and intersect.

   Ⓒ They are coplanar and do not intersect.

   Ⓓ They are not coplanar and do not intersect.

Items 2–5. Lines ℓ and m are intersected by transversal t. $\ell \parallel m$

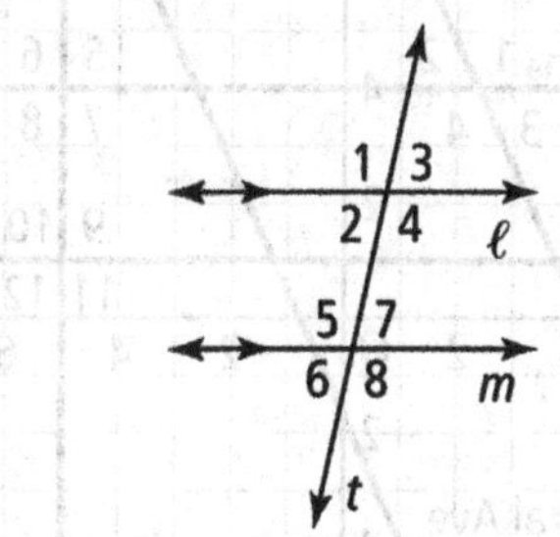

2. Which of the following angles are supplementary to $\angle 2$? Select all that apply.

   Ⓐ $\angle 5$ Ⓑ $\angle 6$ Ⓒ $\angle 7$ Ⓓ $\angle 8$

3. Which of the following angles are congruent to $\angle 6$? Select all that apply.

   Ⓐ $\angle 1$ Ⓑ $\angle 2$ Ⓒ $\angle 3$ Ⓓ $\angle 4$

4. By which postulate or theorem is $\angle 1 \cong \angle 8$?

   Ⓐ Alternate Exterior Angles Theorem

   Ⓑ Alternate Interior Angles Theorem

   Ⓒ Corresponding Angles Theorem

   Ⓓ Same-Side Interior Angles Postulate

5. If $m\angle 4 = 105$, what is $m\angle 5$?

6. Write two equations relating the measure of $\angle 4$ to the measures of $\angle 1$, $\angle 2$, and $\angle 3$.

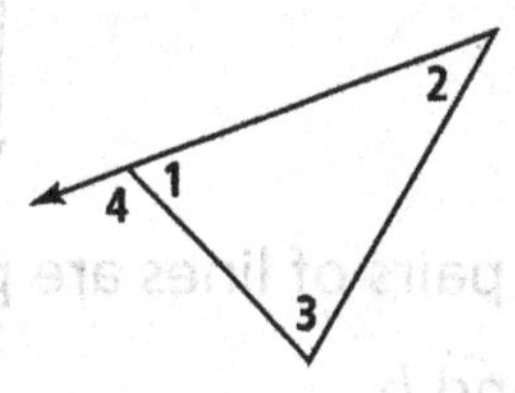

Items 7–9. A triangle is shown.

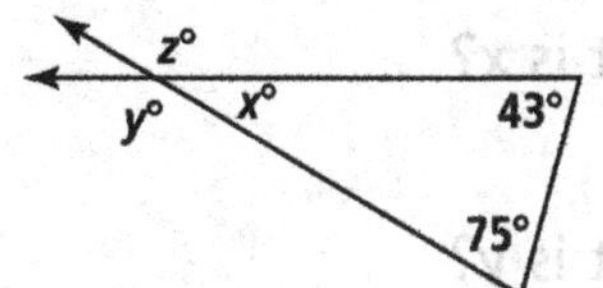

7. What is x?

   Ⓐ 32 Ⓒ 118

   Ⓑ 62 Ⓓ 242

8. What is y?

9. Which of the following statements are true? Select all that apply.

   Ⓐ $x = y$ Ⓒ $y = z$

   Ⓑ $x + y = 180$ Ⓓ $x + z = 180$

10. In $\triangle DEF$, $m\angle D = 53$ and $m\angle F = 68$. What is $m\angle E$?

   Ⓐ 15 Ⓒ 121

   Ⓑ 59 Ⓓ 239

Items 11–15. Lines *a*, *b*, *c*, and *d* intersect as shown.

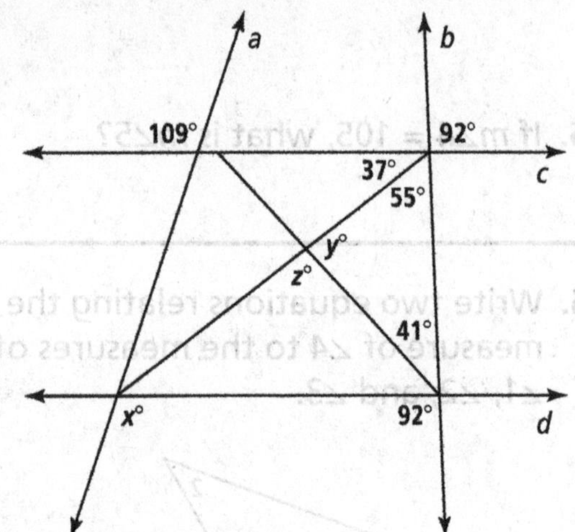

11. Which pairs of lines are parallel?
   Ⓐ *a* and *b*
   Ⓑ *a* and *c*
   Ⓒ *c* and *d*
   Ⓓ *b* and *d*

12. What is *x*?

13. What is *y*?
   Ⓐ 37
   Ⓑ 84
   Ⓒ 88
   Ⓓ 92

14. What is *z*?
   Ⓐ 84
   Ⓑ 92
   Ⓒ 96
   Ⓓ 109

15. If the slope of line *d* is given, the slope of which other line is known?

16. What is the equation of a line that is perpendicular to the line $y = 2x + 1$ and passes through the point (4, 6)?
   Ⓐ $y = -\frac{1}{2}x + 6$
   Ⓑ $y = 2x + 6$
   Ⓒ $y = -\frac{1}{2}x + 8$
   Ⓓ $y = 2x + 8$

17. What is the slope of a line parallel to the line $y = 3x - 4$?

Items 18–20. Part of a city map is shown.

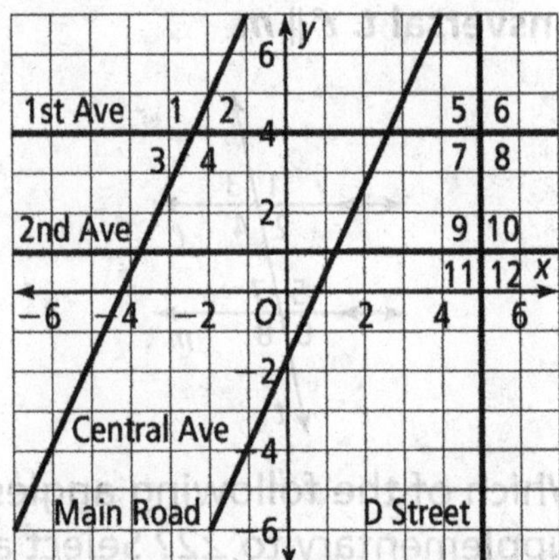

18. Which street is perpendicular to 1st Ave?
   Ⓐ 2nd Ave
   Ⓑ Main Road
   Ⓒ Central Ave
   Ⓓ D Street

19. A city planner wants to build a road parallel to 2nd Ave. What is the slope of the new road?

20. If $m\angle 5 = x$, which angles have a measure of $180 - x$? Select all that apply.
   Ⓐ ∠2
   Ⓑ ∠3
   Ⓒ ∠7
   Ⓓ ∠11

Name ______________________

7 Performance Assessment Form A

Luis is making a simple camera. The diagram shows how an object is projected onto the film.

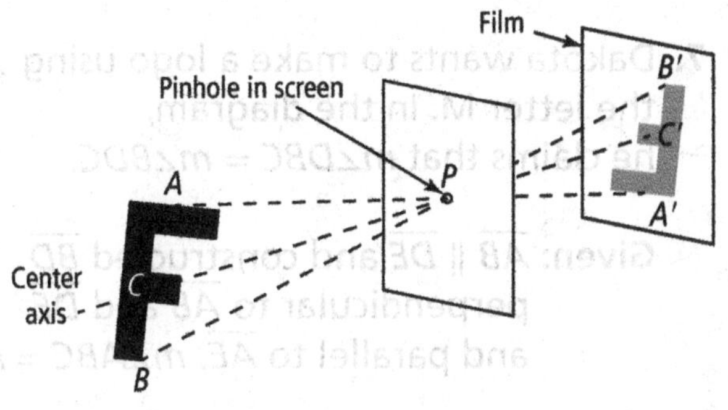

1. Show that if the center axis bisects $\angle APB$, then it bisects $\angle A'PB'$.

2. Luis uses a shoe box that is 14 inches long. He places the pinhole P in the center of the front, which is $7\frac{1}{2}$ in. × $5\frac{1}{8}$ in. If he needs to leave a half-inch border on the film, what is the largest image he can make?

3. In order to rotate an image 45°, Luis tries to rotate the shoe box 45°. His photo shown does not appear to be a rotation of 45°. Estimate the slopes of the parallel line segments.

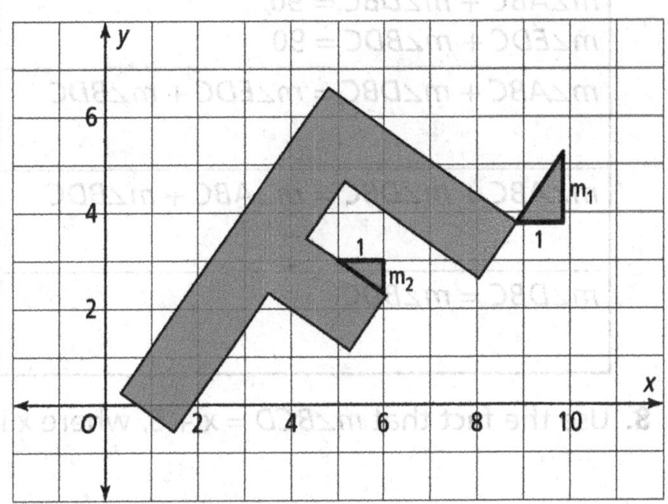

4. Show that there are perpendicular line segments in his photo.

5. Malia drew the slope triangles on the image. She explained, "If Luis had rotated the box 45°, then the legs of the slope triangles would be congruent." What should the slopes be according to Malia?

6. Malia claims that the closer the camera is to the object, the bigger the image. What relationship has she noticed that supports her claim?

7. Dakota wants to make a logo using the letter M. In the diagram, he claims that $m\angle DBC = m\angle BDC$.

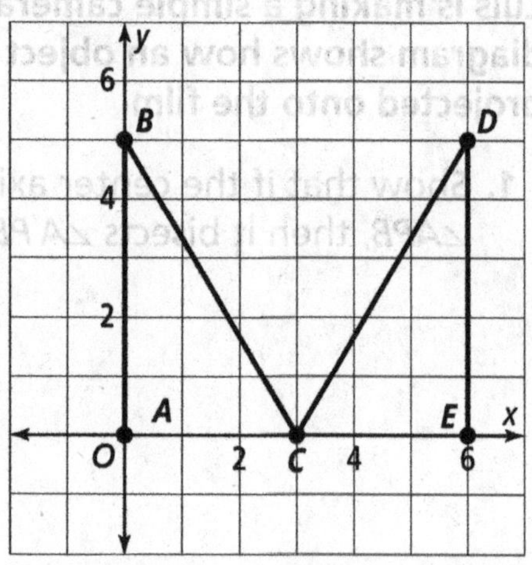

Given: $\overline{AB} \parallel \overline{DE}$ and constructed $\overline{BD}$ perpendicular to $\overline{AB}$ and $\overline{DE}$ and parallel to $\overline{AE}$, $m\angle ABC = m\angle EDC$

Prove: $m\angle DBC = m\angle BDC$

Complete the proof.

$\overline{AB} \parallel \overline{DE}$, $\overline{BD} \parallel \overline{AE}$, $\overline{BD} \perp \overline{AB}$, $\overline{BD} \perp \overline{DE}$ $m\angle ABC = m\angle EDC$	
$\angle ABD$, $\angle BDE$ are right angles.	
$m\angle ABC + m\angle DBC = 90$, $m\angle EDC + m\angle BDC = 90$	
$m\angle ABC + m\angle DBC = m\angle EDC + m\angle BDC$	
$m\angle ABC + m\angle DBC = m\angle ABC + m\angle BDC$	
$m\angle DBC = m\angle BDC$	

8. Use the fact that $m\angle BCD = x + 3$, where x is $m\angle DBC$. Find x.

9. Find $m\angle BCD$ using the fact that $m\angle BCD = x + 3$.

Name ______________________________

7 Performance Assessment Form B

LaTanya is using a microscope to study the anatomy of an amoeba. The diagram shows how the image is enlarged by the microscope.

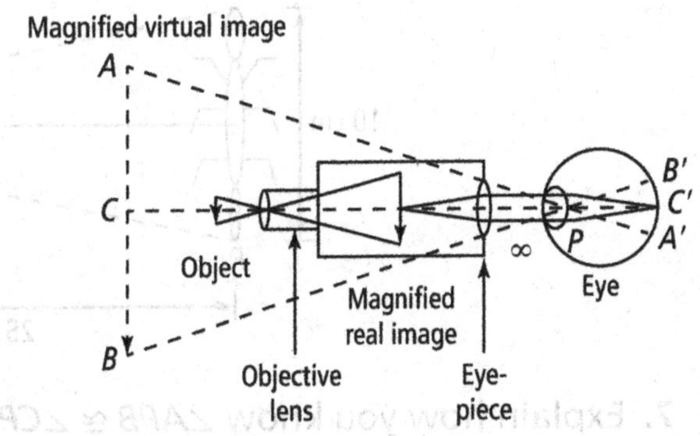

1. Show that if the center axis bisects $\angle APB$, then it bisects $\angle A'PB'$.

2. LaTanya enlarges the image 100 times to make a detailed sketch in her notebook. If the diameter of the amoeba on the slide is 1.04 mm, what is the size of the image she sees?

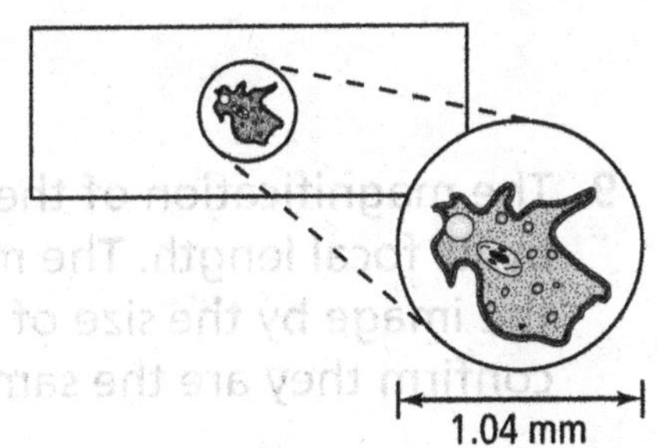

3. To change the orientation of the amoeba, LaTanya tries to rotate the slide 45°. Did she rotate the slide 45°? How can you tell?

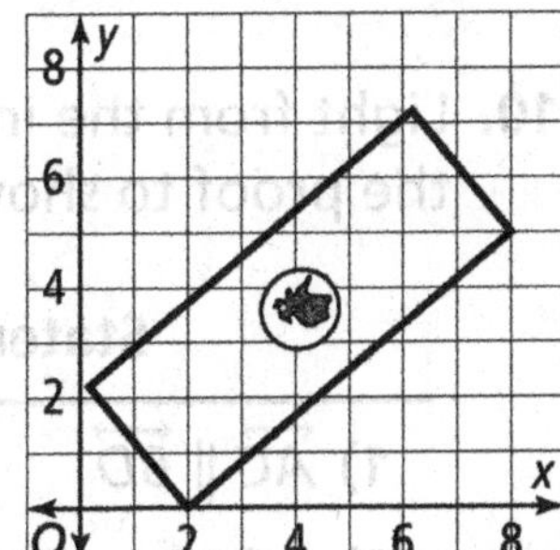

4. Estimate the slopes of the parallel line segments of the slide. Show that the edges of the slide are perpendicular.

5. Avery draws the slope triangles on the image. She says, "If LaTanya had rotated the slide 45°, then the legs of the slope triangles would be congruent." What should the slopes be according to Avery?

6. LaTanya claims that the closer the objective lens is to the slide, the bigger the image is. How is her claim supported by the diagram of the microscope lenses in Item 1?

Zachary uses a hand lens with a focal length of 5 cm to examine an insect 2 cm long. He holds the lens so the insect and his eye are both at the focal length from the insect. He sees an image 25 cm beyond the lens, the distance at which his eye focuses when using relaxed vision.

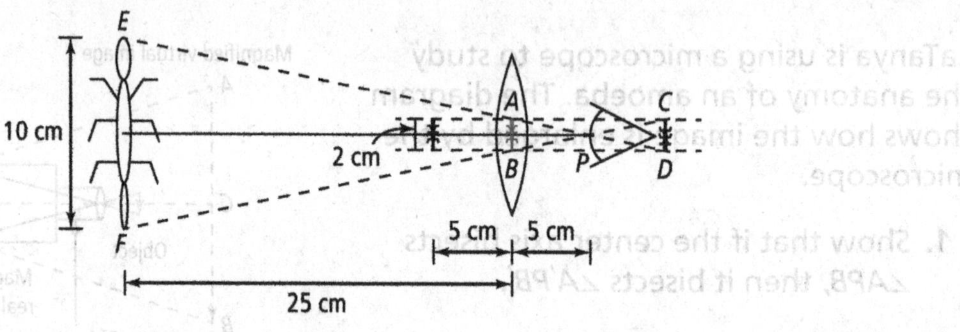

7. Explain how you know $\angle APB \cong \angle CPD$.

8. Point A and point B lie on $\overline{EP}$ and $\overline{FP}$, respectively. Is $\angle APB \cong \angle EPF$? Explain.

9. The magnification of the lens is the distance from the lens to the image divided by its focal length. The magnification can also be found by dividing the size of the image by the size of the subject. Calculate the magnification both ways and confirm they are the same value.

10. Light from the insect travels in parallel rays to the lens, so $\overleftrightarrow{AC} \parallel \overleftrightarrow{BD}$. Complete the proof to show $\angle APB \cong \angle CPD$.

Statements	Reasons
1) $\overleftrightarrow{AC} \parallel \overleftrightarrow{BD}$	1)
2) $\angle CAD \cong \angle BDA$ and $\angle ACB \cong \angle DBC$	2)
3) $m\angle CAD = m\angle BDA$ and $m\angle ACB = m\angle DBC$	3)
4) $m\angle CAD + m\angle ACB + m\angle APC = 180$ and $m\angle ACB + m\angle DBC + m\angle BPD = 180$	4)
5) $m\angle APC = m\angle BPD$	5)
6) $\angle APB \cong \angle BPD$	6)

Name

Benchmark Test 3

1. Marisol buys 3 pounds of cheese and 3 pounds of sausage for a total cost of $36. The sausage costs $2.00 less per pound than the cheese. What is the combined cost of 1 pound of cheese and 1 pound of sausage?

   Ⓐ $16

   Ⓑ $12

   Ⓒ $8

   Ⓓ $6

2. Write a compound inequality for the graph below.

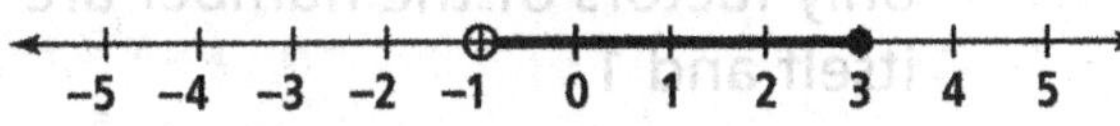

3. Write the equation in standard form of the line that has *x*-intercept 7 and *y*-intercept 4.

4. The cost of having one shirt laundered is $6. Each additional shirt costs $4. Write the explicit and recursive formulas to represent the situation.

   explicit formula:

   recursive formula:

5. Which *r*-value suggests a strong negative correlation?

   Ⓐ $r = 0.97351$

   Ⓑ $r = -0.27331$

   Ⓒ $r = -0.97351$

   Ⓓ $r = 0.27331$

6. What is the solution of the system of equations?

   $4x - 3y = -1$
   $3x - 9y = 33$

7. Find the vertex of the graph of $f(x) = -0.75|x + 3|$. Tell whether the graph opens *upward* or *downward*.

8. To rent a canoe costs $15 for the first hour and $12 for each additional hour or fraction of an hour. Which point is NOT included in the graph of this step function?

Ⓐ (2.5, 39)

Ⓑ (3.2, 51)

Ⓒ (3.0, 39)

Ⓓ (4.5, 51)

9. If $DM = 60$, what is the value of r?

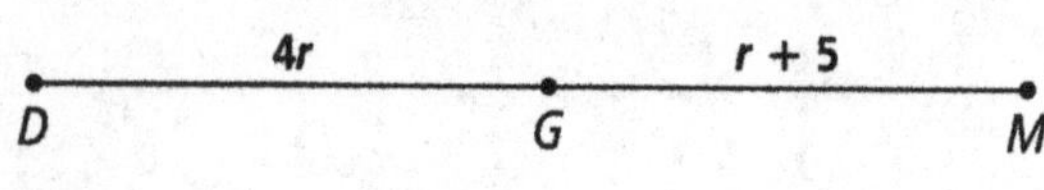

Ⓐ 11

Ⓑ 55

Ⓒ 13

Ⓓ 65

10. What is the distance between points $A(2, 9)$ and $B(-2, 6)$? Round to the nearest whole number.

11. Consider the conjecture, "Any number divisible by 3 is divisible by 6." Is the number a counterexample?

	Yes	No
12	❑	❑
21	❑	❑
23	❑	❑
30	❑	❑
33	❑	❑
45	❑	❑

12. Which number is a counterexample for the conditional below?

If a number is divisible by 6, then it is divisible by 18.

Ⓐ 18 Ⓒ 24

Ⓑ 36 Ⓓ 54

13. Which conditional has a true converse? Select all that apply.

Ⓐ If a quadrilateral is a square, then it has four congruent sides.

Ⓑ If a polygon is a triangle, then it has 3 sides.

Ⓒ If a quadrilateral is a rectangle, then it has two pairs of parallel sides.

Ⓓ If a number is even, then it is divisible by 2.

Ⓔ If a number is prime, then the only factors of the number are itself and 1.

14. Which statement below is true?

Ⓐ If $p \rightarrow q$ is true, then $q \rightarrow p$ is true.

Ⓑ If $p \rightarrow q$ is true and p is true, then q is true.

Ⓒ If $p \rightarrow q$ and $q \rightarrow r$ are true, then $q \rightarrow p$ is true.

Ⓓ If $p \rightarrow q$ and $q \rightarrow r$ are true, then $r \rightarrow p$ is true.

15. Use the Law of Detachment to write a conclusion from the following statements.

If a person wants to be an engineer, then that person needs to get a degree in engineering. Michael wants to be an engineer.

16. What is the value of x?

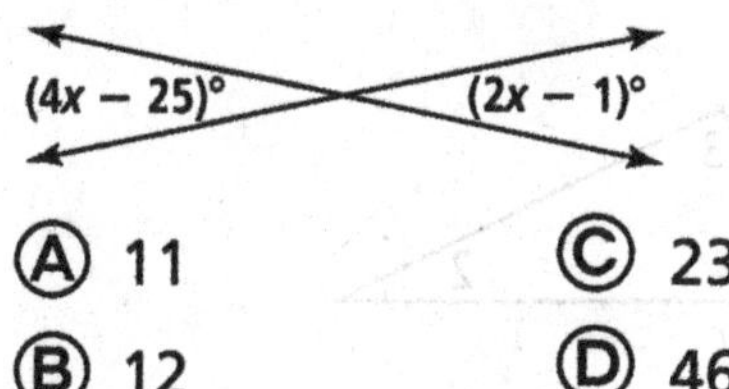

Ⓐ 11 Ⓒ 23

Ⓑ 12 Ⓓ 46

17. The statement "Angle 1 is congruent to angle 3" is justified by the

_______________.

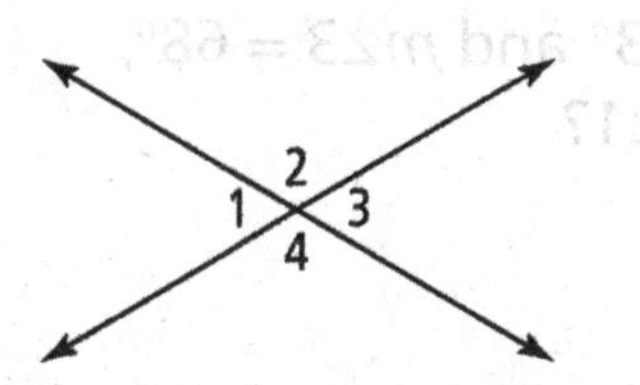

18. Identify two statements that contradict each other.

I. $\angle M$ is an obtuse angle.

II. $m\angle M + m\angle P = 90°$

III. $180° - m\angle M = 25°$

IV. $m\angle P = 120°$

Ⓐ I and II Ⓒ I and III

Ⓑ I and IV Ⓓ III and IV

19. James Cook was the first person to cross the Antarctic Circle. Prove the following conditional statement by proving the contrapositive.

If a person was the first to cross the Antarctic Circle, then that person was James Cook.

Fill in the blanks to write the contrapositive.

If a person _______________ James Cook, then that person _______________ the first person to cross the Antarctic Circle.

Fill in the blanks to complete the proof.

Since James Cook was the first person to cross the Antarctic Circle, the contrapositive is _______________.

Since the contrapositive is _______________, the _______________ must be true.

20. Which pairs of angles are corresponding angles? Select all that apply.

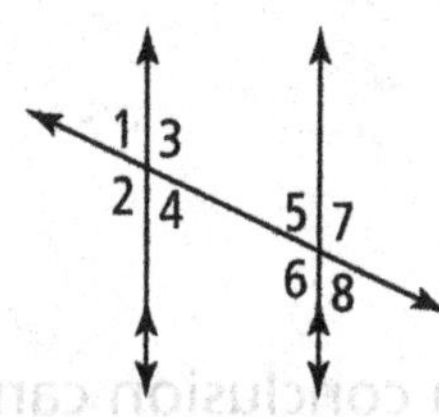

Ⓐ $\angle 1$ and $\angle 5$

Ⓑ $\angle 1$ and $\angle 2$

Ⓒ $\angle 2$ and $\angle 8$

Ⓓ $\angle 3$ and $\angle 7$

Ⓔ $\angle 4$ and $\angle 8$

For Items 21 and 22, use the parallel lines shown.

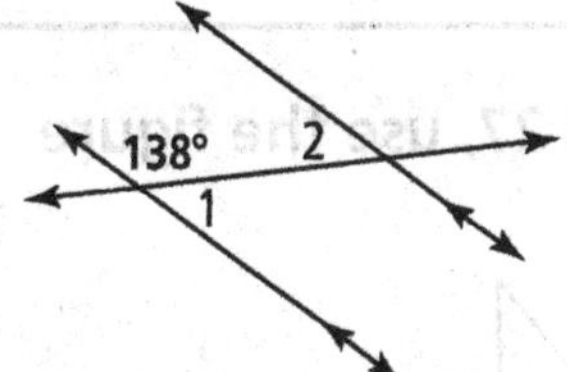

21. What is $m\angle 1$?

Ⓐ 42° Ⓒ 96°

Ⓑ 48° Ⓓ 138°

22. What is $m\angle 2$?

Ⓐ 42° Ⓒ 96°

Ⓑ 48° Ⓓ 138°

For Items 23–25, use the diagram shown.

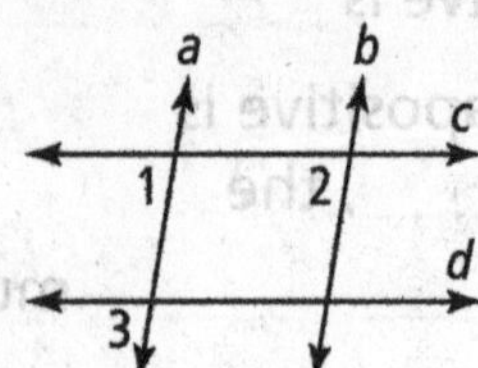

23. If $\angle 1 \cong \angle 3$, which conclusion can be made?

Ⓐ $a \parallel b$

Ⓑ $c \parallel d$

Ⓒ $c \perp a$

Ⓓ $b \perp d$

24. If $\angle 1 \cong \angle 2$, which conclusion can be made?

Ⓐ $a \parallel b$

Ⓑ $c \parallel d$

Ⓒ $c \perp a$

Ⓓ $b \perp d$

25. If $a \parallel b$ and $m\angle 1 = 65°$, what is $m\angle 2$?

For Items 26 and 27, use the figure shown.

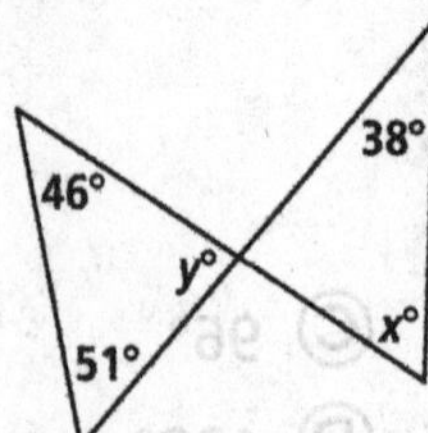

26. What is the value of y?

Ⓐ 83 Ⓑ 89 Ⓒ 96 Ⓓ 97

27. What is the value of x?

Ⓐ 38 Ⓑ 59 Ⓒ 83 Ⓓ 96

For Items 28 and 29, use the triangle shown.

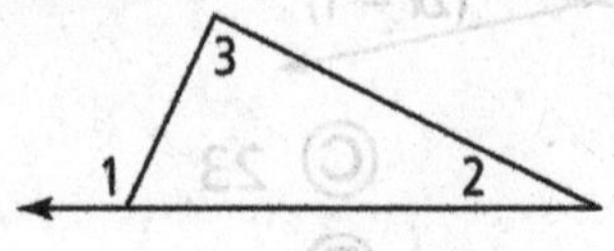

28. If $m\angle 1 = 98°$ and $m\angle 2 = 19°$, what is $m\angle 3$?

29. If $m\angle 2 = 23°$ and $m\angle 3 = 68°$, what is $m\angle 1$?

Ⓐ 23°

Ⓑ 68°

Ⓒ 89°

Ⓓ 91°

---

30. What is an equation of the line that is perpendicular to the line $y = -\frac{2}{3}x - 1$ and passes through the point (–4, 2)?

8 Readiness Assessment

Items 1–4. Lines ℓ and m are intersected by transversal t. $\ell \parallel m$.

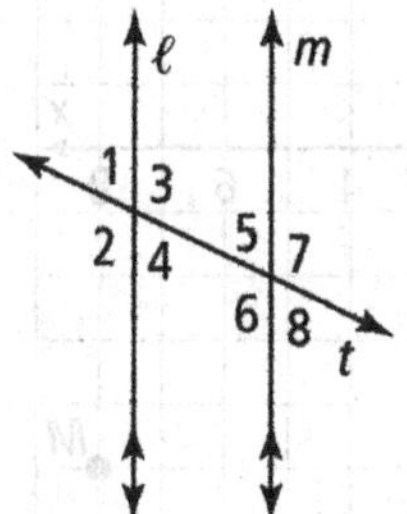

1. Which of the following angles are supplementary to ∠7? Select all that apply.
   Ⓐ ∠5 Ⓒ ∠6
   Ⓑ ∠3 Ⓓ ∠8

2. Which of the following angles are congruent to ∠6? Select all that apply.
   Ⓐ ∠1 Ⓒ ∠2
   Ⓑ ∠3 Ⓓ ∠4

3. By which postulate or theorem is ∠4 ≅ ∠8?
   Ⓐ Alternate Exterior Angles Theorem
   Ⓑ Alternate Interior Angles Theorem
   Ⓒ Corresponding Angles Theorem
   Ⓓ Same-Side Interior Angles Postulate

4. If $m\angle 3 = 126°$, what is $m\angle 5$?

Items 5–6. Triangle *ABC* is similar to triangle *XYZ*.

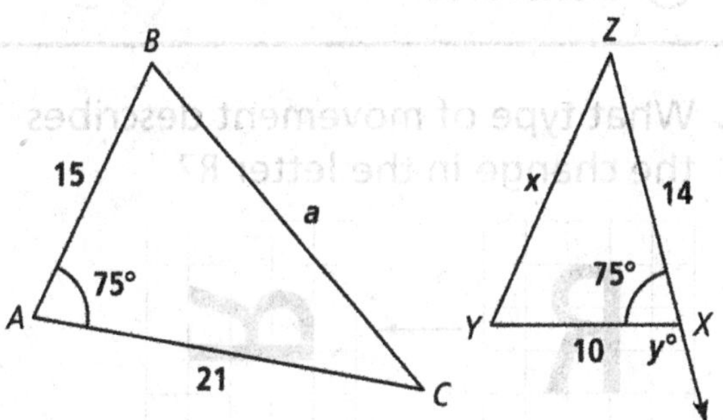

5. Let $a = 24$. What is x?

6. What is y?

Items 7–9. Use the triangles shown.

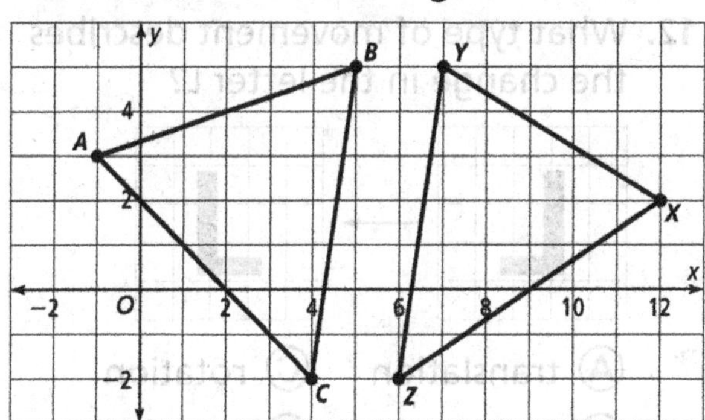

7. What is the exact value of *BC*?
   Ⓐ 3.16 Ⓒ 7.07
   Ⓑ $5\sqrt{2}$ Ⓓ 25

8. What is the best description of the relationship between triangle *ABC* and triangle *XYZ*?
   Ⓐ congruent Ⓒ neither
   Ⓑ similar Ⓓ cannot be determined

9. Is $\overline{AC}$ perpendicular to $\overline{XZ}$? Explain.

10. What type of lines intersect and are coplanar? Select all that apply.

Ⓐ parallel

Ⓑ perpendicular

Ⓒ segments

Ⓓ transversal

11. What type of movement describes the change in the letter R?

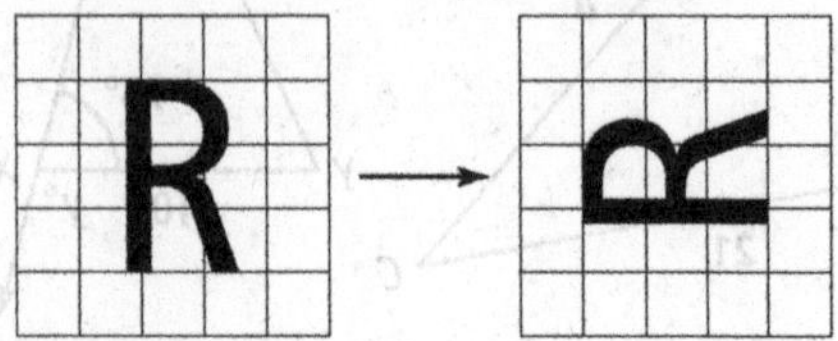

Ⓐ translation Ⓒ rotation

Ⓑ reflection Ⓓ cannot be determined

12. What type of movement describes the change in the letter L?

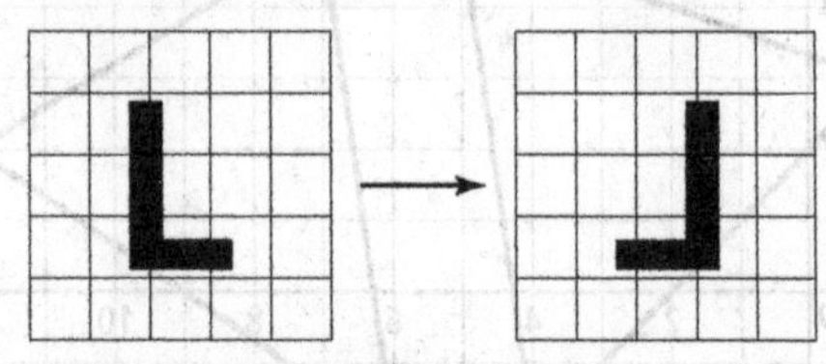

Ⓐ translation Ⓒ rotation

Ⓑ reflection Ⓓ cannot be determined

13. What type of movement describes the change in the letter F?

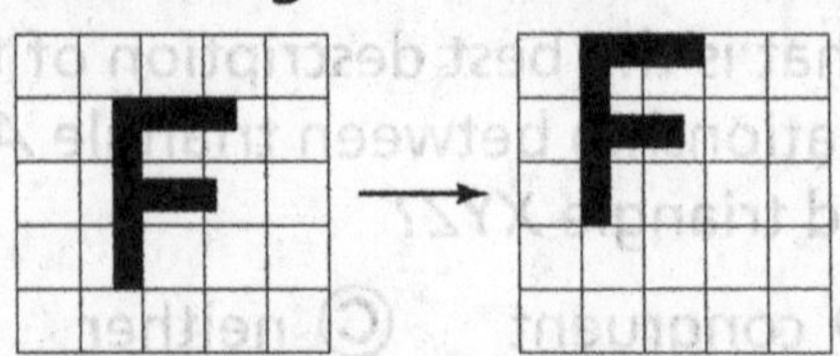

Ⓐ translation Ⓒ rotation

Ⓑ reflection Ⓓ cannot be determined

Items 14–18. Use the coordinates plotted below.

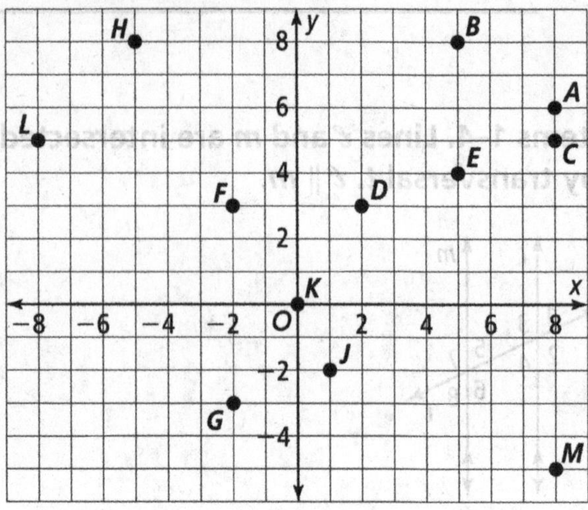

14. Which point is a reflection of C across the x-axis?

15. Which point is a 90° counterclockwise rotation of B around K?

16. Which point is a translation of A up 2 and left 13?

17. Which points are rotations of F around K?

18. Which description matches the movement of point G to point D? Select all that apply.

Ⓐ translating down 6 and left 4

Ⓑ reflecting across the y-axis followed by reflecting across the x-axis

Ⓒ rotating 180° clockwise around K

Ⓓ rotating 180° counterclockwise around K

Ⓔ cannot be determined

19. How would you describe movements that result in an image in the same position?

Ⓐ similar Ⓒ different

Ⓑ equivalent Ⓓ like

Name ______________________

8-1 Lesson Quiz

Reflections

1. Which of the following does a rigid motion preserve?
   Ⓐ side lengths only
   Ⓑ angle measures only
   Ⓒ side lengths and angle measures
   Ⓓ neither side lengths nor angle measures

2. What is the rule used to transform $\triangle ABC$ to its image?
   $A(-3, 5)$, $B(2, 8)$, $C(-4, -5)$ and $A'(-3, -5)$, $B'(2, -8)$, $C'(-4, 5)$
   Ⓐ $R_m(x, y) = (-y, -x)$, where the equation of line m is $y = -x$
   Ⓑ $R_n(x, y) = (y, x)$, where the equation of line n is $y = -x$
   Ⓒ $R_{y\text{-axis}}(x, y) = (-x, y)$
   Ⓓ $R_{x\text{-axis}}(x, y) = (x, -y)$

For Items 3–5, use $\triangle ABC$ as shown.

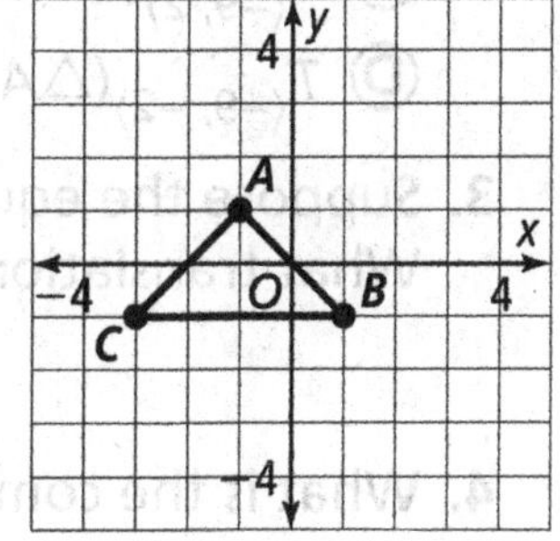

3. Suppose the equation of line s is $y = 2$. What are the coordinates of C' of $\triangle A'B'C'$ for R_s?

4. Suppose the equation of line t is $y = x$. Graph $\triangle A'B'C'$ for R_t.

5. After a reflection, the image vertices are $A'(5, 1)$, $B'(3, -1)$, and $C'(7, -1)$. What is the line of reflection?

Name ____________________

8-2 Lesson Quiz

Translations

For Items 1 and 2, use $\triangle ABC$.

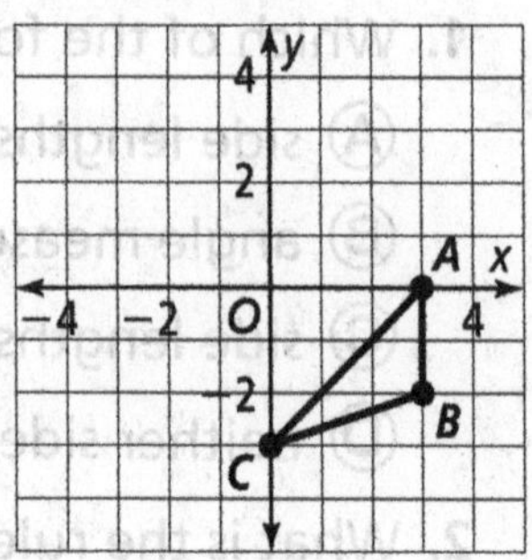

1. What are the vertices of $\triangle A'B'C'$ produced by $T_{\langle -3,\ 6\rangle}(\triangle ABC) = \triangle A'B'C'$?

   Ⓐ $A'(0, 6)$, $B'(0, 4)$, $C'(-3, 3)$

   Ⓑ $A'(6, 6)$, $B'(6, 4)$, $C'(3, 3)$

   Ⓒ $A'(0, -6)$, $B'(0, -8)$, $C'(-3, 9)$

   Ⓓ $A'(6, -6)$, $B'(6, -8)$, $C'(3, 9)$

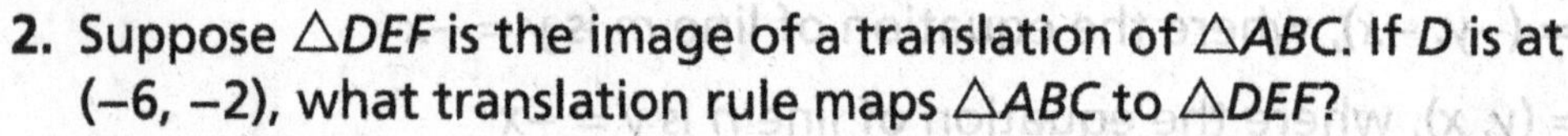

2. Suppose $\triangle DEF$ is the image of a translation of $\triangle ABC$. If D is at $(-6, -2)$, what translation rule maps $\triangle ABC$ to $\triangle DEF$?

   Ⓐ $T_{\langle 9,\ 2\rangle}(\triangle ABC) = \triangle DEF$

   Ⓑ $T_{\langle 9,\ -2\rangle}(\triangle ABC) = \triangle DEF$

   Ⓒ $T_{\langle -9,\ 2\rangle}(\triangle ABC) = \triangle DEF$

   Ⓓ $T_{\langle -9,\ -2\rangle}(\triangle ABC) = \triangle DEF$

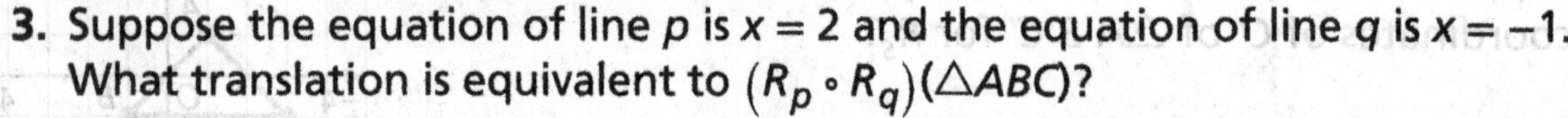

3. Suppose the equation of line p is $x = 2$ and the equation of line q is $x = -1$. What translation is equivalent to $(R_p \circ R_q)(\triangle ABC)$?

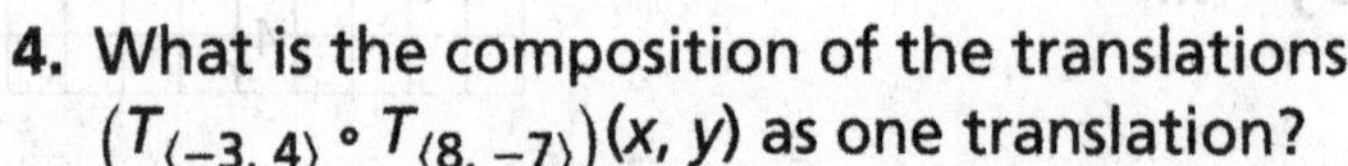

4. What is the composition of the translations $(T_{\langle -3,\ 4\rangle} \circ T_{\langle 8,\ -7\rangle})(x, y)$ as one translation?

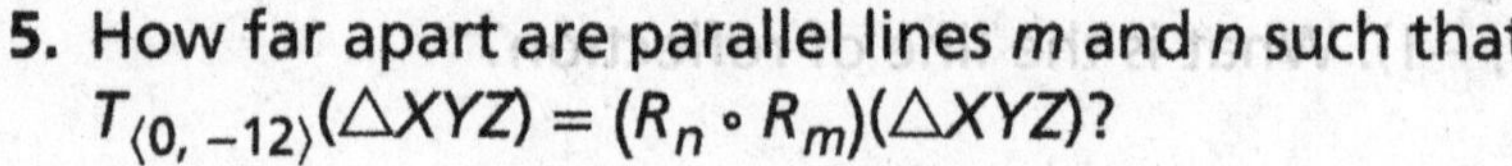

5. How far apart are parallel lines m and n such that $T_{\langle 0,\ -12\rangle}(\triangle XYZ) = (R_n \circ R_m)(\triangle XYZ)$?

Name ______________________________

8-3 Lesson Quiz

Rotations

For Items 1–2, use $\triangle BCD$ in the figure shown.

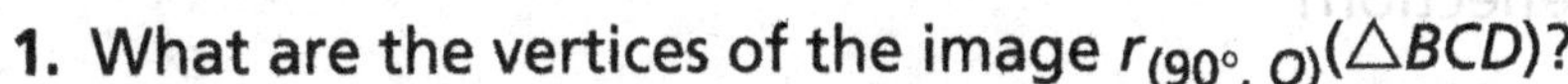

1. What are the vertices of the image $r_{(90°,\ O)}(\triangle BCD)$?

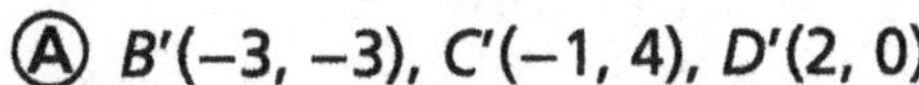

Ⓐ $B'(-3, -3)$, $C'(-1, 4)$, $D'(2, 0)$

Ⓑ $B'(3, 3)$, $C'(1, -4)$, $D'(-2, 0)$

Ⓒ $B'(3, -3)$, $C'(1, 4)$, $D'(0, 2)$

Ⓓ $B'(-3, -3)$, $C'(-1, -4)$, $D'(0, -2)$

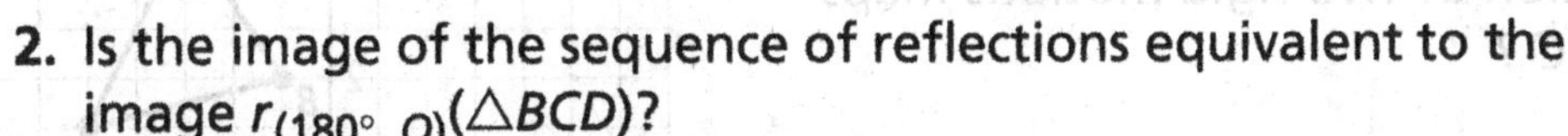

2. Is the image of the sequence of reflections equivalent to the image $r_{(180°,\ O)}(\triangle BCD)$?

$(R_{x\text{-axis}} \circ R_{y\text{-axis}})(\triangle BCD)$	Yes	No
$(R_{y\text{-axis}} \circ R_{x\text{-axis}})(\triangle BCD)$	Yes	No

3. $\overline{AB}$ is rotated 120° clockwise about B. Then $\overline{AB}$ is rotated 45° counterclockwise about A. What is the image of A as a composition of transformations?

Ⓐ $(r_{(120°,\ B)} \circ r_{(-45°,\ A)})(A)$

Ⓑ $(r_{(-45°,\ A)} \circ r_{(120°,\ B)})(A)$

Ⓒ $(r_{(-120°,\ B)} \circ r_{(45°,\ A)})(A)$

Ⓓ $(r_{(45°,\ A)} \circ r_{(-120°,\ B)})(A)$

4. Suppose $r_{(140°,\ P)}(A) = B$ and $(R_{\overleftrightarrow{PD}} \circ R_{\overleftrightarrow{PC}})(A) = B$. What is $m\angle CPD$?

5. You are given the rotation $r_{(45°,\ P)}$. How many times does the rotation need to be applied to a figure to map the figure onto itself?

8-4 Lesson Quiz

Classification of Rigid Motions

1. Can the following composition of rigid motions be described as a single translation, rotation, or reflection?

$R_m \circ R_n$	Yes	No
$T_{\langle c,\, d\rangle} \circ T_{\langle a,\, b\rangle}$	Yes	No
$T_{\langle a,\, b\rangle} \circ R_m$	Yes	No

For Items 2–3, use the figure showing $\triangle ABC$.

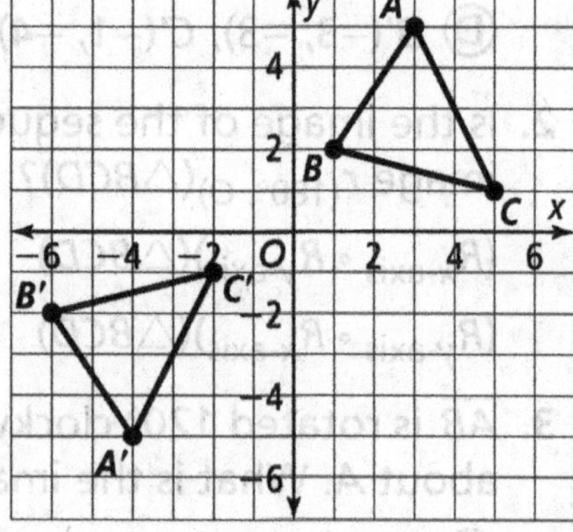

2. Which composition of two rigid motions maps $\triangle ABC$ to $\triangle A'B'C'$?

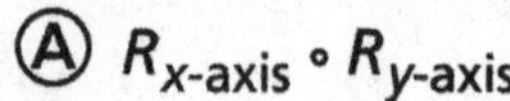

Ⓐ $R_{x\text{-axis}} \circ R_{y\text{-axis}}$

Ⓑ $R_{y\text{-axis}} \circ R_{x\text{-axis}}$

Ⓒ $T_{\langle -7,\, 0\rangle} \circ R_{x\text{-axis}}$

Ⓓ $T_{\langle -7,\, 0\rangle} \circ R_{y\text{-axis}}$

3. Suppose m is the line with equation $y = -4$ and $\triangle A'B'C'$ is mapped to $\triangle A''B''C''$ by applying the glide reflection $T_{\langle 3,\, 0\rangle} \circ R_m$. What are the coordinates of $\triangle A''B''C''$?

Ⓐ $A''(-1, -3)$, $B''(-3, -6)$, $C''(1, -7)$

Ⓑ $A''(-7, -3)$, $B''(-8, -6)$, $C''(-5, -7)$

Ⓒ $A''(-2, -5)$, $B''(0, -2)$, $C''(-3, -1)$

Ⓓ $A''(-8, -3)$, $B''(-6, 4)$, $C''(-9, 0)$

For Items 4–5, use the figure showing $\triangle DEF$ and $\triangle D'E'F'$.

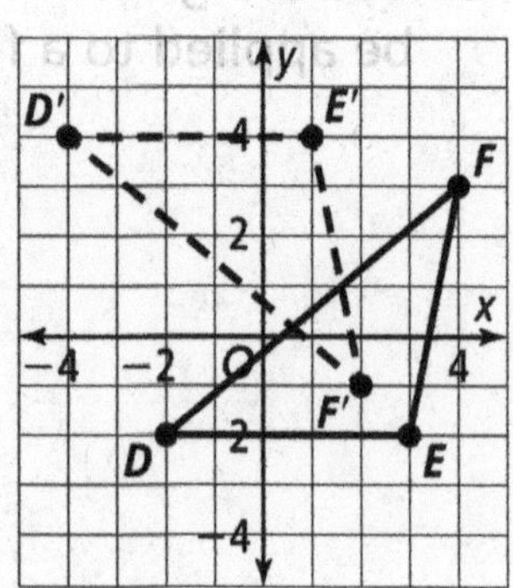

4. What is a glide reflection that maps $\triangle DEF$ onto $\triangle D'E'F'$?

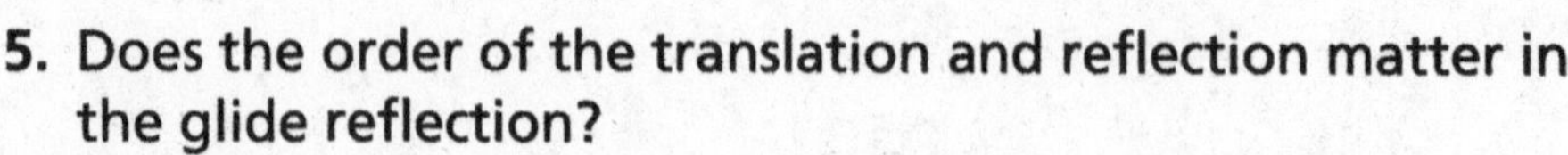

5. Does the order of the translation and reflection matter in the glide reflection?

8-5 Lesson Quiz

Symmetry

For Items 1–3, use the regular pentagon shown.

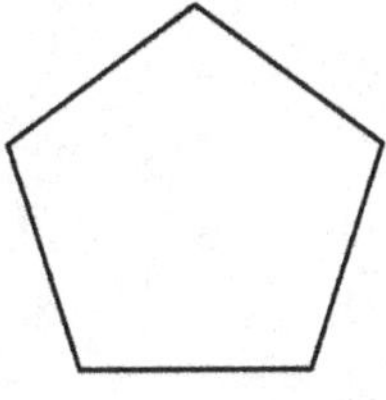

1. How many lines of symmetry does the pentagon have?

   Ⓐ 0
   Ⓑ 1
   Ⓒ 3
   Ⓓ 5

2. What is the least angle of rotation that maps the pentagon onto itself?

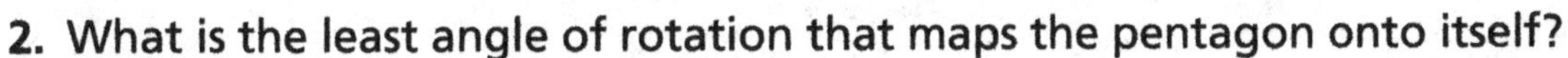

3. Does the pentagon have the following types of symmetry?

Reflectional	Yes	No
Point	Yes	No

For Items 4–5, use the figure shown.

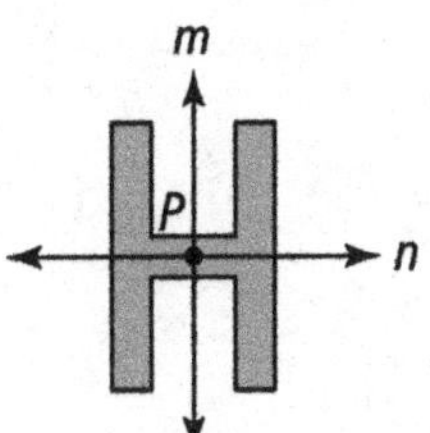

4. What reflections map the figure onto itself?

5. Which rotation maps the figure onto itself?

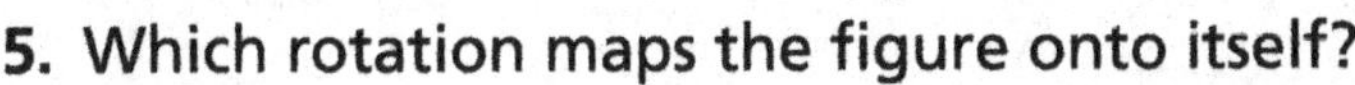

   Ⓐ $r_{(45°, P)}$
   Ⓑ $r_{(90°, P)}$
   Ⓒ $r_{(180°, P)}$
   Ⓓ $r_{(270°, P)}$

Name

PearsonRealize.com

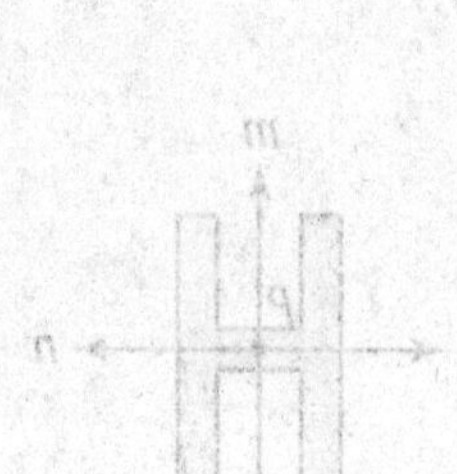

Name ______________________________

8 Topic Assessment Form A

1. What is a rule for the translation of $\triangle RST$? Select all that apply.

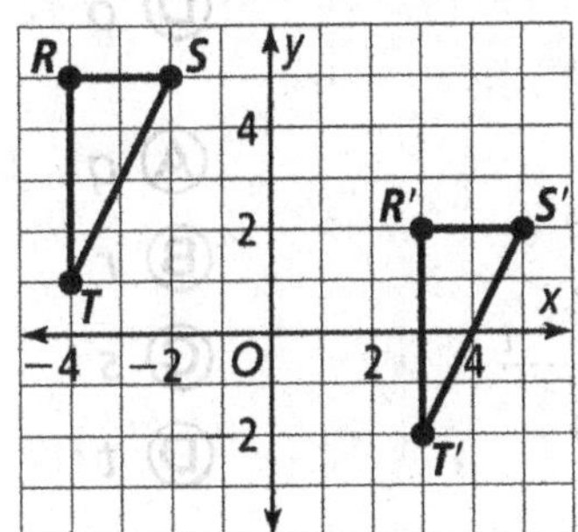

Ⓐ $T_{\langle -7, 3\rangle}$

Ⓑ 7 units down; 3 units right

Ⓒ 7 units up; 3 units left

Ⓓ $T_{\langle 7, -3\rangle}$

Items 2–5. Find the coordinates of the vertices of each image.

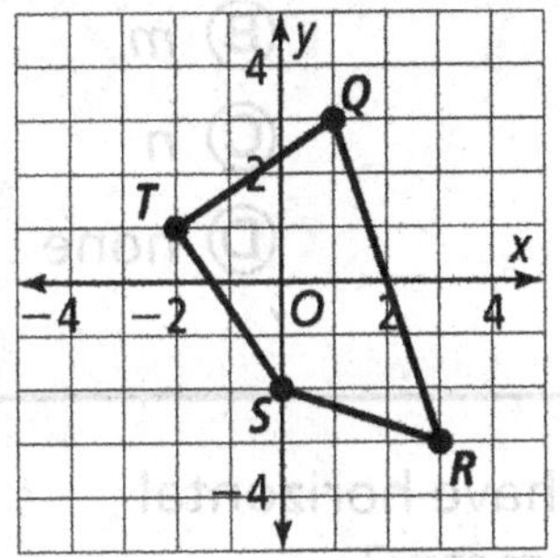

2. $R_{x\text{-axis}}(QRST)$

3. $r_{(90°, O)}(QRST)$

4. $T_{\langle 3, -2\rangle}(QRST)$

5. $(R_{y\text{-axis}} \circ T_{\langle 2, 0\rangle})(QRST)$

Items 6–7. What rigid motion maps the solid-line figure onto the dotted-line figure?

6. 

7. 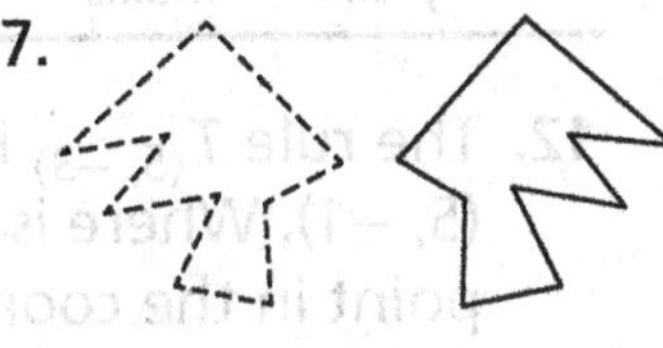

8. Which of the descriptions is true for the graph?

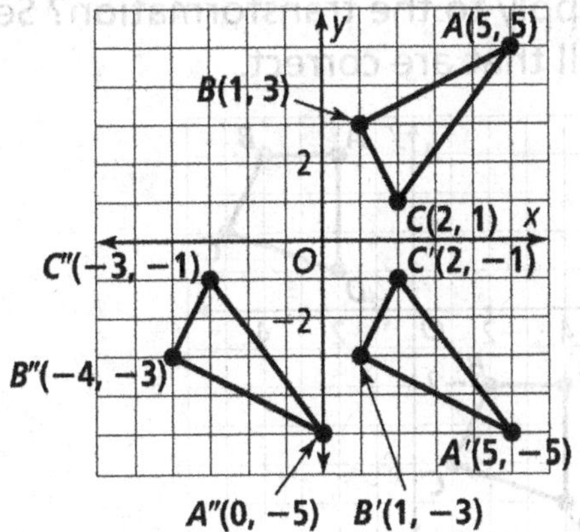

Ⓐ $\triangle A'B'C'$ is $T_{\langle 0, -2\rangle}(\triangle ABC)$

Ⓑ $\triangle A'B'C'$ is $(T_{\langle 0, -2\rangle} \circ R_{x\text{-axis}})(\triangle ABC)$

Ⓒ $\triangle A'B'C'$ is $R_{x\text{-axis}}(\triangle ABC)$

Ⓓ $\triangle A'B'C'$ is $r_{90°}(\triangle ABC)$

9. Point $P'(5, -4)$ is the image of point $P(2, 3)$ under a translation. What is the image of $(6, -2)$ under the same translation?

Ⓐ (7, −1)

Ⓑ (13, −3)

Ⓒ (9, −9)

Ⓓ (3, 5)

10. Which capital letters have one or more lines of symmetry? Select all that apply.

Ⓐ X Ⓑ Z Ⓒ H Ⓓ C

11. Point T is at (−2, 5). What are the coordinates of point T' after $R_{y\text{-axis}} \circ R_{x\text{-axis}}$?

12. The rule $T_{\langle 5, -3 \rangle}$ is used for point (5, −1). Where is the translated point in the coordinate system?

Ⓐ Quadrant I
Ⓑ Quadrant II
Ⓒ Quadrant III
Ⓓ Quadrant IV

13. Which of the following descriptions apply to the transformation? Select all that are correct.

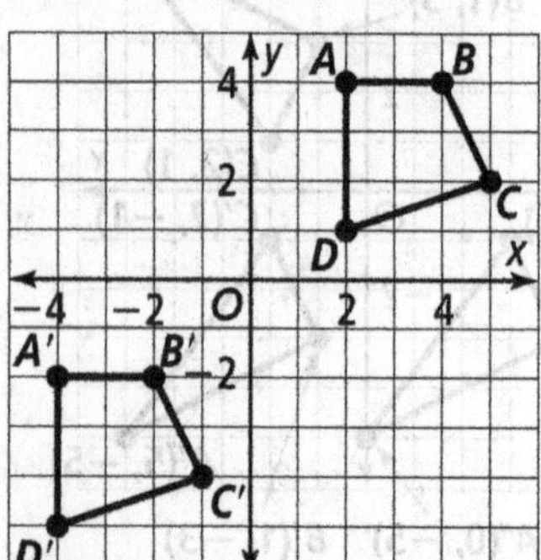

Ⓐ $T_{\langle -6, -6 \rangle}$
Ⓑ 6 units down; 6 units left
Ⓒ 6 units up; 6 units right
Ⓓ $T_{\langle 6, 6 \rangle}$

14. If a figure is translated with the rule $T_{\langle -3, 3 \rangle}$, which translation moves the image back to the original position?

Ⓐ $T_{\langle 3, -3 \rangle}$
Ⓑ $T_{\langle -3, 3 \rangle}$
Ⓒ $T_{\langle 0, 3 \rangle}$
Ⓓ $T_{\langle -3, 0 \rangle}$

Items 15–18. Find the lines of symmetry for each shape. Select all that apply.

15.

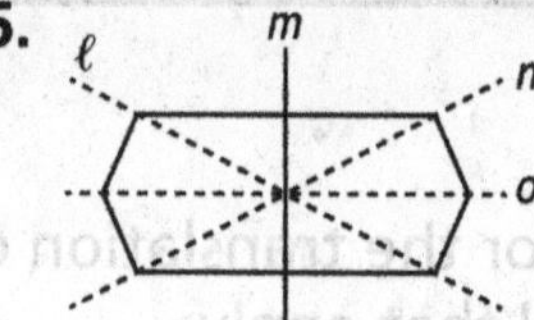

Ⓐ ℓ
Ⓑ m
Ⓒ n
Ⓓ o

16.

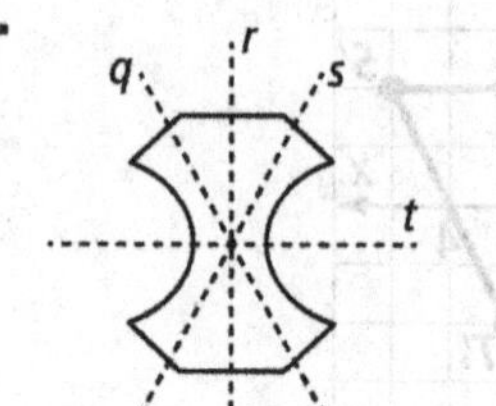

Ⓐ q
Ⓑ r
Ⓒ s
Ⓓ t

17.

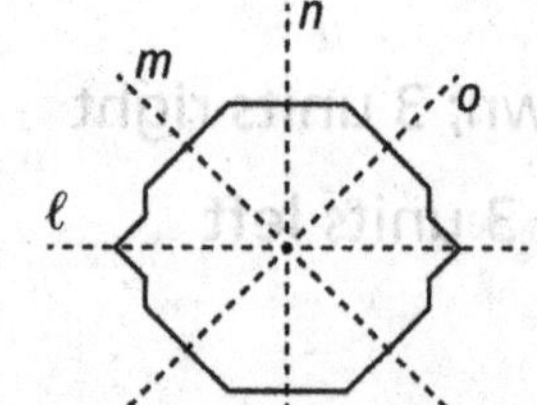

Ⓐ ℓ
Ⓑ m
Ⓒ n
Ⓓ o

18.

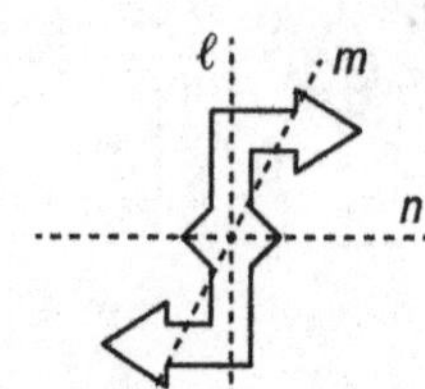

Ⓐ ℓ
Ⓑ m
Ⓒ n
Ⓓ none

19. Which words have horizontal reflection symmetry?

Ⓐ BOO
Ⓑ PIP
Ⓒ RADAR
Ⓓ EXCEED

20. Which shape is an example of rotational symmetry?

Ⓐ 

Ⓒ  

Ⓑ 

Ⓓ  

Name ______________________________

8 Topic Assessment Form B

1. What is a rule for the translation of $\triangle RST$? Select all that apply.

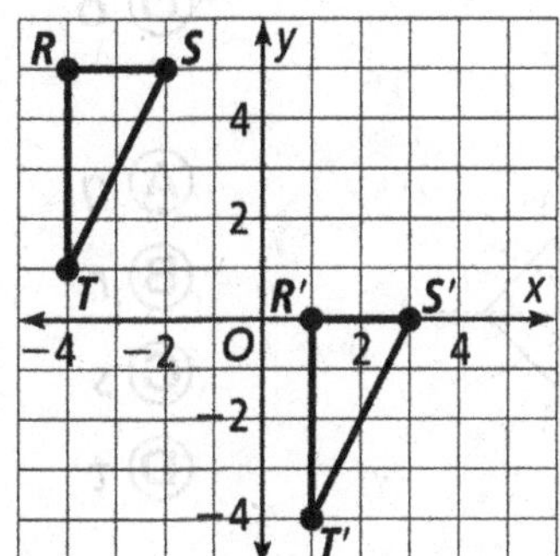

Ⓐ $T_{\langle 5, -5 \rangle}$
Ⓑ 5 units down; 5 units right
Ⓒ 5 units up; 5 units left
Ⓓ $T_{\langle -5, 5 \rangle}$

Items 2–5. Find the coordinates of the vertices of each image.

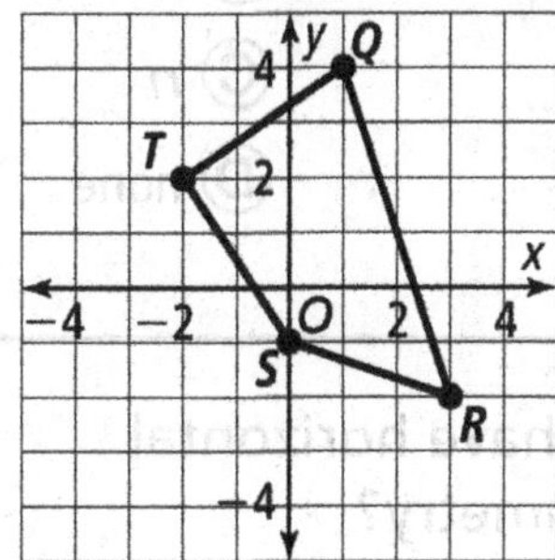

2. $R_{x\text{-axis}}(QRST)$

3. $r_{(180°, O)}(QRST)$

4. $T_{\langle -2, -3 \rangle}(QRST)$

5. $(R_{y\text{-axis}} \circ T_{\langle 3, 0 \rangle})(QRST)$

Items 6–7. What rigid motion maps the solid-line figure onto the dotted-line figure?

6. **7.**

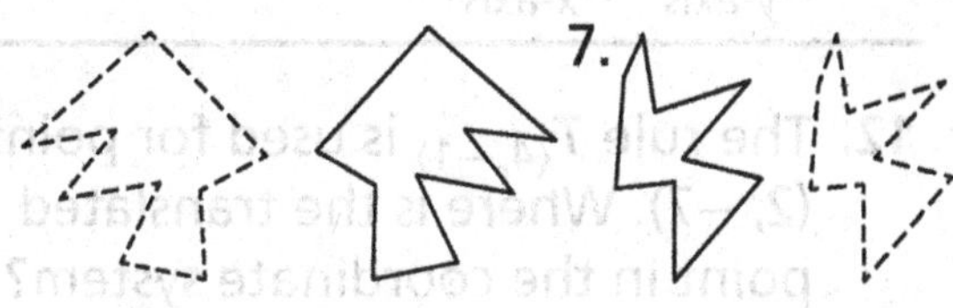

8. Which of the descriptions is true for the graph?

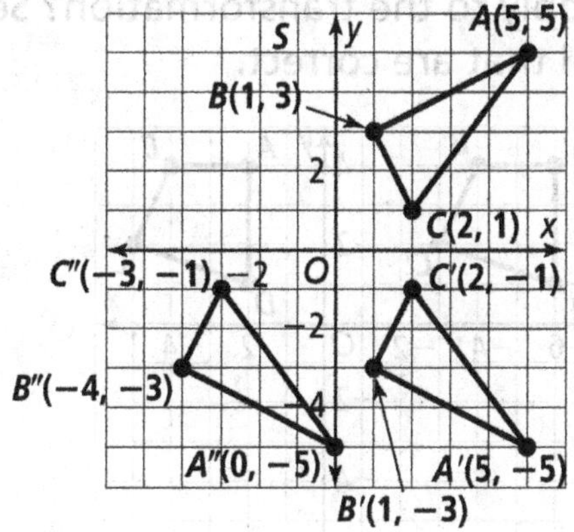

Ⓐ $\triangle A''B''C''$ is $T_{\langle -5, 0 \rangle}(\triangle A'B'C')$
Ⓑ $\triangle A''B''C''$ is $(T_{\langle -5, 0 \rangle} \circ R_{x\text{-axis}})(\triangle A'B'C')$
Ⓒ $\triangle A''B''C''$ is $R_{x\text{-axis}}(\triangle A'B'C')$
Ⓓ $\triangle A''B''C''$ is $r_{90°}(\triangle A'B'C')$

9. Point $P'(-3, 2)$ is the image of point $P(3, 8)$ under a translation. What is the image of $(0, -6)$ under the same translation?

Ⓐ $(-3, -4)$
Ⓑ $(0, 6)$
Ⓒ $(0, 10)$
Ⓓ $(-6, -12)$

10. Which capital letters have one or more lines of symmetry? Select all that apply.

Ⓐ V Ⓑ M Ⓒ N Ⓓ O

11. Point T is at (−6, 4). What are the coordinates of point T' after $R_{y\text{-axis}} \circ R_{x\text{-axis}}$?

12. The rule $T_{\langle 4, -1 \rangle}$ is used for point (2, −7). Where is the translated point in the coordinate system?

Ⓐ Quadrant I Ⓒ Quadrant III

Ⓑ Quadrant II Ⓓ Quadrant IV

13. Which of the following descriptions apply to the transformation? Select all that are correct.

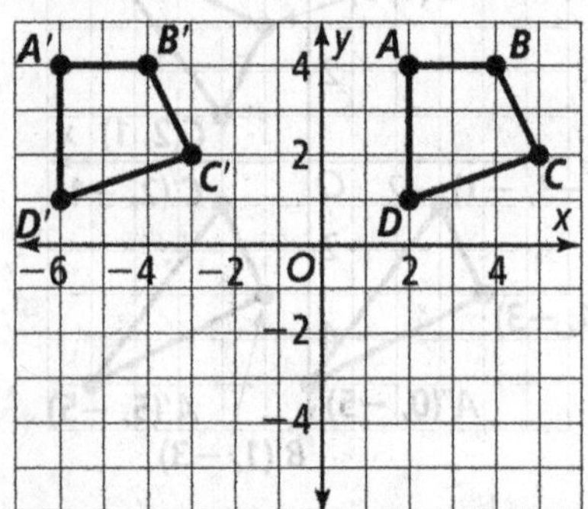

Ⓐ $T_{\langle -8, 0 \rangle}$

Ⓑ 8 units down

Ⓒ 8 units left

Ⓓ $T_{\langle 0, -8 \rangle}$

14. If a figure is translated with the rule $T_{\langle -5, 3 \rangle}$, which translation moves the image back to the original position?

Ⓐ $T_{\langle 5, -3 \rangle}$

Ⓑ $T_{\langle -5, 3 \rangle}$

Ⓒ $T_{\langle 0, 5 \rangle}$

Ⓓ $T_{\langle -5, 0 \rangle}$

Items 15–18. Find the lines of symmetry for each shape. Select all that apply.

15.

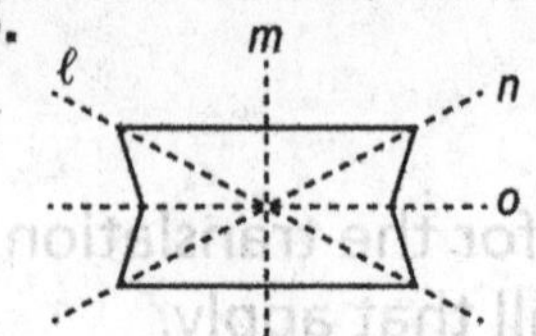

Ⓐ ℓ

Ⓑ m

Ⓒ n

Ⓓ o

16.

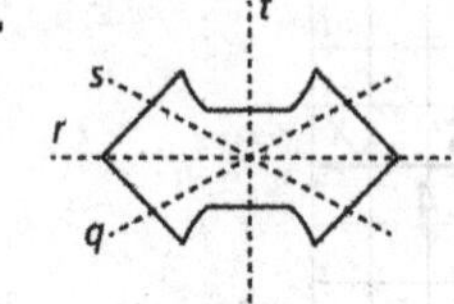

Ⓐ q

Ⓑ r

Ⓒ s

Ⓓ t

17.

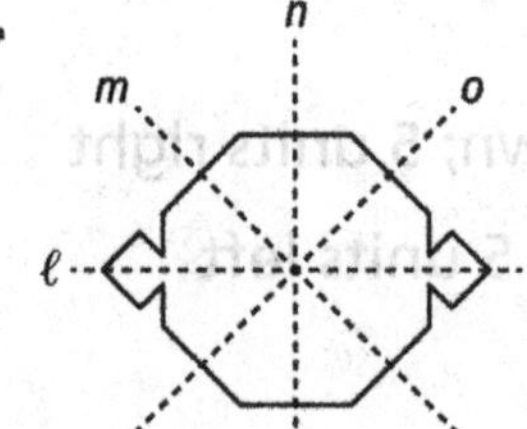

Ⓐ ℓ

Ⓑ m

Ⓒ n

Ⓓ o

18.

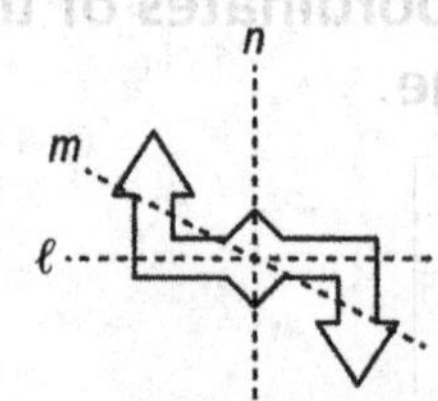

Ⓐ ℓ

Ⓑ m

Ⓒ n

Ⓓ none

19. Which words have horizontal reflection symmetry?

Ⓐ BOOK Ⓒ CHECK

Ⓑ POP Ⓓ SUCCEED

20. Which shape is an example of rotational symmetry?

Ⓐ 

Ⓒ 

Ⓑ 

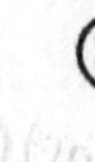

Ⓓ 

Name ____________________

8 Performance Assessment Form A

Derek is designing a series of icons for the Snippet App. He has hired you to check some icons and to create some new ones. The icons will incorporate reflection, translation, rotation, glide reflection, and symmetry.

Use what you know about transformations to answer Items 1 and 2.

1. Classify the transformation for the features inside each circle as *reflection, translation, rotation,* or *glide reflection*.

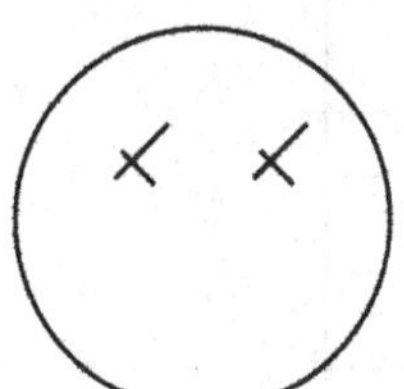

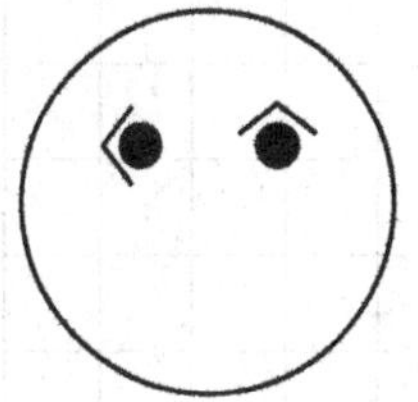

Ⓐ __________ Ⓑ  __________ Ⓒ  __________ Ⓓ __________

2. The keypad will have the following symbols. Which symbols have symmetry? Classify each symbol by listing the letter above it next to appropriate type of symmetry.

A	B	C	D	E	F	G	H	I	J	K	L
♈	♉	♊	♋	♌	♍	♎	♏	♐	♑	♒	♓

Reflection ____________________

Translation ____________________

Rotation ____________________

3. Create an icon by reflecting the shape according to the rule $R_{\ell}(\triangle ABC)$.

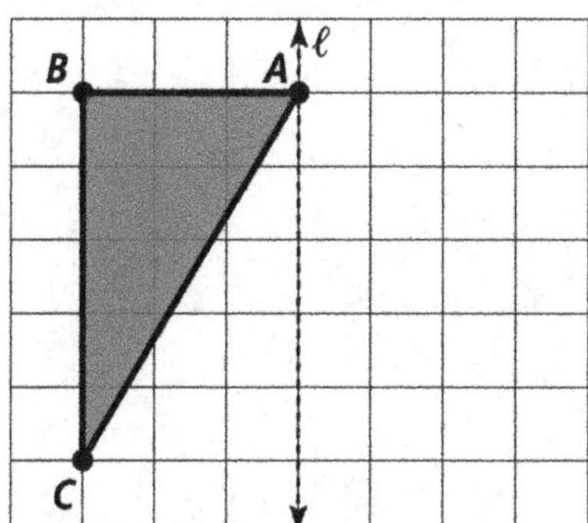

4. Create an icon by translating the shape according to the rule $T_{\langle 3, -5 \rangle}$.

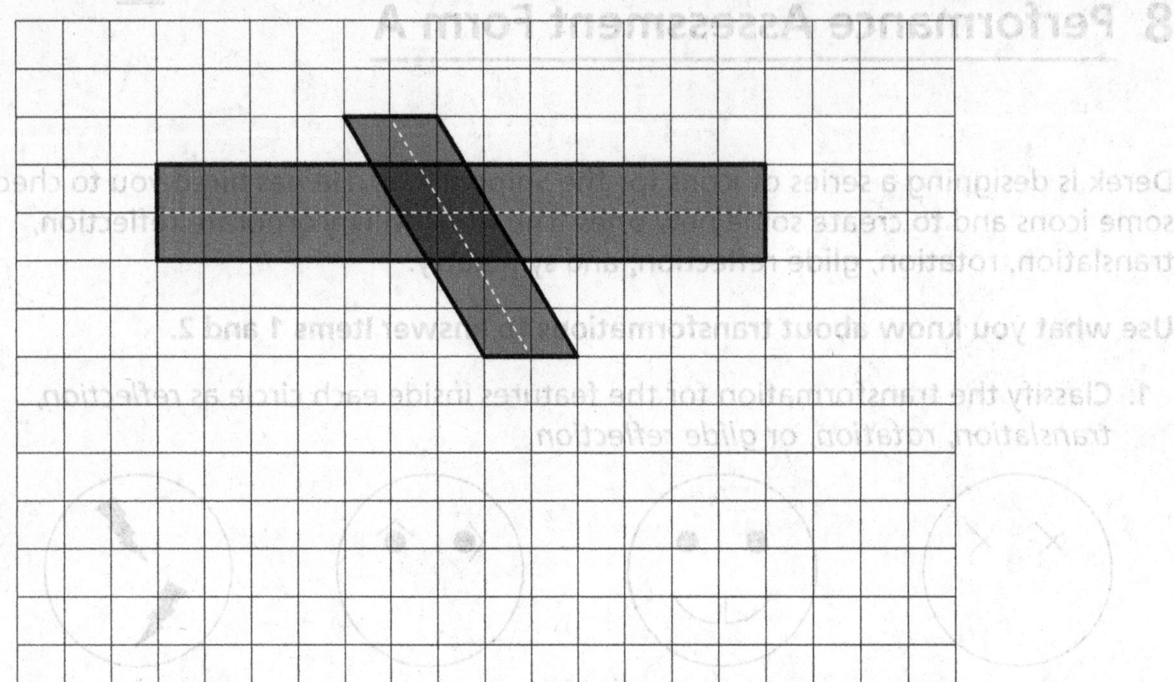

5. Create an icon by rotating the shape according to the rule $r_{(-45°, P)}$.

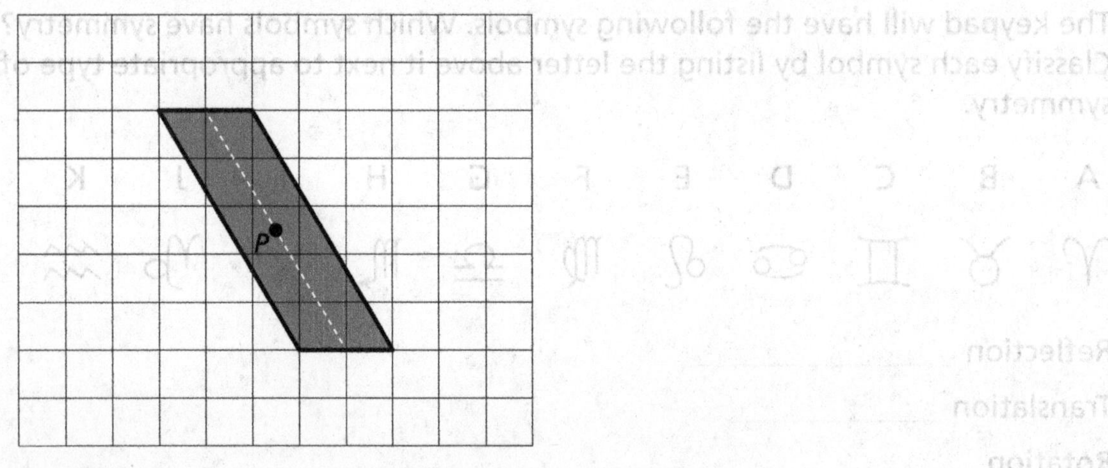

6. Create an icon according to the rule $T_{\langle 0, 3 \rangle} \circ R_{\ell}(\triangle CDE)$.

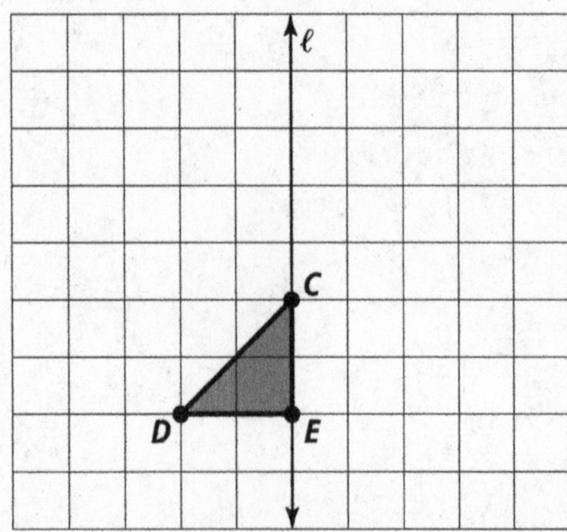

Name ______________________

8 Performance Assessment Form B

Jamie is studying ancient symbols and the Greek alphabet for logo designs. She needs you to analyze the symbols for reflection, translation, rotation, glide reflection, and symmetry.

Use what you know about transformations to answer Items 1 and 2.

1. Classify the transformation for each symbol as *reflection, translation, rotation,* or *glide reflection*.

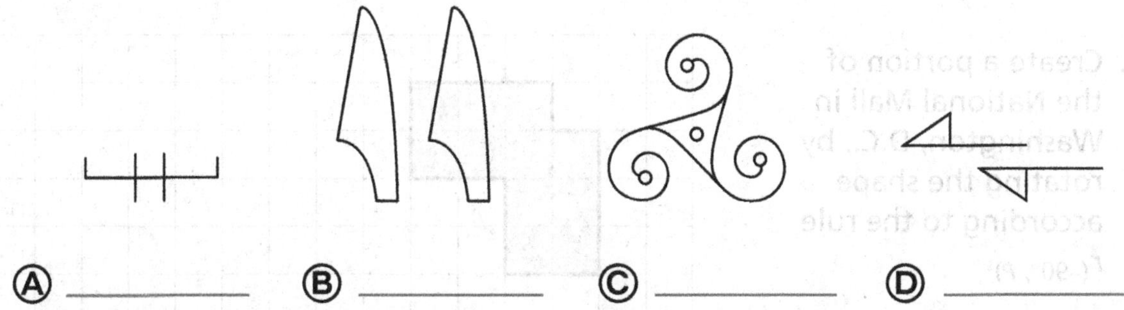

Ⓐ ____________ Ⓑ ____________ Ⓒ ____________ Ⓓ ____________

2. Which of the following symbols have symmetry? Classify each character by listing the letter above it next to the correct type of symmetry.

A	B	C	D	E	F	G	H	I	J	K	L
Α	Β	Γ	Δ	Ε	Ζ	Η	Θ	Ι	Κ	Λ	Ξ

Reflection ____________________

Translation ____________________

Rotation ____________________

Dyani is studying city planning. She recognizes that transformations are a big part of laying out a city. She asks you to do some of the drawings.

Use your mathematical expertise to answer Items 3–6.

3. Create a portion of the National Mall in Washington, D.C., by reflecting the shape according to the rule R_ℓ.

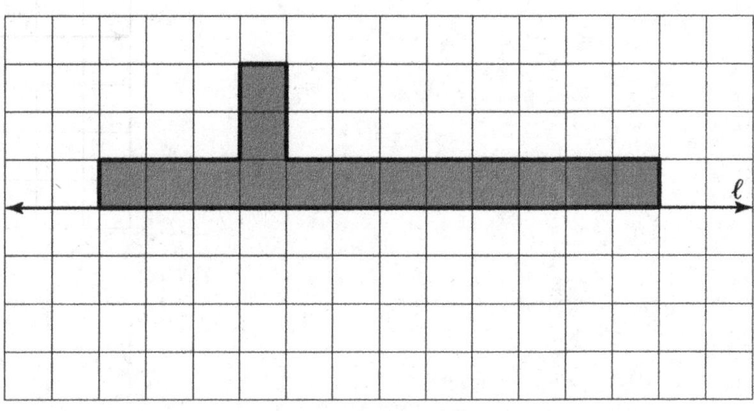

4. Create a portion of the National Mall in Washington, D.C., by translating the shape according to the rule $T_{\langle 5,\,0\rangle}$.

5. Create a portion of the National Mall in Washington, D.C., by rotating the shape according to the rule $r_{(-90^\circ,\,P)}$.

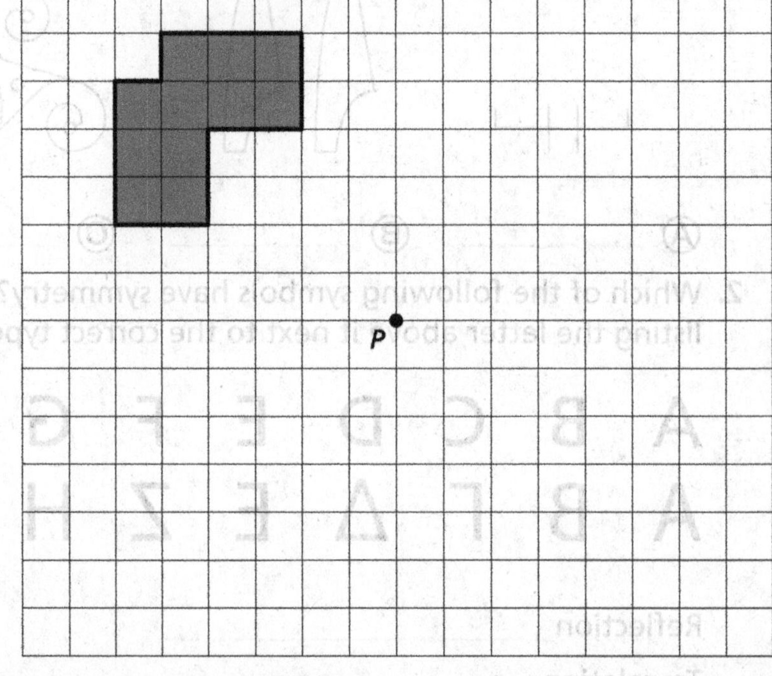

6. Create a portion of the National Mall in Washington, D.C., according to the rule $T_{\langle 4,\,0\rangle} \circ R_{\ell}(ABCD)$.

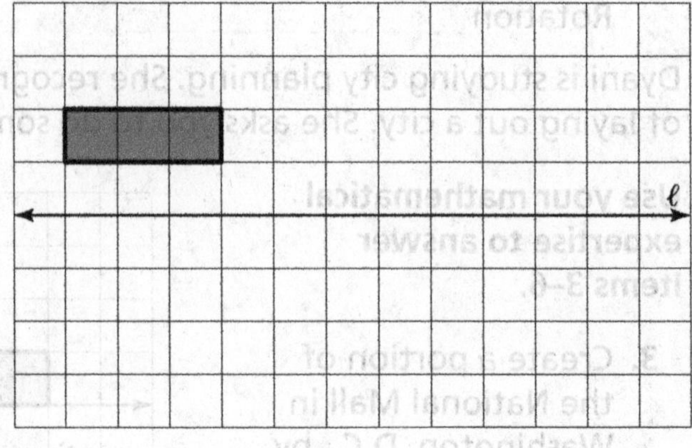

Name ______________________

9 Readiness Assessment

Items 1–4. In the figure shown, the measures of all angles are equal, and $AB = EF$.

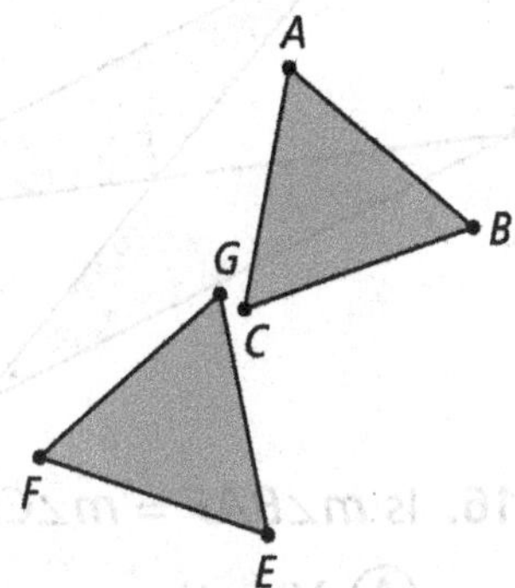

1. What type of transformation appears to map $\triangle ABC$ onto $\triangle EFG$?
   Ⓐ reflection
   Ⓑ translation
   Ⓒ rotation
   Ⓓ none of the above

2. What type of triangle is $\triangle ABC$? What type of triangle is $\triangle EFG$? Select all that apply.
   Ⓐ $\triangle ABC$: right; $\triangle EFG$: right
   Ⓑ $\triangle ABC$: equilateral; $\triangle EFG$: equilateral
   Ⓒ $\triangle ABC$: isosceles; $\triangle EFG$: isosceles
   Ⓓ $\triangle ABC$: scalene; $\triangle EFG$: scalene
   Ⓔ none of the above

3. What are the measures of the angles in $\triangle ABC$? What are the measures of the angles in $\triangle EFG$?
   Ⓐ 60°; 60°; 60° Ⓒ 90°; 45°; 45°
   Ⓑ 90°; 60°; 30° Ⓓ 70°; 60°; 50°

4. Is $\triangle EFG$ the same size and shape as $\triangle ABC$? Explain.

Items 5–7. Use the figure shown.

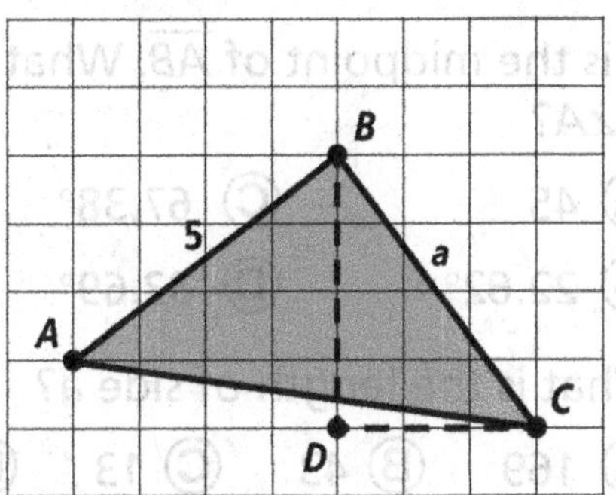

5. What is the measure of side a?

6. What type of triangle is $\triangle ABC$? Select all that apply.
   Ⓐ right Ⓒ isosceles
   Ⓑ equilateral Ⓓ scalene

7. What is the exact length of $\overline{AC}$?

8. What is the area of $\odot X$ expressed in terms of π?
   Ⓐ 4.5π
   Ⓑ 9π
   Ⓒ 20.25π
   Ⓓ 81π

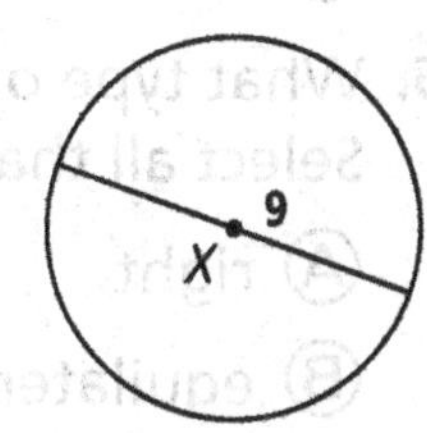

9. Write an expression in terms of π to represent the area of circle P.

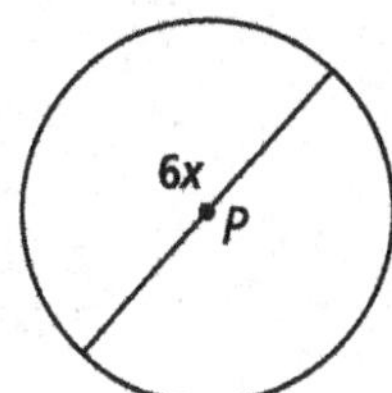

Items 10–15. Use the figure shown.

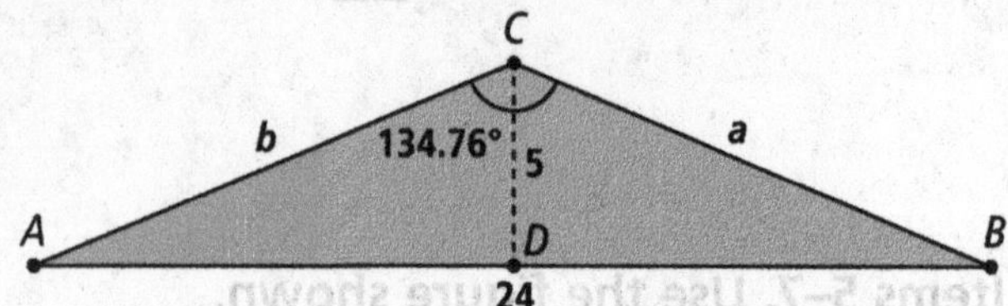

10. D is the midpoint of $\overline{AB}$. What is $m\angle A$?

Ⓐ 45 Ⓒ 67.38°

Ⓑ 22.62° Ⓓ 33.69°

11. What is the length of side a?

Ⓐ 169 Ⓑ 43 Ⓒ 13 Ⓓ 12

12. What is the length of side b?

Ⓐ 169 Ⓑ 43 Ⓒ 13 Ⓓ 12

13. What is $m\angle BCD$?

14. What type of triangle is $\triangle ABC$? Select all that apply.

Ⓐ right

Ⓑ equilateral

Ⓒ isosceles

Ⓓ obtuse

15. What type of triangle is $\triangle ACD$? Select all that apply.

Ⓐ right

Ⓑ equilateral

Ⓒ isosceles

Ⓓ obtuse

Items 16–19. In the figure, $\overline{AB}$ is parallel to $\overline{CE}$. Point F is the midpoint of $\overline{AE}$ and $\overline{BC}$.

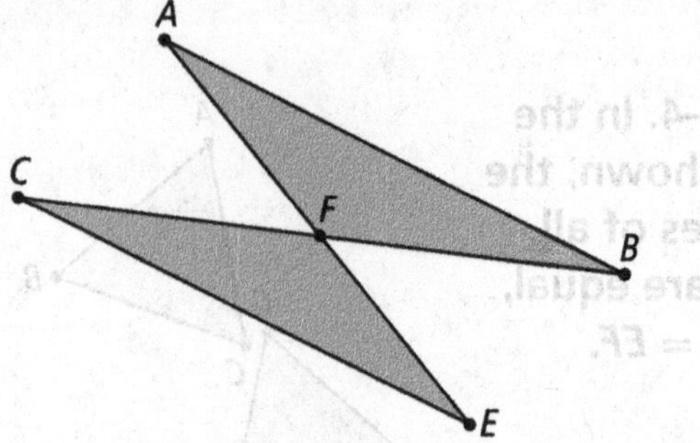

16. Is $m\angle BAF = m\angle CEF$? Explain.

Ⓐ Yes; they are vertical angles.

Ⓑ Yes; they are alternate interior angles.

Ⓒ Yes; they are alternate exterior angles.

Ⓓ No; the triangles are different sizes.

17. Which statement is true?

Ⓐ $CF = AF$

Ⓑ $CF = EF$

Ⓒ $EF = BF$

Ⓓ $AF = EF$

18. Is $m\angle AFB = m\angle CFE$? Explain.

Ⓐ Yes; they are vertical angles.

Ⓑ Yes; they are alternate interior angles.

Ⓒ Yes; they are alternate exterior angles.

Ⓓ No; the triangles are different sizes.

19. Is $\triangle FBA$ the same size and shape as $\triangle FCE$? Explain.

Name ______________________________

9-1 Lesson Quiz

Congruence

Use the graph of two triangles for Items 1 and 2.

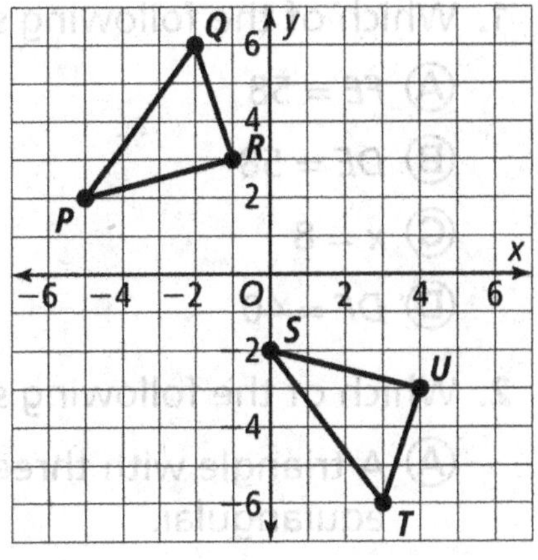

1. Triangle *PQR* is reflected across the line $y = 0$. The image is then translated 5 units to the right, resulting in $\triangle STU$. Which of the following statements are true? Select all that apply.

Ⓐ $PQ = ST$

Ⓑ $PQ = TU$

Ⓒ $m\angle R = m\angle U$

Ⓓ $m\angle P = m\angle U$

2. In the graph, $\triangle PQR \cong \triangle STU$. Complete the statement below to describe a composition of rigid motions that maps $\triangle PQR$ to $\triangle STU$.

Reflect $\triangle PQR$ across the line __________. Then translate the resulting image __________ units to the right.

Use the graph of four triangles for Items 3 and 4.

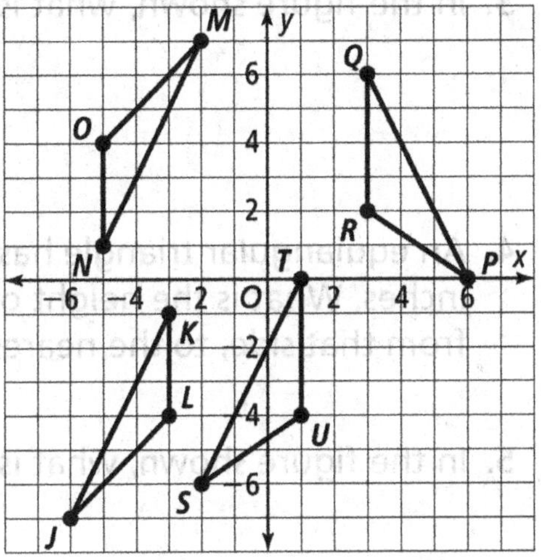

3. Which of the following statements is true?

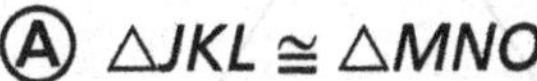

Ⓐ $\triangle JKL \cong \triangle MNO$

Ⓑ $\triangle JKL \cong \triangle PQR$

Ⓒ $\triangle STU \cong \triangle MNO$

Ⓓ $\triangle STU \cong \triangle JKL$

4. Complete the statement below to prove that $\triangle MNO$ is not congruent to $\triangle PQR$.

The segment $\overline{QR}$ cannot be mapped to ______ by any composition of rigid motions.

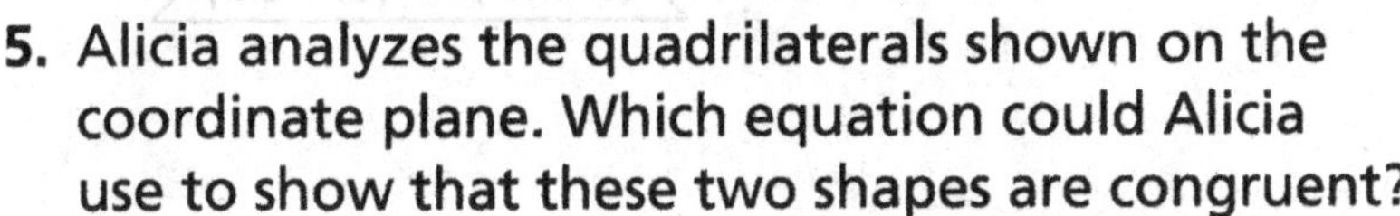

5. Alicia analyzes the quadrilaterals shown on the coordinate plane. Which equation could Alicia use to show that these two shapes are congruent?

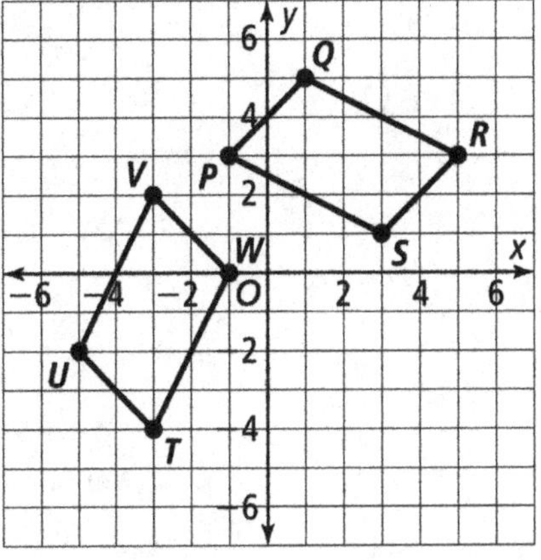

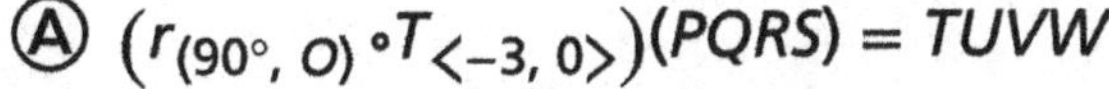

Ⓐ $(r_{(90°,\, O)} \circ T_{\langle -3,\, 0\rangle})(PQRS) = TUVW$

Ⓑ $(r_{(90°,\, O)} \circ T_{\langle 0,\, -3\rangle})(PQRS) = TUVW$

Ⓒ $(r_{(180°,\, O)} \circ T_{\langle -3,\, 0\rangle})(PQRS) = TUVW$

Ⓓ $(r_{(180°,\, O)} \circ T_{\langle 0,\, -3\rangle})(PQRS) = TUVW$

Name ______________________________

9-2 Lesson Quiz

Isosceles and Equilateral Triangles

1. Which of the following statements is incorrect?

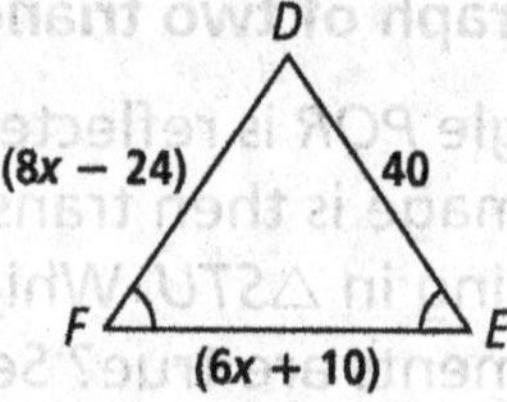

Ⓐ $FE = 58$

Ⓑ $DE = 58$

Ⓒ $x = 8$

Ⓓ $DF = 40$

2. Which of the following statements is incorrect?

Ⓐ A triangle with three congruent sides is equiangular.

Ⓑ The Isosceles Triangle Theorem can be applied to equilateral triangles.

Ⓒ The measure of each angle of an equilateral triangle is 120°.

Ⓓ A triangle with three congruent angles is equilateral.

3. In the figure shown, what is $m\angle A$?

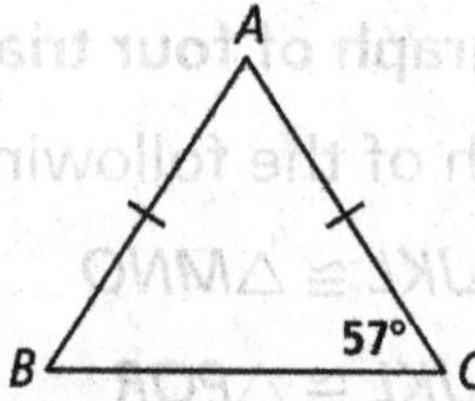

4. An equiangular triangle has one side of length six inches. What is the height of the triangle, drawn from that side, to the nearest tenth of an inch?

5. In the figure shown, what is the value of x?

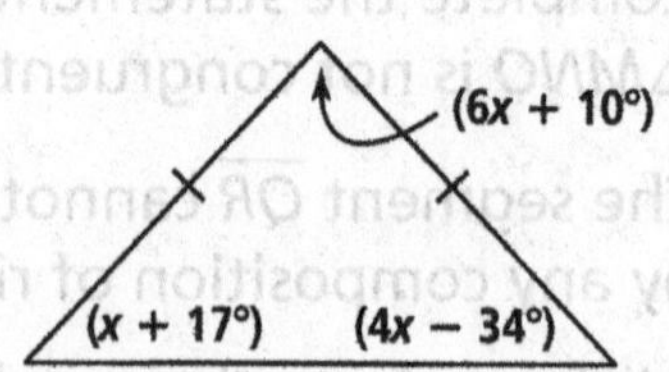

Name ______________________

9-3 Lesson Quiz

Proving and Applying the SAS and SSS Congruence Criteria

1. In the figure shown, which composition of rigid motions will map one triangle onto the other?

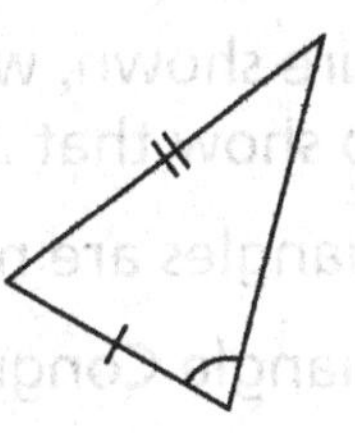
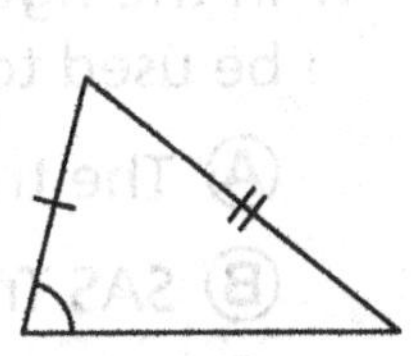

   Ⓐ a glide reflection
   Ⓑ a reflection followed by a translation
   Ⓒ two translations
   Ⓓ a rotation followed by a translation

2. Which theorem shows that $\triangle ABC \cong \triangle DEF$?

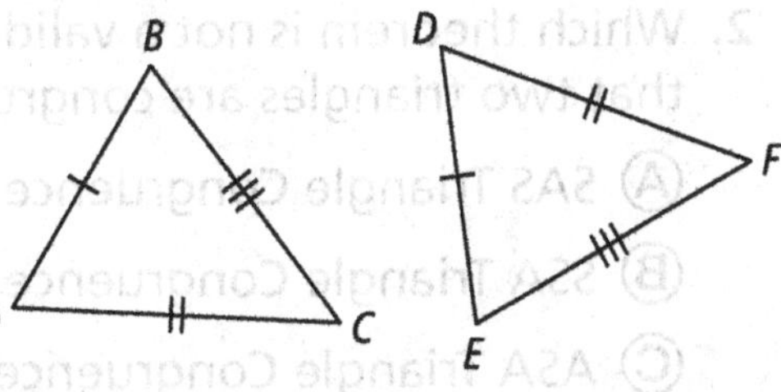

   Ⓐ The triangles are not congruent.
   Ⓑ SAS Triangle Congruence Theorem
   Ⓒ Isosceles Triangle Theorem
   Ⓓ SSS Triangle Congruence Theorem

3. In the figure shown, what additional information is needed to show that $\triangle ABC \cong \triangle DEF$ by SSS?

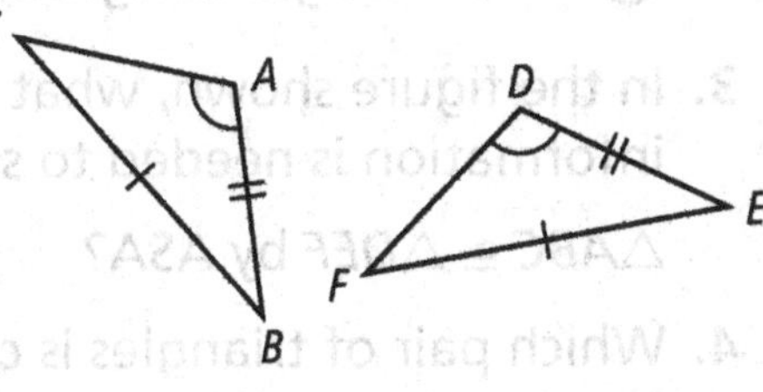

4. Which are necessary conditions to apply the SAS Triangle Congruence Theorem? Select all that apply.

   Ⓐ Two sides and the included angle of a triangle are congruent to the corresponding parts of another triangle.
   Ⓑ Two angles and the included side of one triangle are congruent to the corresponding parts of another triangle.
   Ⓒ An angle and the two sides collinear with the angle's rays are congruent to the corresponding parts of another triangle.
   Ⓓ Two sides and any angle of one triangle are congruent to the corresponding parts of another triangle.

5. In the figure shown, what is the value of x?

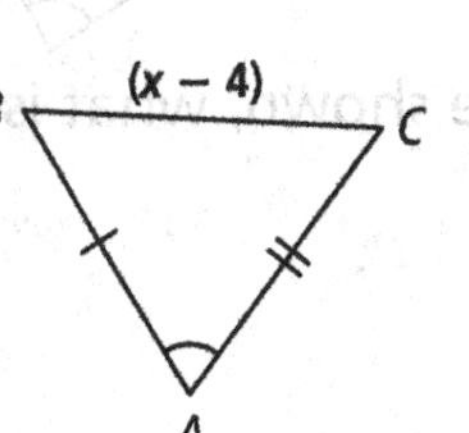

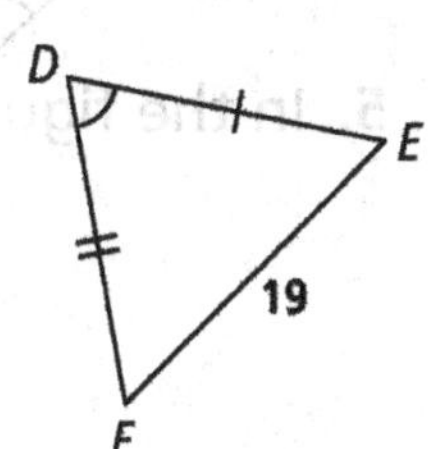

Name ____________________

9-4 Lesson Quiz

Proving and Applying the ASA and AAS Congruence Criteria

1. In the figure shown, which theorem can be used to show that $\triangle ABC \cong \triangle DEF$?

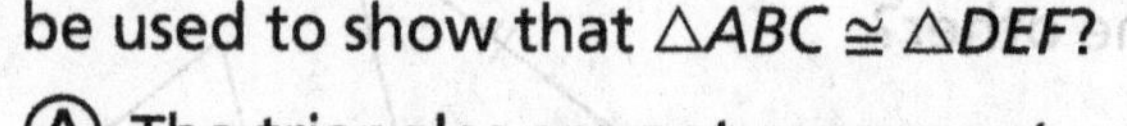

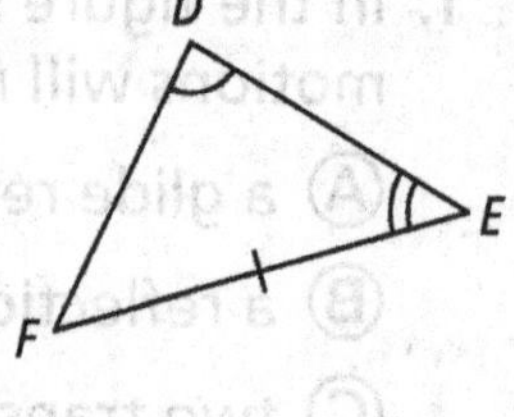

Ⓐ The triangles are not congruent.

Ⓑ SAS Triangle Congruence Theorem

Ⓒ AAS Triangle Congruence Theorem

Ⓓ ASA Triangle Congruence Theorem

2. Which theorem is not a valid theorem to show that two triangles are congruent?

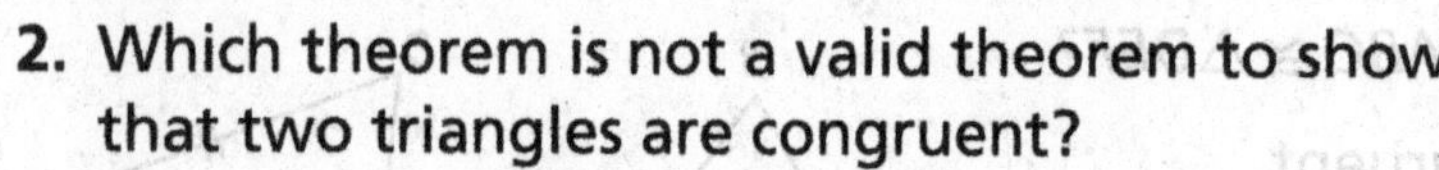

Ⓐ SAS Triangle Congruence Theorem

Ⓑ SSA Triangle Congruence Theorem

Ⓒ ASA Triangle Congruence Theorem

Ⓓ AAS Triangle Congruence Theorem

3. In the figure shown, what additional information is needed to show that $\triangle ABC \cong \triangle DEF$ by ASA?

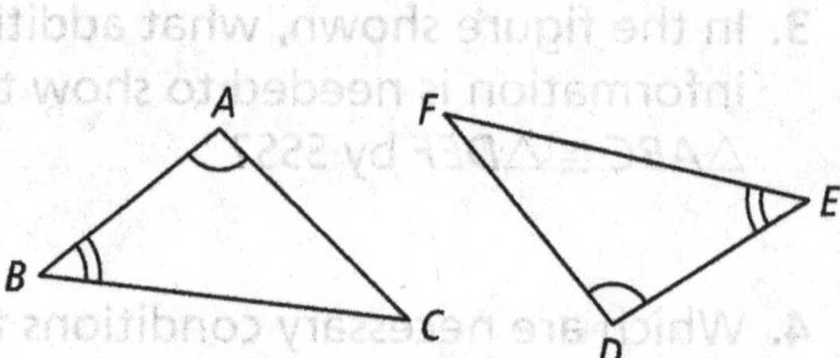

4. Which pair of triangles is congruent by ASA? Select all that apply.

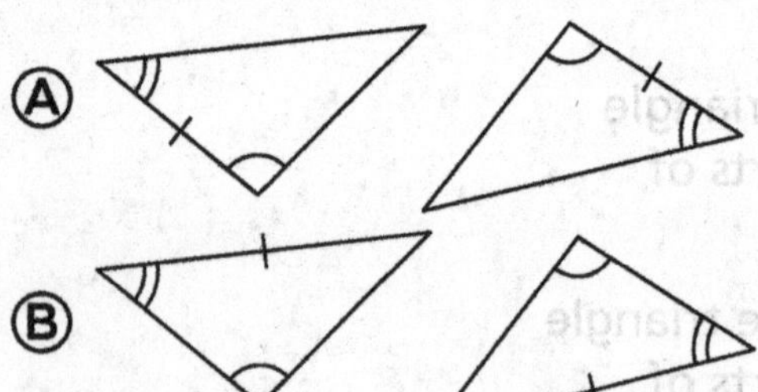

Ⓐ

Ⓑ

Ⓒ

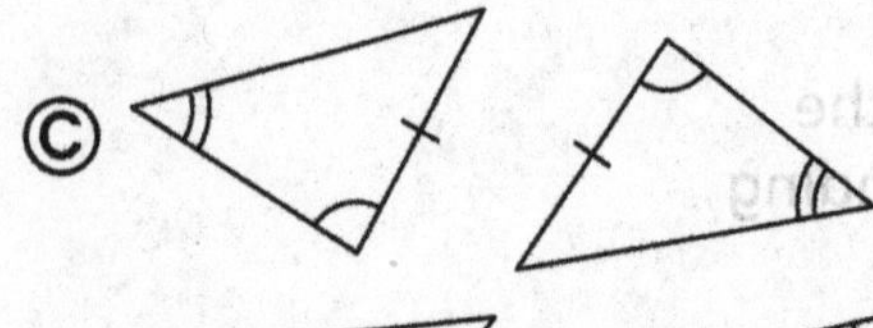

Ⓓ

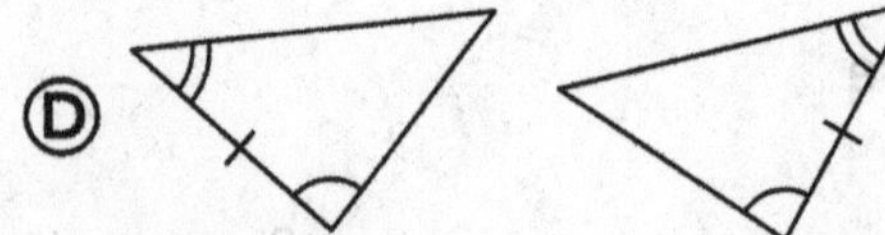

5. In the figure shown, what is the value of x?

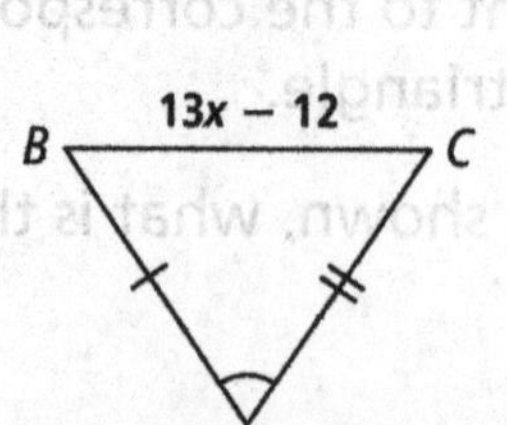

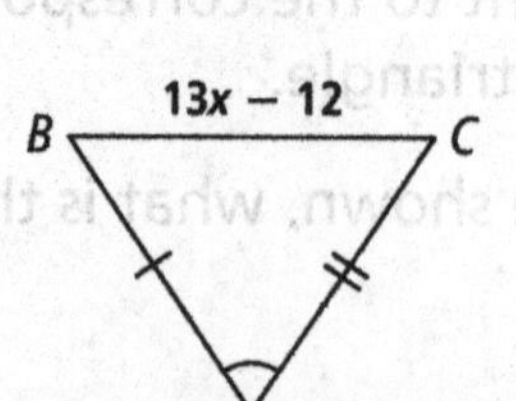

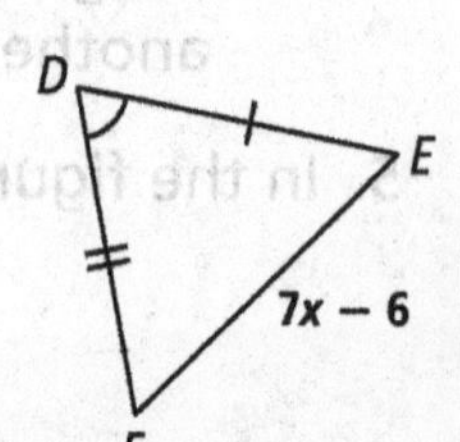

Name ______________________________

9-5 Lesson Quiz

Congruence in Right Triangles

1. Which pair of triangles can be proven congruent using the Hypotenuse-Leg Theorem?

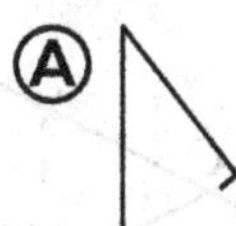
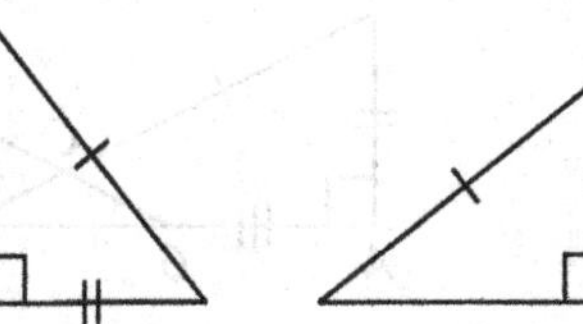

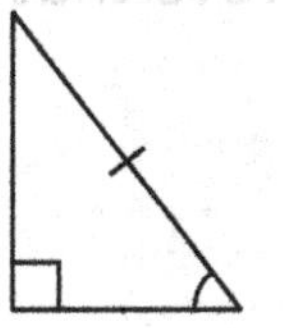
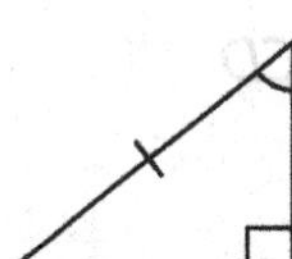
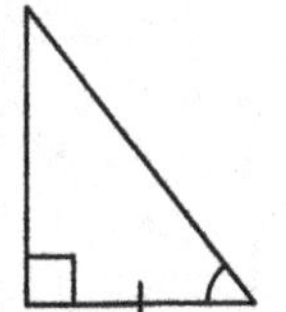
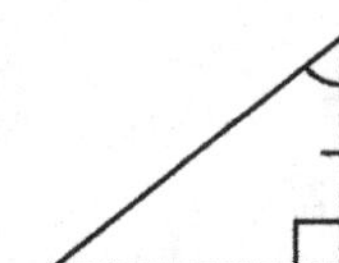

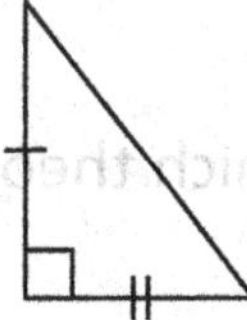
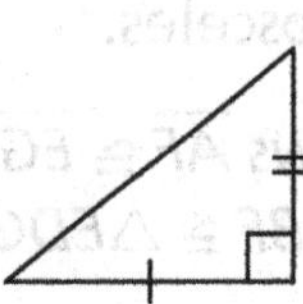

2. Which theorem would show that the two right triangles are congruent?

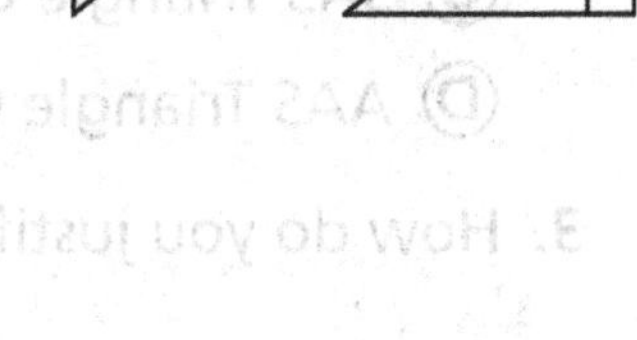

Ⓐ SAS Triangle Congruence Theorem

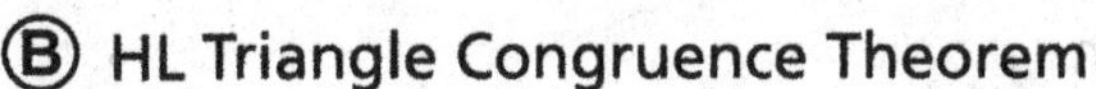
Ⓑ HL Triangle Congruence Theorem

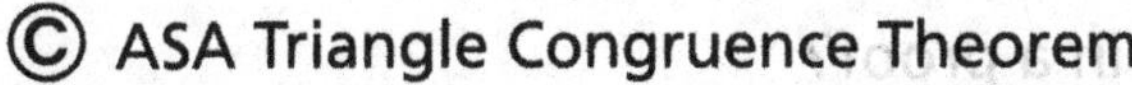
Ⓒ ASA Triangle Congruence Theorem

Ⓓ AAS Triangle Congruence Theorem

3. In the figure, what theorem can be used to show that $\triangle ABC \cong \triangle DEF$?

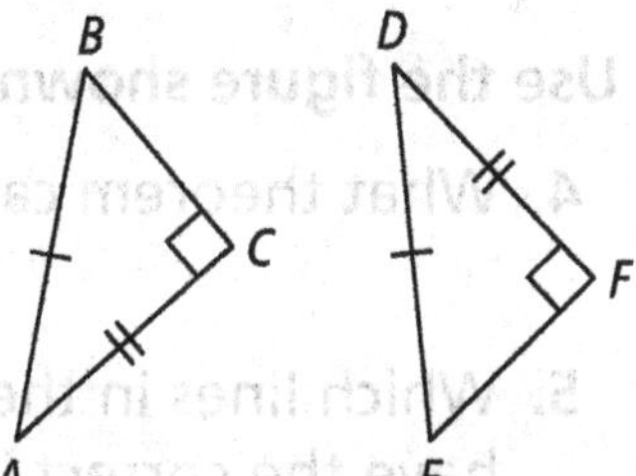

4. For the figures shown, which information can be used to show that $\triangle ABC \cong \triangle DEF$? Select all that apply.

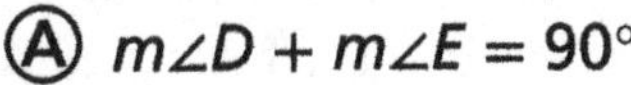
Ⓐ $m\angle D + m\angle E = 90°$

Ⓑ $m\angle D = 37°$

Ⓒ $\angle E \cong \angle B$

Ⓓ $\angle F$ is a right angle.

5. If $y = 5$, is there sufficient information to show that $\triangle ABC \cong \triangle DEF$? Explain.

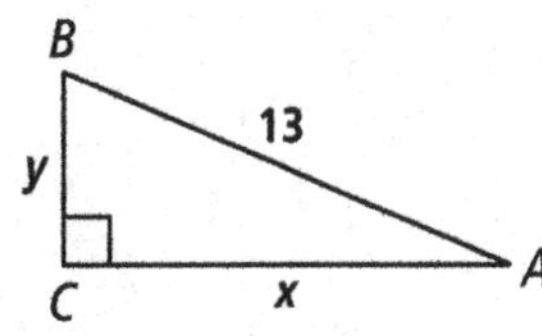

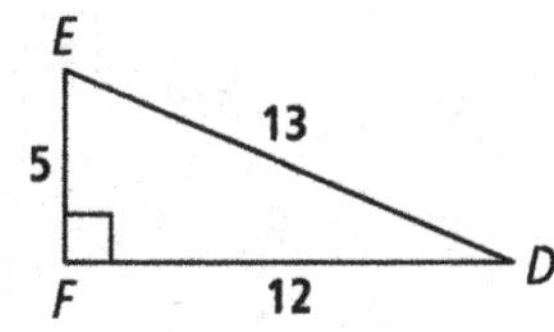

Name ______________________________

9-6 Lesson Quiz

Congruence in Overlapping Triangles

Use the diagram shown for Items 1–3.

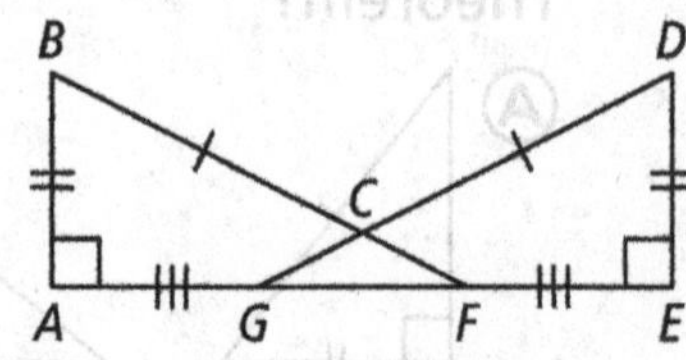

1. Which is a needed step to prove that $\triangle ABF \cong \triangle EDG$?

   Ⓐ $\angle BCD \cong \angle BCD$

   Ⓑ $\overline{GF} \cong \overline{GF}$

   Ⓒ $\angle BCG \cong \angle DCF$

   Ⓓ $\triangle CFG$ is isosceles.

2. If a proof shows $\overline{AF} \cong \overline{EG}$, which theorem would show that $\triangle ABF \cong \triangle EDG$?

   Ⓐ HL Triangle Congruence Theorem

   Ⓑ ASA Triangle Congruence Theorem

   Ⓒ SAS Triangle Congruence Theorem

   Ⓓ AAS Triangle Congruence Theorem

3. How do you justify $\overline{GF} \cong \overline{GF}$ as a step in a proof?

Use the figure shown for Items 4 and 5.

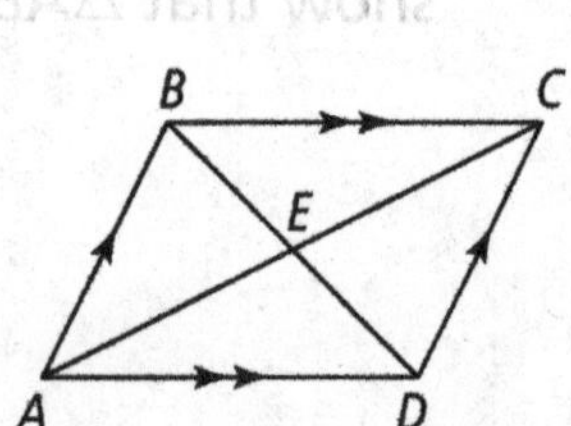

4. What theorem can be used to show that $\angle ABE \cong \angle CDE$?

5. Which lines in the following proof of $\triangle ABC \cong \triangle CDA$ have the correct justification? Select all that apply

   Ⓐ $\overline{AC} \cong \overline{AC}$, Reflexive Property of Congruence

   Ⓑ $\angle ACB \cong \angle CAD$, Alternate Interior Angles Theorem

   Ⓒ $\angle BAC \cong \angle DCA$, Alternate Interior Angles Theorem

   Ⓓ $\triangle ABC \cong \triangle CDA$, SAS Triangle Congruence Theorem

Name ______________________________

9-7 Lesson Quiz

Polygons in the Coordinate Plane

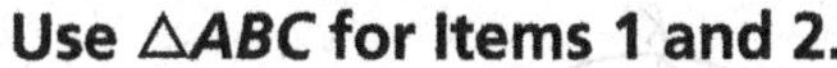

Use △*ABC* for Items 1 and 2.

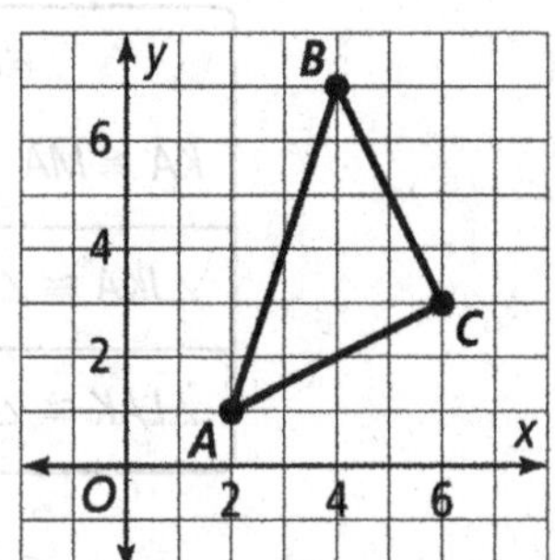

1. What kind of triangle is △*ABC*? Select all that apply.

Ⓐ scalene

Ⓑ right

Ⓒ isosceles

Ⓓ equilateral

2. What is the area of △*ABC*?

Ⓐ $2\sqrt{5}$

Ⓑ $4\sqrt{5}$

Ⓒ 10

Ⓓ 20

Use *DEFG* for Items 3–5.

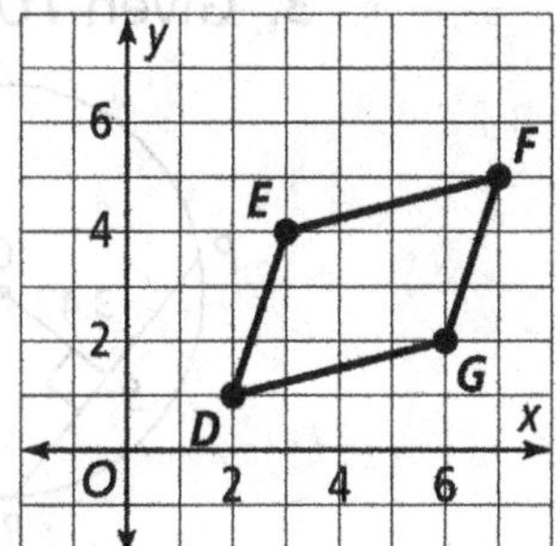

3. What is the perimeter of *DEFG*?

4. What is the relationship between $\overline{DE}$ and $\overline{FG}$? Select all that apply.

Ⓐ parallel

Ⓑ perpendicular

Ⓒ proportional

Ⓓ equal length

5. What type of quadrilateral is *DEFG*?

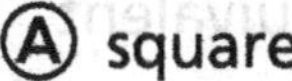

Ⓐ square

Ⓑ rhombus

Ⓒ trapezoid

Ⓓ parallelogram

9-8 Lesson Quiz

Chords

1. Is each statement true for ⊙*A*?

	Yes	No
$\overline{KA} \cong \overline{MA}$	❑	❑
$\angle JKA \cong \angle MLA$	❑	❑
$\angle LAK \cong \angle MAJ$	❑	❑

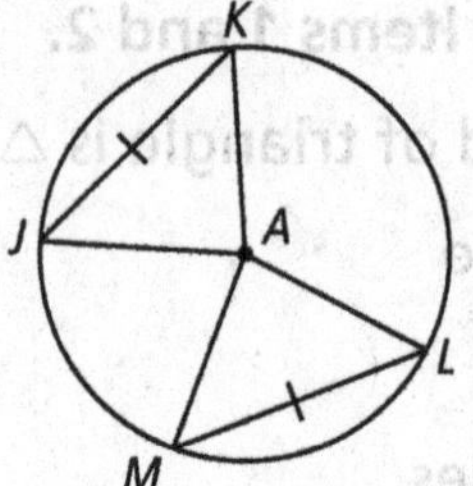

2. In ⊙*Q*, *DE* = *FG*. Which must be true? Select all that apply.

Ⓐ $DE \cong FG$

Ⓑ $\overline{EF} \cong \overline{QD}$

Ⓒ $\triangle DQE \cong \triangle FQE$

Ⓓ $\triangle FQE \cong \triangle FQG$

Ⓔ $\angle DQE \cong \angle GQF$

3. Given *TU* = 7.4, what is *PS* in ⊙*C*? Round to the nearest tenth.

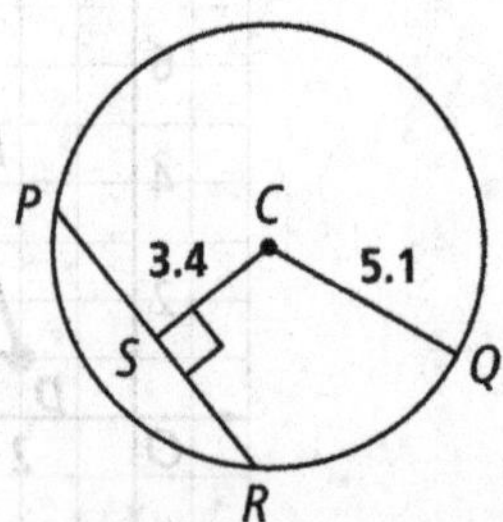

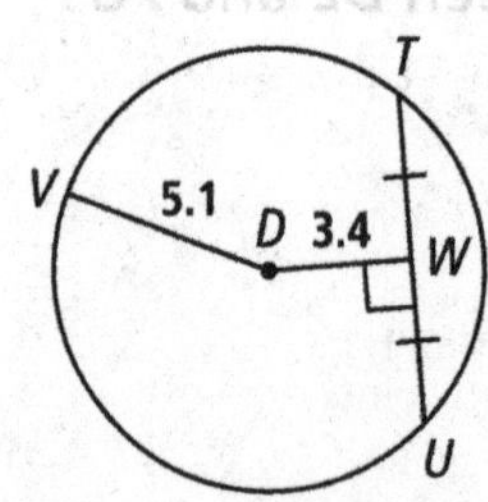

4. In ⊙*Z*, chords $\overline{JK}$ and $\overline{LM}$ are congruent. Which must be equivalent to the distance from $\overline{JK}$ to point *Z*?

Ⓐ the distance from $\overline{JK}$ to $\overline{LM}$

Ⓑ the distance from $\overline{LM}$ to point *Z*

Ⓒ the distance from point *K* to $\overline{LM}$

Ⓓ the distance from point *J* to point *Z*

5. Given ⊙*N* with chord $\overline{AB}$, which point lies on the perpendicular bisector of $\overline{AB}$?

Ⓐ *A*

Ⓑ *B*

Ⓒ *N*

Ⓓ none of these points

9 Topic Assessment Form A

1. What theorem shows that $\triangle ACE \cong \triangle BCD$?

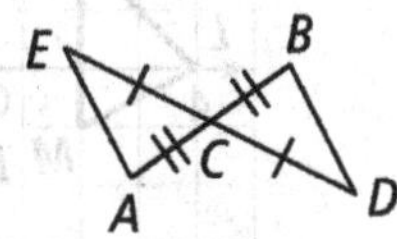

Ⓐ HL Ⓒ ASA
Ⓑ AAS Ⓓ SAS

2. What composition of rigid motions maps $\triangle PQR$ to $\triangle XZY$?

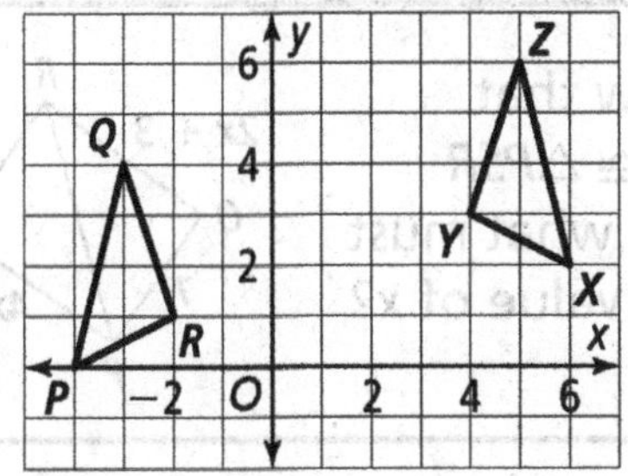

Ⓐ $T_{<1, 3>} \circ r_{(270°, O)}$
Ⓑ $R_{x=0} \circ T_{<0, 2>}$
Ⓒ $T_{<6, 2>} \circ R_{x=-2}$
Ⓓ $R_{y=-2} \circ T_{<6, 0>}$

Items 3–4. $\triangle JKL$ and $\triangle LMN$ are shown.

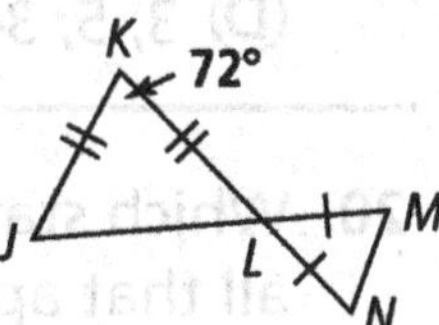

3. What is $m\angle KJL$?

4. What is $m\angle LNM$?

5. What additional piece of information is needed to show that $\triangle DEF \cong \triangle PQR$ by ASA?

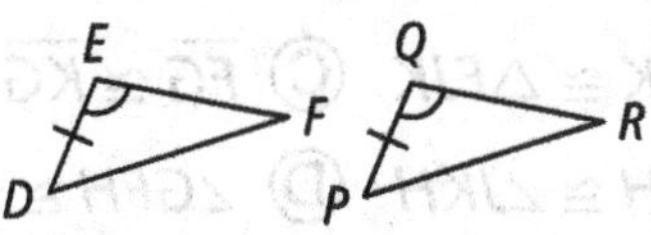

Ⓐ $\angle F \cong \angle R$ Ⓒ $\overline{DF} \cong \overline{PR}$
Ⓑ $\angle D \cong \angle P$ Ⓓ $\overline{EF} \cong \overline{QR}$

Items 6–7. Refer to the diagram shown.

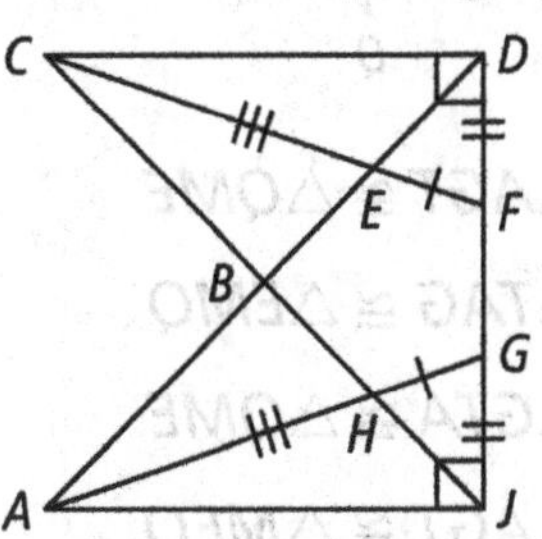

6. What theorem shows that $\triangle AJG \cong \triangle CDF$?

7. Which can be proven? Select all that apply.

Ⓐ $\angle CED \cong \angle AHJ$ Ⓒ $\overline{CB} \cong \overline{DB}$
Ⓑ $\overline{AB} \cong \overline{CB}$ Ⓓ $\angle DAG \cong \angle JCF$

For Items 8–9, use the graph.

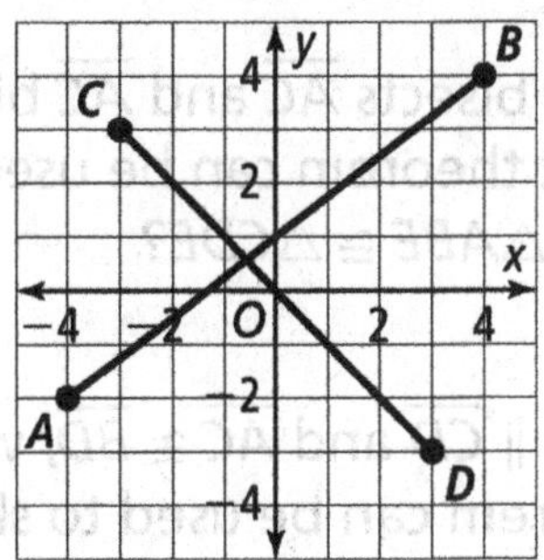

8. What is AB?

9. What are the coordinates of the point $\frac{1}{4}$ of the way from A to B?

10. Which of the following cannot be used to prove that two triangles are congruent?

Ⓐ AAA Ⓒ SSS
Ⓑ ASA Ⓓ HL

11. Which statement is correct?

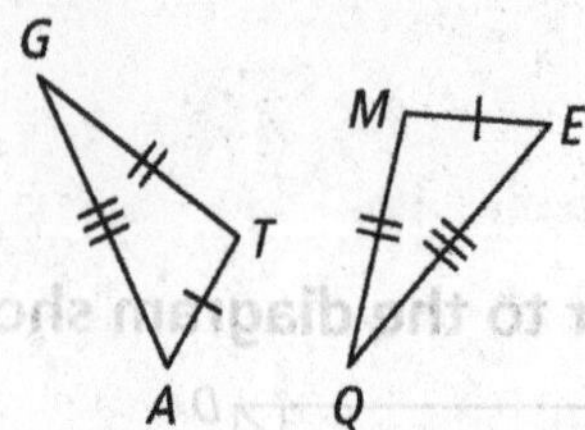

Ⓐ $\triangle AGT \cong \triangle QME$

Ⓑ $\triangle TAG \cong \triangle EMQ$

Ⓒ $\triangle GTA \cong \triangle QME$

Ⓓ $\triangle AGT \cong \triangle MEQ$

Items 12–14. Refer to the diagram shown.

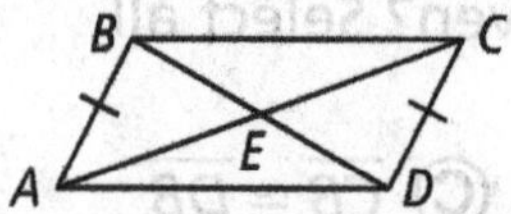

12. If $\angle BAC \cong \angle DCA$, what theorem can be used to show that $\triangle ABE \cong \triangle CDE$?

13. If $\overline{BD}$ bisects $\overline{AC}$ and $\overline{AC}$ bisects $\overline{BD}$, what theorem can be used to show that $\triangle ABE \cong \triangle CDE$?

14. If $\overline{AB} \parallel \overline{CD}$ and $\overline{AC} \cong \overline{BD}$, what theorem can be used to show that $\triangle ACD \cong \triangle CAB$?

Items 15–16. Refer to the diagram shown.

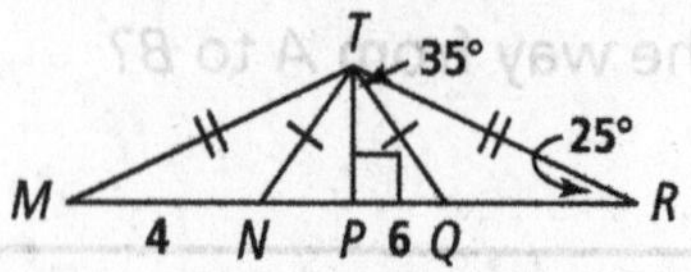

15. What is $m\angle MNT$?

16. What is MR?

17. Which triangle is congruent to $\triangle KLM$?

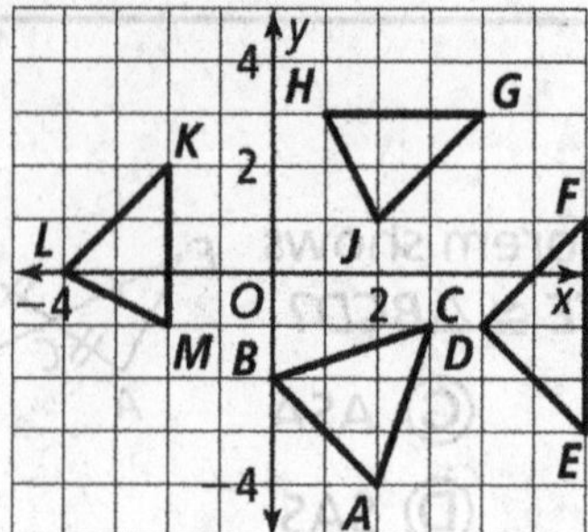

Ⓐ $\triangle GJH$ Ⓒ $\triangle FDE$

Ⓑ $\triangle CBA$ Ⓓ none

---

18. To show that $\triangle RQP \cong \triangle PSR$ by SSS, what must be the value of x?

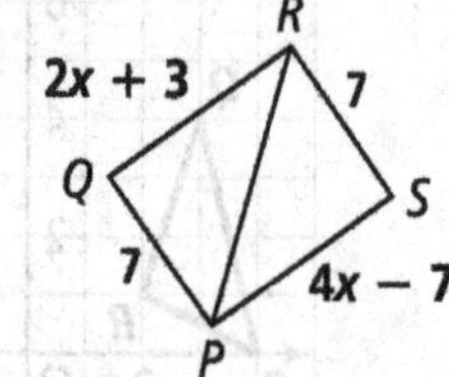

---

19. Which could be the lengths of the sides of a right triangle?

Ⓐ 8, 15, 17

Ⓑ 6, 12, 18

Ⓒ 4, 7, 22

Ⓓ 3, 5, 34

---

20. Which statements are true? Select all that apply.

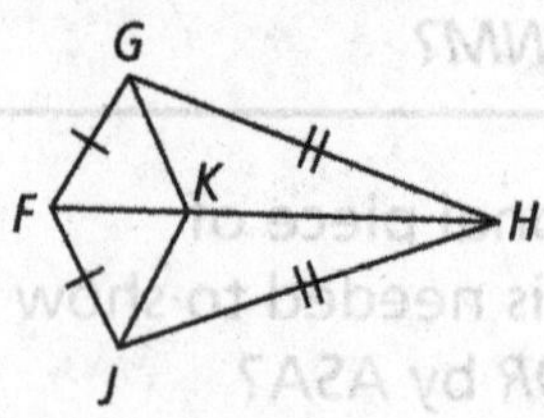

Ⓐ $\triangle FGK \cong \triangle FJK$ Ⓒ $\overline{FG} \cong \overline{KG}$

Ⓑ $\angle GKH \cong \angle JKH$ Ⓓ $\angle GFH \cong \angle JFH$

Name ____________________

enVision Integrated
MATHEMATICS I
PearsonRealize.com

9 Topic Assessment Form B

1. What theorem shows that $\triangle TNP \cong \triangle TMQ$?

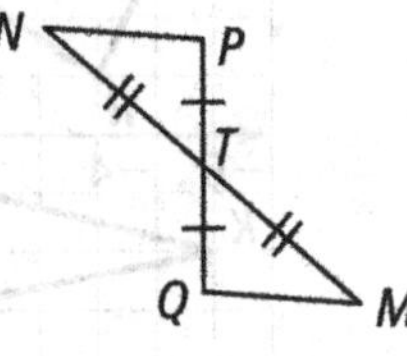

Ⓐ AAS Ⓒ SAS

Ⓑ ASA Ⓓ HL

2. What composition of rigid motions maps $\triangle ABC$ to $\triangle TUV$?

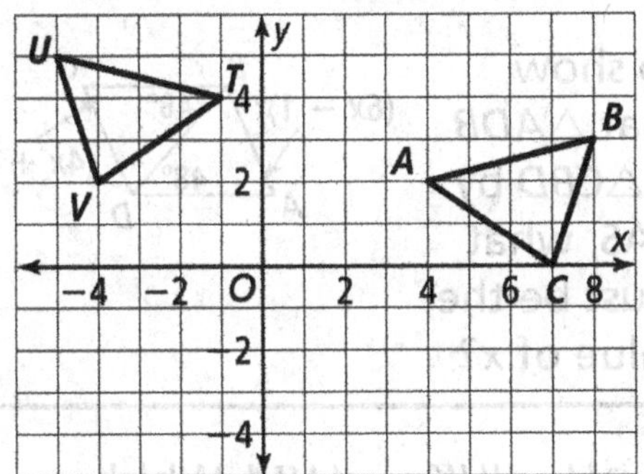

Ⓐ $R_{x=0} \circ T_{<3, 2>}$

Ⓑ $T_{<1, 0>} \circ r_{(90°, O)}$

Ⓒ $R_{x=1} \circ R_{y=3}$

Ⓓ $T_{<1, 2>} \circ R_{x=1}$

Items 3–4. $\triangle ABC$ and $\triangle CDE$ are shown.

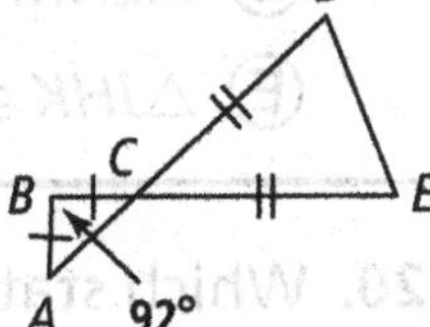

3. What is $m\angle BAC$?

4. What is $m\angle CDE$?

5. What additional piece of information is needed to show that $\triangle GHJ \cong \triangle MNP$ by SAS?

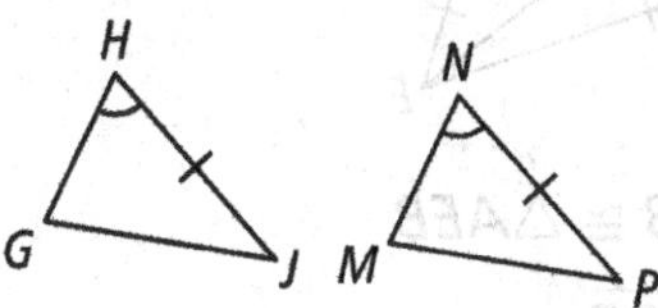

Ⓐ $\angle G \cong \angle M$ Ⓒ $\overline{GH} \cong \overline{MN}$

Ⓑ $\angle J \cong \angle P$ Ⓓ $\overline{GJ} \cong \overline{MP}$

Items 6–7. Refer to the diagram shown.

6. What theorem shows that $\triangle NTM \cong \triangle SMT$?

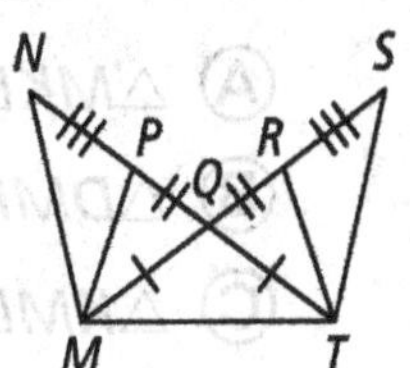

7. Which can be proven? Select all that apply.

Ⓐ $\angle MPT \cong \angle TRM$

Ⓑ $\overline{PT} \cong \overline{MT}$

Ⓒ $\overline{PM} \cong \overline{RT}$

Ⓓ $\triangle NQM \cong \triangle SQT$

Use $\triangle ABC$ for Items 8 and 9.

8. What type of triangle is $\triangle ABC$? Select all that apply.

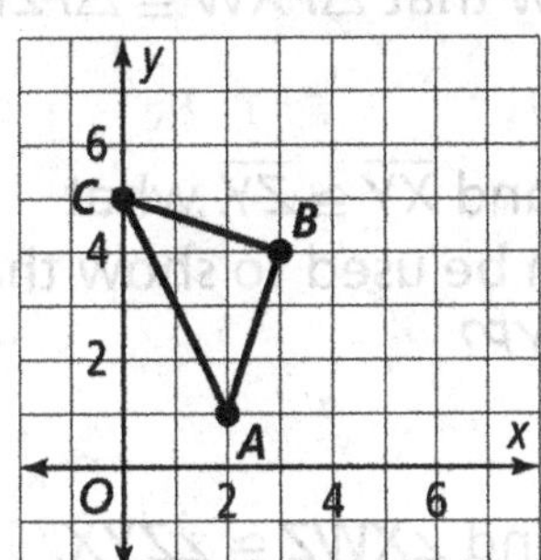

Ⓐ equilateral Ⓒ isosceles

Ⓑ right Ⓓ scalene

9. What is the area of $\triangle ABC$?

Ⓐ 10 Ⓒ $2\sqrt{10}$

Ⓑ 5 Ⓓ $\sqrt{10}$

10. Which of the following cannot be used to prove that two triangles are congruent?

Ⓐ AAS Ⓒ SSA

Ⓑ HL Ⓓ SSS

11. Which statement is correct?

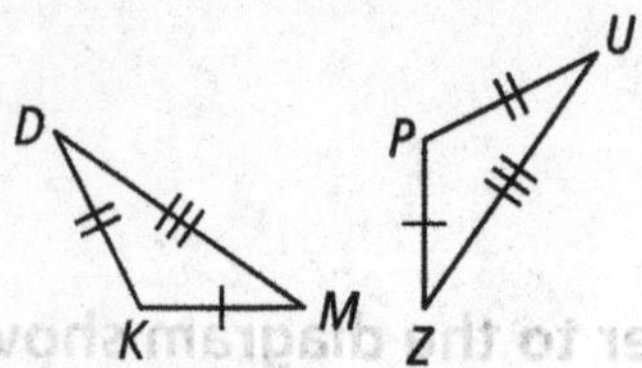

Ⓐ $\triangle MKD \cong \triangle ZUP$

Ⓑ $\triangle DMK \cong \triangle PUZ$

Ⓒ $\triangle KMD \cong \triangle PUZ$

Ⓓ $\triangle DKM \cong \triangle UPZ$

Items 12–14. Refer to the diagram shown.

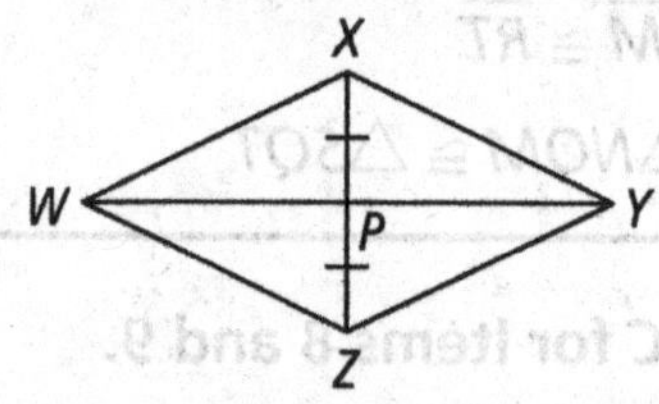

12. If $\overline{WX} \cong \overline{WZ}$, what theorem can be used to show that $\triangle PXW \cong \triangle PZW$?

13. If $\overline{XZ} \perp \overline{WY}$ and $\overline{XY} \cong \overline{ZY}$, what theorem can be used to show that $\triangle XYP \cong \triangle ZYP$?

14. If $\overline{XW} \parallel \overline{YZ}$ and $\angle XWZ \cong \angle ZYX$, what theorem can be used to show that $\triangle XWZ \cong \triangle ZYX$?

Items 15–16. Refer to the diagram shown.

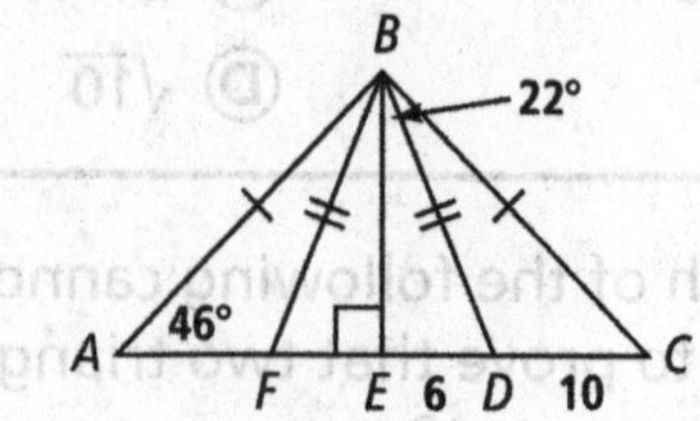

15. What is $m\angle BFD$?

16. What is AC?

17. Which triangle is congruent to $\triangle XYZ$?

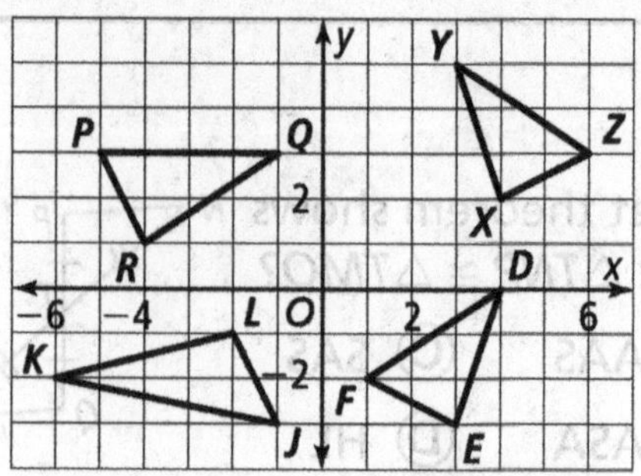

Ⓐ $\triangle RQP$

Ⓑ $\triangle LKJ$

Ⓒ $\triangle EDF$

Ⓓ none

---

18. To show that $\triangle ADB \cong \triangle CBD$ by AAS, what must be the value of x?

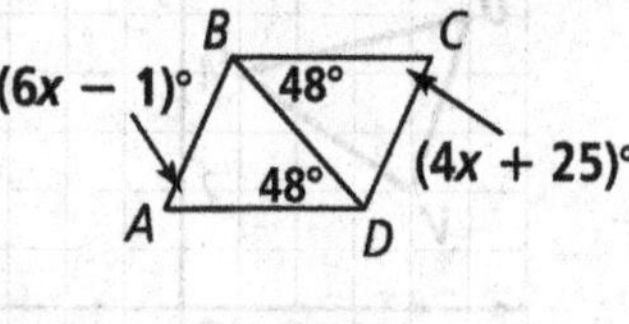

---

19. In ⊙H, $\angle JHK \cong \angle LHM$. Which statement must be true? Select all that apply.

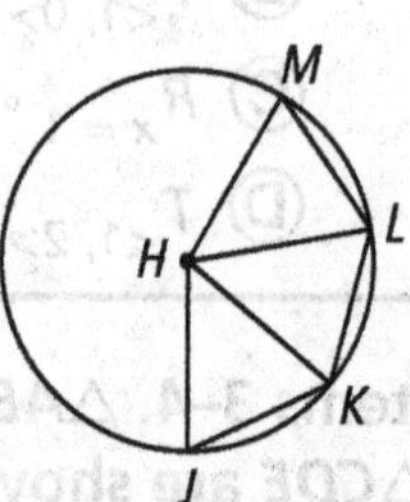

Ⓐ $\triangle LHK \cong \triangle JHK$

Ⓑ $\overline{ML} \cong \overline{JK}$

Ⓒ $\overparen{MLK} \cong \overparen{LKJ}$

Ⓓ $\triangle LHM \cong \triangle LHK$

Ⓔ $\triangle JHK \cong \triangle LHM$

---

20. Which statements are true? Select all that apply.

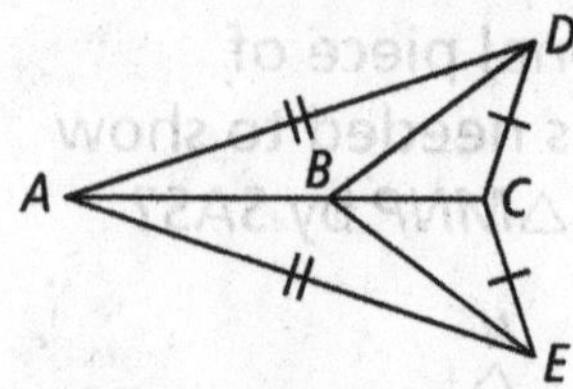

Ⓐ $\triangle ADB \cong \triangle AEB$

Ⓑ $\overline{BD} \cong \overline{BE}$

Ⓒ $\angle BDC \cong \angle BEC$

Ⓓ $\overline{AB} \cong \overline{BE}$

Name ______________________________

9 Performance Assessment Form A

Darren is designing a leather collar for his rescued dog, Galgo. He has leather stamps in the shapes shown.

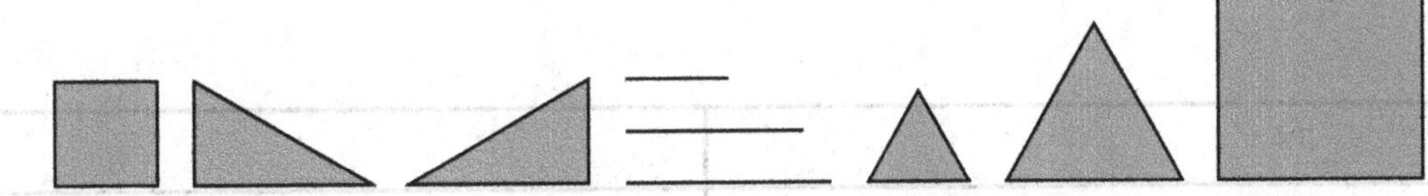

The lengths of the sides of the stamps are 1 cm, $\sqrt{3}$ cm, and 2 cm. The two rectangles are squares, and the two triangles on the right are equilateral triangles. The collar is 2 cm wide. Darren wants the design to use overlapping triangles, triangles that share a side, or both. He also wants the pattern to repeat several times around the collar.

1. Continue the design shown that Darren started.

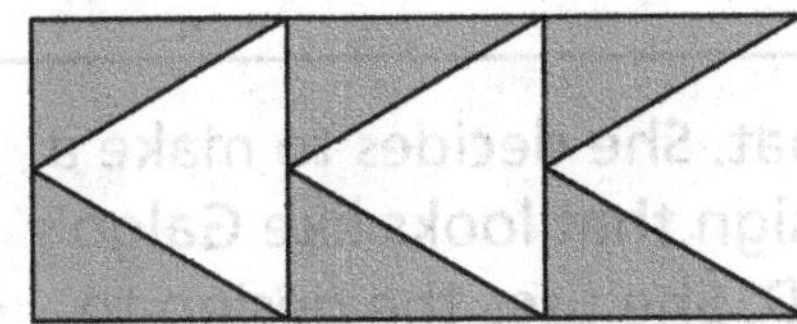

2. Add labels to the figures on the collar and write a proof that shows two of the small triangles are congruent.

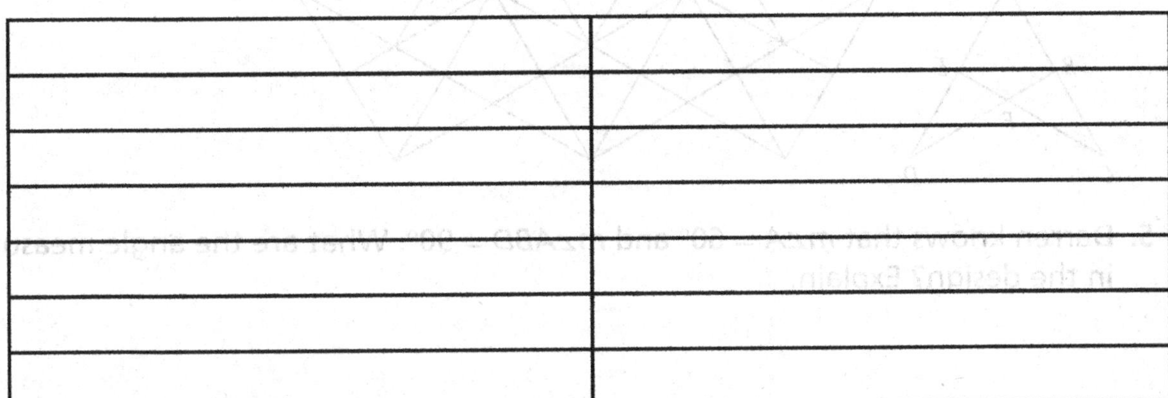

3. Are two of the stamps congruent right triangles? Explain.

4. Make your own repeating design between the two horizontal lines for Galgo's collar and show that two of the triangles in your design, other than the shapes of the stamps, are congruent.

Darren asks his grandmother to make his dog a coat. She decides to make a quilted coat from scraps of fabric. She draws a design that looks like Galgo's head with nose at *A* and tips of the ears at *C* and *D*. She uses the design to draw a quilt pattern without overlaps or gaps along the sides.

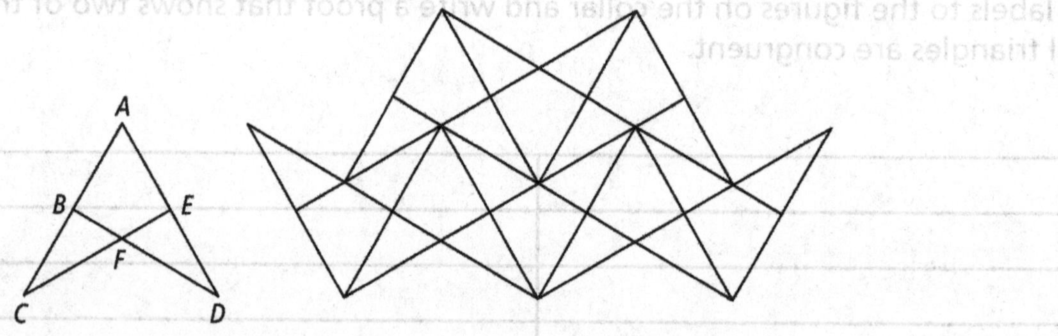

5. Darren knows that $m\angle A = 60°$ and $m\angle ABD = 90°$. What are the angle measures in the design? Explain.

Name ____________________

9 Performance Assessment Form B

Yama is designing a company logo. The company president requested for the logo to be made of triangles. Yama is proposing the design shown.

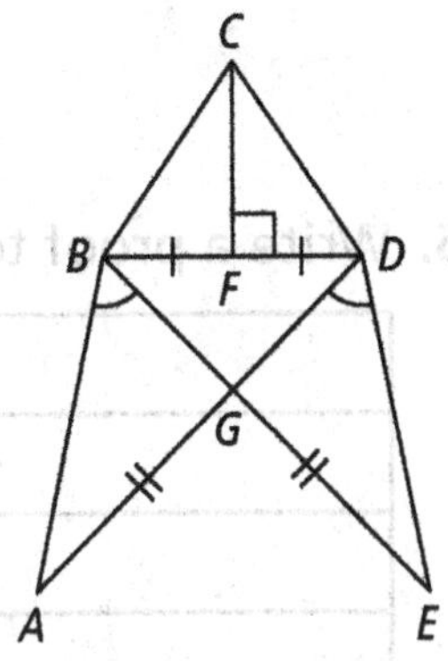

1. Identify two triangles in the diagram that are congruent. Draw separate diagrams of the two triangles, including any information that is shown in Yama's diagram.

2. Write a proof to show the two triangles are congruent.

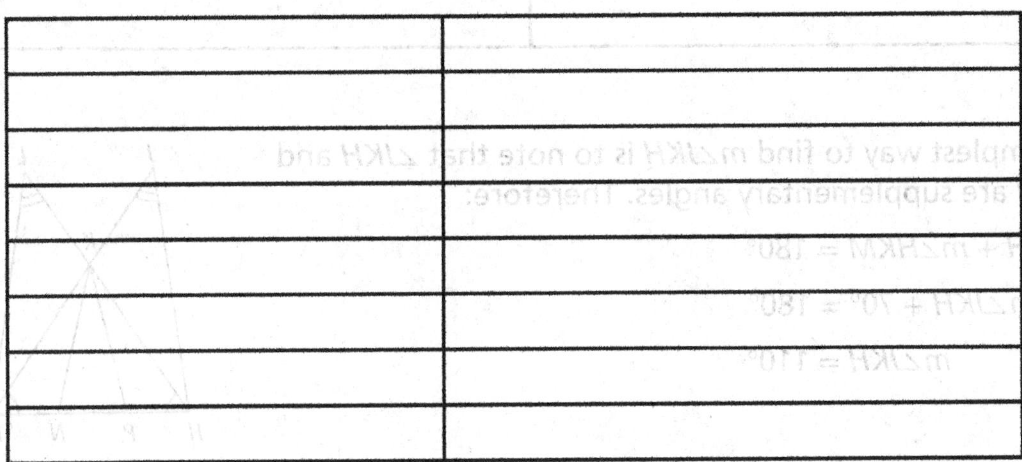

3. Identify an isosceles triangle in the diagram. Explain how you know.

4. Design your own logo that includes at least four triangles. At least two of the triangles must be congruent. Mark congruent angles and segments and right angles in your diagram.

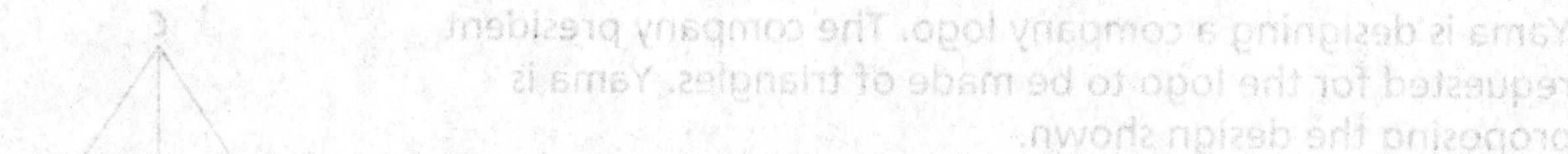

5. Write a proof to show that two of the triangles in your design are congruent.

6. The simplest way to find $m\angle JKH$ is to note that $\angle JKH$ and $\angle HKM$ are supplementary angles. Therefore:

$$m\angle JKH + m\angle HKM = 180°$$

$$m\angle JKH + 70° = 180°$$

$$m\angle JKH = 110°$$

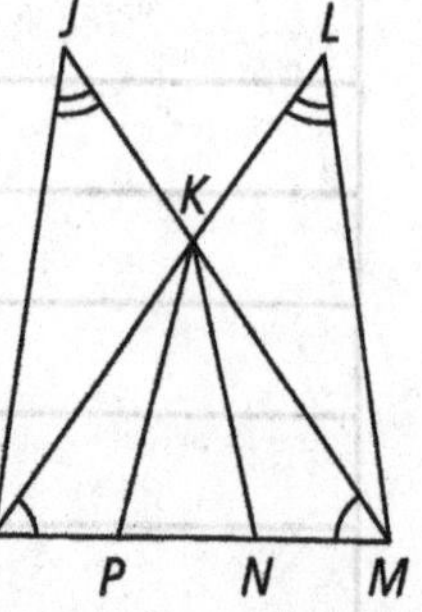

Name ___

Benchmark Test 4

1. Kelley has to work 45 hours at her job to earn enough money to buy a phone. She works 3 hours each day. If she has worked x days, write a linear equation to represent how many more hours Kelley must work to afford the phone.

2. For the graph of the equation you wrote in Item 3, what does the y-intercept represent?

   Ⓐ Total hours still needed to work after x days

   Ⓑ Work hours completed each day

   Ⓒ Total number of workdays needed to earn the phone

   Ⓓ Total number of work hours needed to earn the phone

3. Identify the domain and range of the relation.

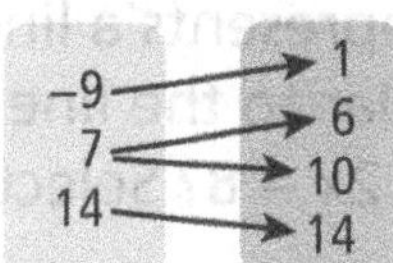

domain: ___

range: ___

4. Solve the equation $\frac{(6^x)^{\frac{1}{3}}}{6^{\frac{2}{3}}} = 36$.

   Ⓐ $x = 8$

   Ⓑ $x = 7$

   Ⓒ $x = 512$

   Ⓓ $x = \frac{4}{3}$

5. If $m\angle NOP = 24°$ and $m\angle NOQ = 110°$, what is $m\angle POQ$?

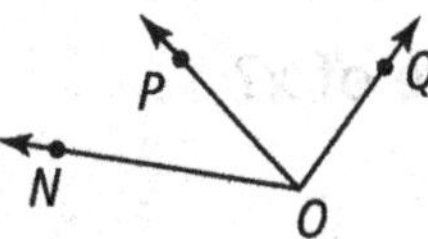

   Ⓐ 62° Ⓑ 86° Ⓒ 134° Ⓓ 156°

6. The angle bisector of $\angle ABC$ is $\overrightarrow{BP}$. If $m\angle ABP$ is $6n°$, what is $m\angle ABC$?

7. What are the coordinates of the point $\frac{4}{5}$ of the way from D to E?

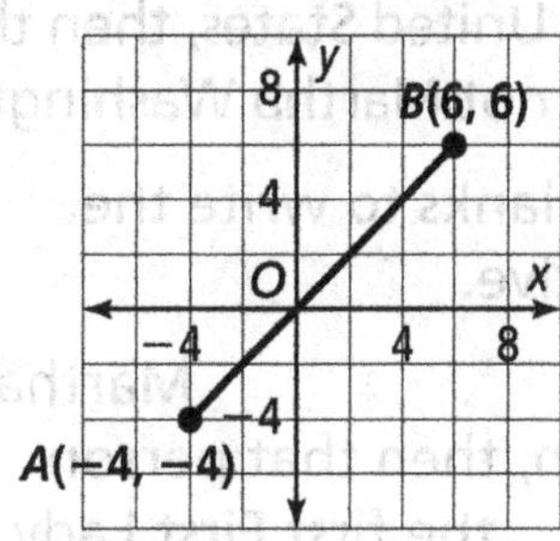

   Ⓐ (−2, −2)

   Ⓑ (0, 0)

   Ⓒ (2, 2)

   Ⓓ (4, 4)

8. Which figure is a counterexample for the conditional?

   If a quadrilateral has four right angles, then it is a square.

   Ⓐ rectangle

   Ⓑ kite

   Ⓒ parallelogram

   Ⓓ rhombus

9. Use the Law of Detachment to make a conclusion.

If a person studies architecture, then that person must take calculus. Caroline is studying architecture.

10. What is the value of x?

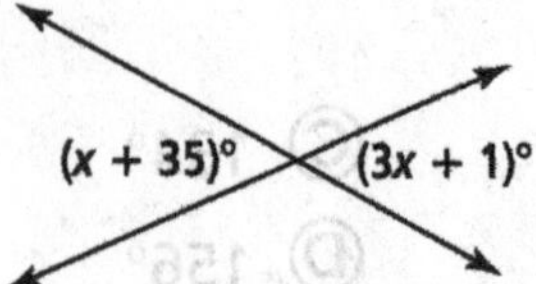

11. Martha Washington was the first First Lady of the United States. Prove the conditional statement by proving the contrapositive.

If a person was not the first First Lady of the United States, then that person was not Martha Washington.

Fill in the blanks to write the contrapositive.

If a person __________ Martha Washington, then that person __________ the first First Lady of the United States.

Fill in the blanks to write the contrapositive.

Since Martha Washington was the first First Lady of the United States, the contrapositive is __________.

Since the contrapositive is __________, the __________ must be true.

12. Which pairs of angles are alternate interior angles? Select all that apply.

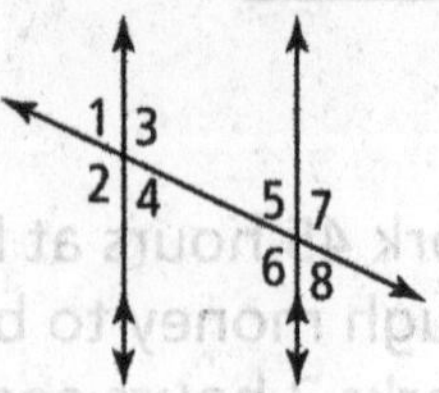

Ⓐ ∠3 and ∠6

Ⓑ ∠3 and ∠8

Ⓒ ∠4 and ∠5

Ⓓ ∠4 and ∠7

Ⓔ ∠1 and ∠8

13. If $a \parallel b$ and $m\angle 2 = 71°$, what is $m\angle 1$?

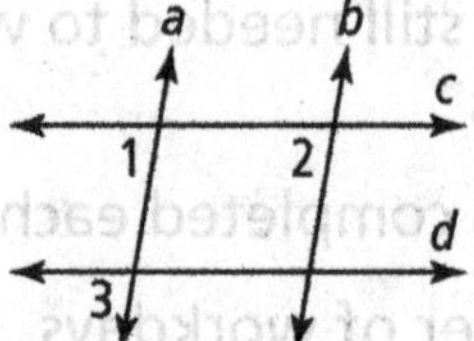

Ⓐ 19°

Ⓑ 71°

Ⓒ 109°

Ⓓ 142°

14. Which equation represents a line that is perpendicular to the line with equation $y = 2x - 8$? Select all that apply.

Ⓐ $y = \frac{1}{2}x + 1$

Ⓑ $y = -\frac{1}{2}x + 1$

Ⓒ $x + 2y = 5$

Ⓓ $-x + 2y = -3$

Ⓔ $-x - 2y = 9$

15. Quadrilateral *ABCD* has coordinates $A(-2, 0)$, $B(0, 4)$, $C(4, 6)$, and $D(2, 2)$. Graph and label quadrilateral *ABCD*, and then graph and label the image $R_{x\text{-axis}}(ABCD) = A'B'C'D'$.

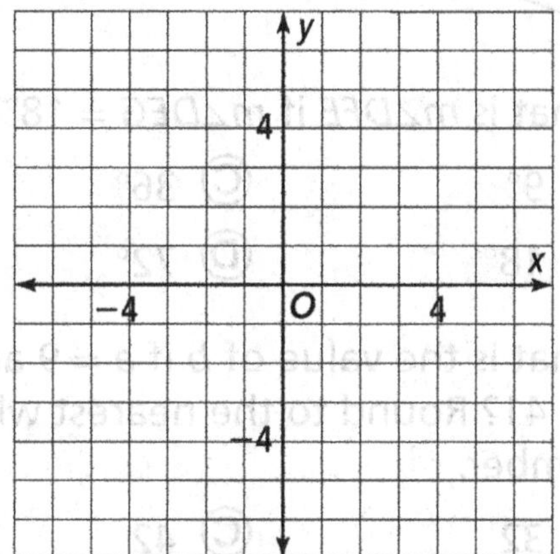

16. If point *B* has coordinates (−8, 1), what are the coordinates of the point when it is reflected across the *y*-axis?

Ⓐ (8, 1)
Ⓑ (−8, −1)
Ⓒ (−8, 1)
Ⓓ (8, −1)

17. What translation rule maps *ABCD* to *A′B′C′D′*?

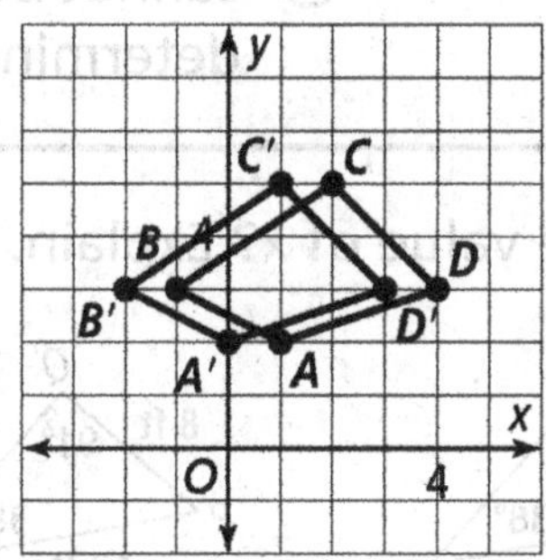

Ⓐ $T_{\langle -1, 0\rangle}$
Ⓑ $T_{\langle 1, 0\rangle}$
Ⓒ $T_{\langle 0, -1\rangle}$
Ⓓ $T_{\langle 0, 1\rangle}$

18. Triangle *ABC* has vertices $A(1, 3)$, $B(2, 5)$, and $C(5, 3)$. If the coordinates of *B′* are (*p*, *q*), what are the values of *p* and *q* after the translation described by the rule $T_{\langle 1, 4\rangle}$?

For Items 19 and 20, use pentagon *ABCDE*.

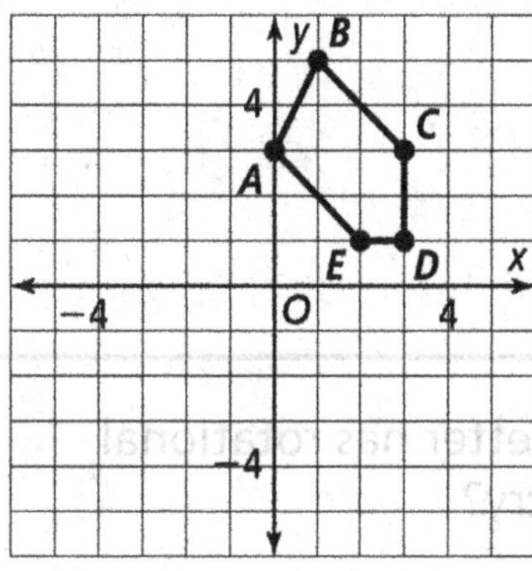

19. What are the coordinates of *B′* after the pentagon is rotated 90° about the origin?

Ⓐ (1, 5)
Ⓑ (−1, 5)
Ⓒ (−5, 1)
Ⓓ (5, 1)

20. What are the coordinates of *E′* after the pentagon is rotated 270° about the origin?

Ⓐ (1, −2)
Ⓑ (1, 2)
Ⓒ (2, −1)
Ⓓ (2, 1)

21. Given △*ABC* with coordinates $A(1, 3)$, $B(4, 5)$, and $C(5, 2)$, what are the coordinates of △*A′B′C′* after the glide reflection described by $T_{\langle -1, 1\rangle} \circ R_{y\text{-axis}}$?

22. Write a rule for the glide reflection that maps △*ABC* with vertices $A(-4, -2)$, $B(-2, 6)$, and $C(4, 4)$ to △*A′B′C′* with vertices $A'(-2, -2)$, $B'(0, -10)$, and $C'(6, -8)$.

23. How many lines of symmetry does a regular decagon have?

Ⓐ 2

Ⓑ 5

Ⓒ 10

Ⓓ 12

---

24. Which letter has rotational symmetry?

Ⓐ E

Ⓑ B

Ⓒ Z

Ⓓ V

---

25. Triangle *JKL* is reflected across the *y*-axis to create $\triangle J'K'L'$. Are the two figures are congruent? Explain.

---

26. Triangles *ABC* and *DEF* are isosceles triangles. Answer yes or no to the statements about the triangles.

	Yes	No
The base angles of $\triangle ABC$ are congruent to the base angles of $\triangle EDF$.	❑	❑
Two sides of $\triangle ABC$ are congruent.	❑	❑
Two angles of $\triangle DEF$ are congruent.	❑	❑
Two sides of $\triangle ABC$ are congruent to two sides of $\triangle EDF$.	❑	❑

For Items 27 and 28, use $\triangle DEF$.

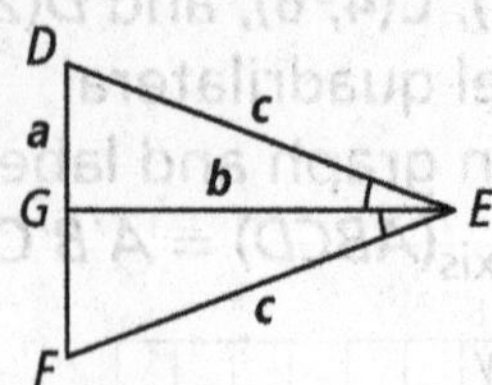

27. What is $m\angle DFE$ if $m\angle DEG = 18°$?

Ⓐ 9°

Ⓑ 18°

Ⓒ 36°

Ⓓ 72°

28. What is the value of *b* if $a = 9$ and $c = 41$? Round to the nearest whole number.

Ⓐ 32

Ⓑ 40

Ⓒ 42

Ⓓ 50

---

29. Which criterion can be used to prove the triangles are congruent?

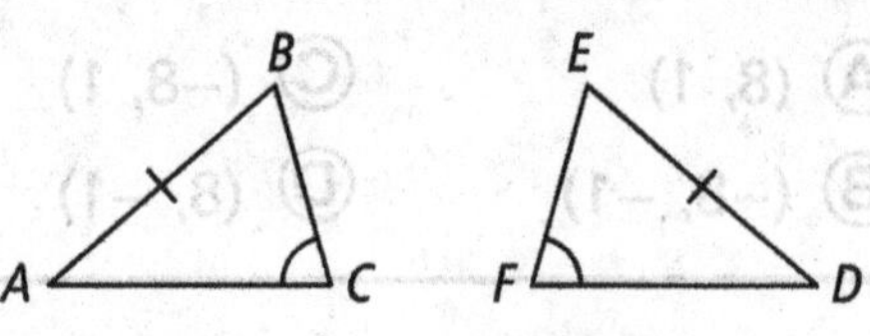

Ⓐ SSS

Ⓑ SAS

Ⓒ SSA

Ⓓ cannot be determined

---

30. What is the value of *x*? Explain.

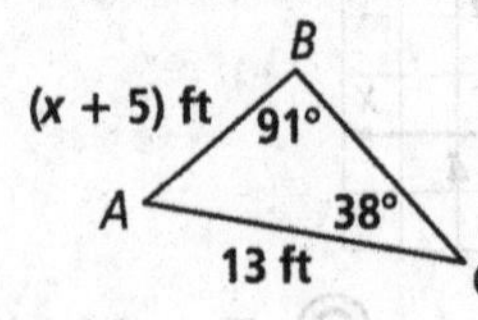

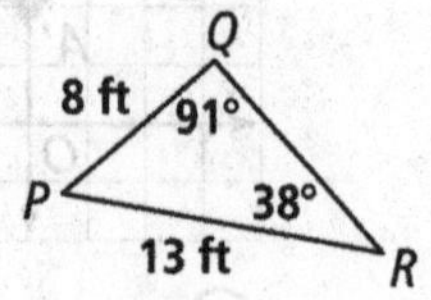

Name ______________________________

10 Readiness Assessment

1. Complete using *increase, decrease,* or *remain constant*: A scatter plot shows a negative association if, as the *x*-values increase, the *y*-values ______.

2. Which best describes a weak correlation of data?

   Ⓐ There is no association between the *x*- and *y*-values.

   Ⓑ There is a negative association between *x*- and *y*-values.

   Ⓒ The data are grouped closely together in one area on the coordinate plane.

   Ⓓ There is a data point that lies far away from other data points.

3. Which ordered pair would be classified as an outlier of the data in the table?

x	1	1.5	2	2.5	3	4	5	5.5
y	63	64	65	93	70	72	74	78

4. A line of best fit for a data set has equation $y = 3x - 4$. What *y*-value would you predict for an *x*-value of 8 in this data set?

   Ⓐ 4　　Ⓒ 16

   Ⓑ 8　　Ⓓ 20

5. Which of the lines could be used to predict other values for the data shown in the scatter plot?

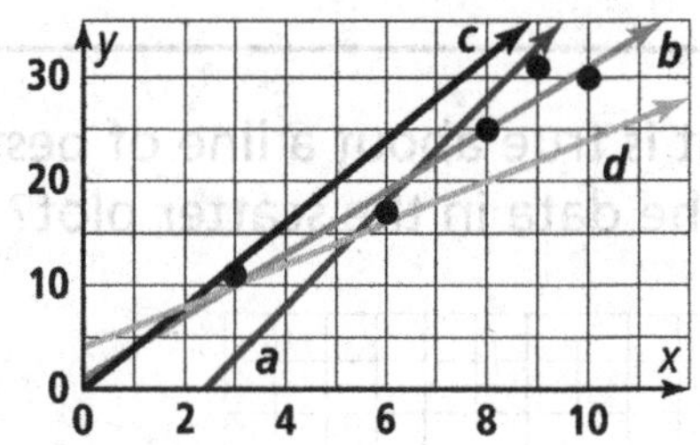

   Ⓐ Line *a*　　Ⓒ Line *c*

   Ⓑ Line *b*　　Ⓓ Line *d*

Use this data set for Items 6 and 7: 1, 3, 5, 6, 8, 12, 14.

6. What is the mean of the data?

7. What is the median of the data?

8. What is the range of the data?

9. What advantage does a scatter plot have over a table of values? Select all that apply.

   Ⓐ The scatter plot visually shows any positive or negative association.

   Ⓑ The scatter plot shows any linear association.

   Ⓒ The scatter plot easily identifies duplicate data values.

   Ⓓ The scatter plot visually shows any outliers of the data.

10. Which equation represents a line of best fit for the set of ordered pairs? {(1, 16), (2, 20), (3, 24), (4, 30), (5, 36)}

Ⓐ $y = 5x + 10$

Ⓑ $y = 10x + 5$

Ⓒ $y = -5x + 10$

Ⓓ $y = -10x + 5$

11. What is true about a line of best fit for the data in the scatter plot?

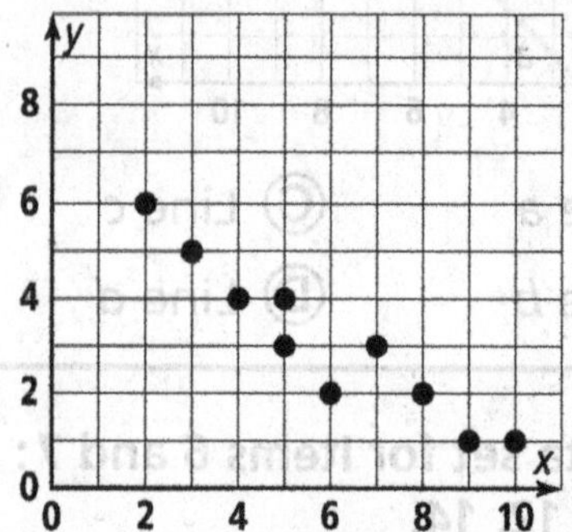

Ⓐ The slope is undefined.

Ⓑ The slope is negative.

Ⓒ The slope is positive.

Ⓓ The slope is zero.

12. Which statement best describes a scatter plot with a linear association?

Ⓐ Most data points are grouped in a small area of the plane.

Ⓑ There is a data point that lies far away from other data.

Ⓒ A line could be drawn so that most data points are close to the line.

Ⓓ The data points approximate a U-shaped curve.

13. If the outlier were removed from this data set, would the mean increase or decrease?
39, 68, 72, 81, 86, 88, 91, 95

14. What is the median of the data?
53, 47, 61, 73, 39

15. What is the definition of the median of a data set?

Ⓐ The median is the average of the data values.

Ⓑ The median is the value in the middle of an ordered data set.

Ⓒ The median is the most frequently occurring data value.

Ⓓ The median is the most likely data value.

16. How far is 80 from the mean of this data set?
110, 130, 100, 120, 150, 80

17. The line plots display data from 2 classes. Which measure would best compare the centers of the data?

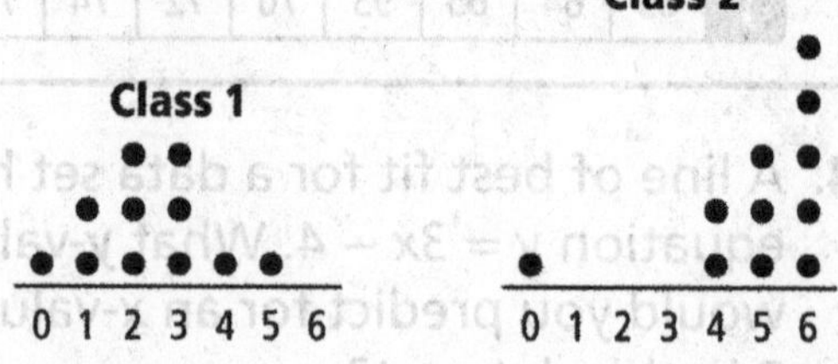

18. If the mean of this set of data is 8, what is x?

4	8	11	14
10	6	8	x

Ⓐ $x = 1$

Ⓑ $x = 3$

Ⓒ $x = 8$

Ⓓ x could be any value.

Name ______________________________

10-1 Lesson Quiz

Analyzing Data Displays

1. The prices of 12 different types of cereal, rounded to the nearest dollar, are shown. Make a dot plot of the data.

4	5	6	4	5	5
5	8	4	3	4	4

2. Cereal Brand X costs $3. Use the data from Item 1. Which description of Brand X is most accurate?

   Ⓐ Brand X costs more than the median price of the cereals in the plot.

   Ⓑ Brand X is an outlier for the data set.

   Ⓒ The price of Brand X is the same as the price that was recorded most often.

   Ⓓ Brand X costs about a dollar less than the price that was recorded most often.

3. The histogram displays the ages of 50 randomly selected users of an online music service. Based on the data, is advertising on the service more likely to reach people who are younger than 30 or people who are 30 and older?

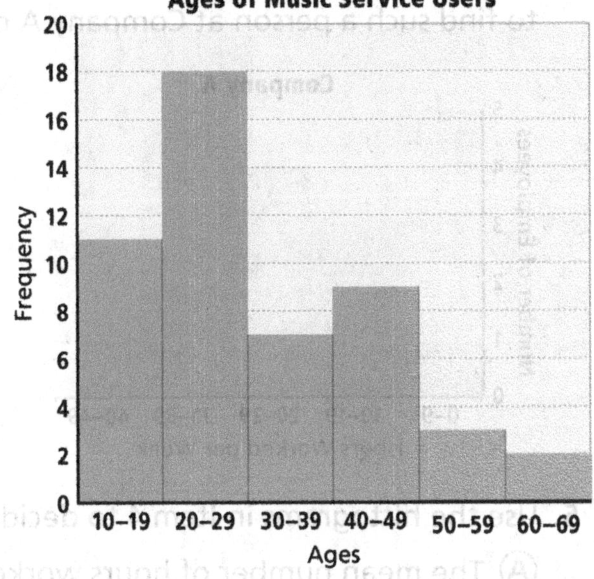

4. The box plot shows the ages of people at a movie screening. What percent of the people are between 20 and 37 years old?

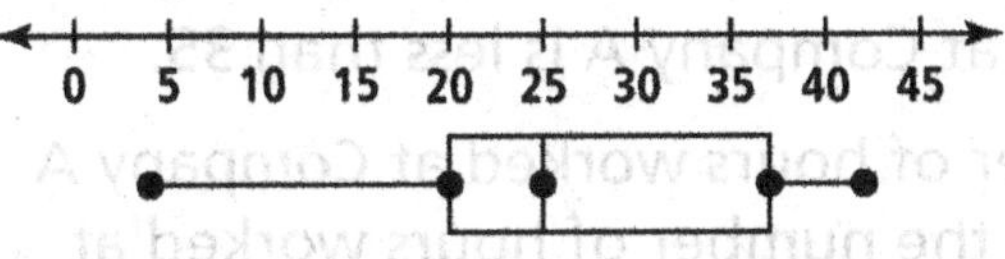

5. Which of the following data displays does not show individual data values but rather shows the number of values that fall within a series of specified ranges?

   Ⓐ histogram Ⓑ box plot Ⓒ dot plot Ⓓ scatter plot

Name ________________________________

10-2 Lesson Quiz

Comparing Data Sets

1. The dot plots show the ages of people at two different movies at a school movie night. Which data set seems to have greater variability?

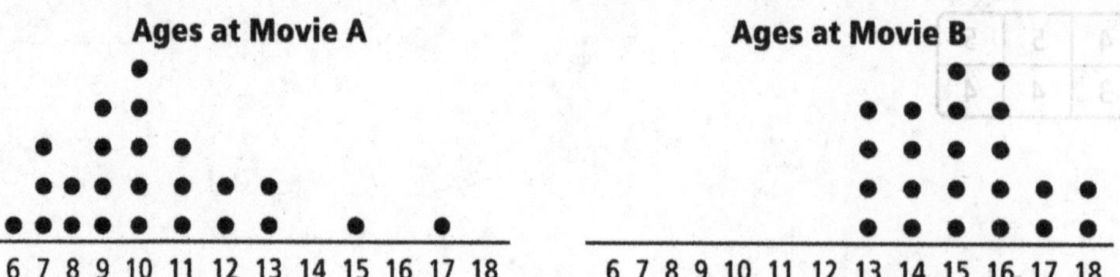

2. Use the data sets in Item 1. What is the mean absolute deviation of the ages at Movie B?

Ⓐ 0 Ⓑ 1.25 Ⓒ 1.4 Ⓓ 16

3. The box plots display the data from Item 1.

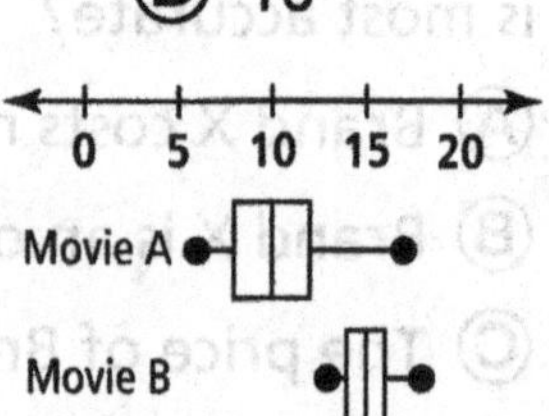

Complete: The box plots show that ______% of the people at Movie A are younger than the youngest person at Movie B.

4. A reporter wants to interview an employee who works fewer than 30 hours per week. Is the reporter more likely to find such a person at Company A or at Company B?

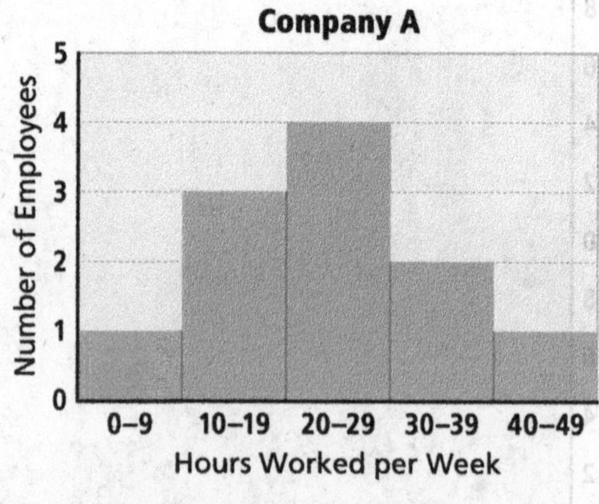

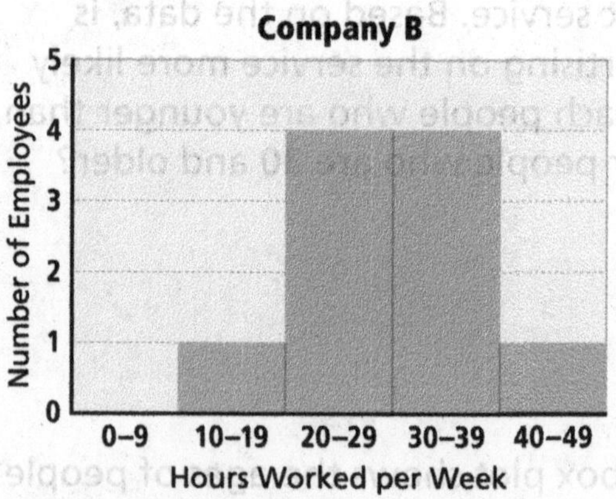

5. Use the histograms in Item 4 to decide which statement is true.

Ⓐ The mean number of hours worked at Company B is less than 25.

Ⓑ The median number of hours worked at Company A is less than 35.

Ⓒ The standard deviation for the number of hours worked at Company A is less than the standard deviation for the number of hours worked at Company B.

Ⓓ The IQR for the number of hours worked at Company B is greater than the IQR for the number of hours worked at Company A.

Name ______________________________

10-3 Lesson Quiz

Interpreting the Shapes of Data Displays

1. The histogram shows the number of books checked out by individual library patrons in one year. What inference can you make based on the shape of the data?

   Complete: Most patrons checked out ____________ 30 books in a year.

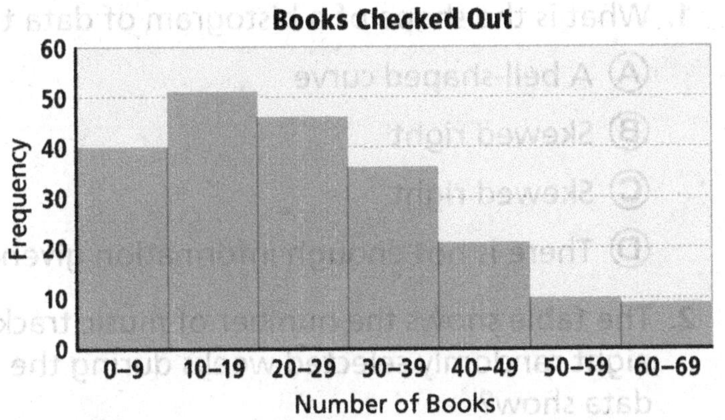

2. For the data in Item 1, is the mean of the number of books checked out likely to be *greater than*, *equal to*, or *less than* the median number of books?

3. A scientist measures the heights of sunflower plants. The histogram shows the results. Which statement is correct?

   Heights

   Frequency: 0, 5, 10, 15, 20, 25, 30, 35

   0–9, 10–19, 20–29, 30–39, 40–49, 50–59

   Height of Plants (inches)

   Ⓐ The data are skewed left, so the mean height is greater than the median height.

   Ⓑ The data are skewed right, so the median height is greater than the mean height.

   Ⓒ The data are skewed left, so the median height is greater than the mean height.

   Ⓓ No conclusion can be made about the relationship between the median height and the mean height based on the histogram.

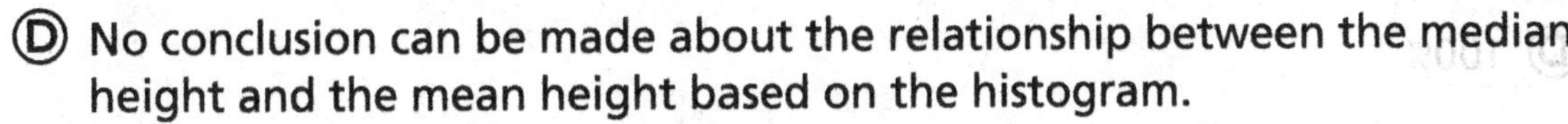

4. Using the data from Item 3, are there more plants with height h in the range 20 in. $\leq h < 40$ in. or in the range $h \geq 40$ in.?

5. Which of the following can be determined exactly from a histogram?

   Ⓐ mean

   Ⓑ median

   Ⓒ MAD

   Ⓓ none of these

10-4 Lesson Quiz

Standard Deviation

1. What is the shape of a histogram of data that form a normal distribution?

   Ⓐ A bell-shaped curve

   Ⓑ Skewed right

   Ⓒ Skewed right

   Ⓓ There is not enough information given to describe the shape.

2. The table shows the number of music tracks downloaded by a student during eight randomly selected weeks during the year. How much variability do the data show?

16	10	12	10	17	14	15	18

   Complete:
   The standard deviation is about __________, which is relatively small. The data __________ show much variability.

3. The table shows Kayden's quiz scores for a semester. What are the mean and the standard deviation, rounded to the nearest hundredth, for the quiz data?

45	48	42	47	43

4. In a data set with a normal distribution, the mean is 98 and the standard deviation is 12. About what percent of the data lie between 74 and 122?

   Ⓐ 68%

   Ⓑ 95%

   Ⓒ 99.7%

   Ⓓ 100%

5. Brand X batteries have a mean life span of 102 hours, with a standard deviation of 6.8 hours. Brand Y batteries have a mean life span of 100 hours, with a standard deviation of 1.4 hours.

   Complete: About 68% of Brand X's batteries have a lifespan between __________ and __________ hours. About 68% of Brand Y's batteries have a lifespan between __________ and __________ hours. The lifespan of a Brand __________ battery is more likely to be consistently close to the mean.

10-5 Lesson Quiz

Two-Way Frequency Tables

1. A school offers two music classes, Band and Choir. Out of 66 students in Band, 36 are male. Twelve males and 42 females are in choir. There are no students who are enrolled in both classes.

   Complete the two-way frequency table to organize the Band and Choir data.

	Band	Choir	Totals
Males			
Females			
Totals			

2. Use the table in Item 1. Which of these statements is true?

   Ⓐ Of the students in music, 10% are males in Choir, and 35% are females in Choir.

   Ⓑ Of the students in music, 55% are males, and 45% are females.

   Ⓒ Of the students in music, 25% are males in Choir, and 75% are males in Band.

   Ⓓ Of the students in music, 25% are females in Choir, and 30% are males in Choir.

3. The table shows the number of athletes in sports at a school in the fall. No students belong in more than one of the groups shown. Complete the table and find the percent of the JV athletes in the cross-country program and the soccer program. Round all percents to the nearest whole percent.

	Soccer	Cross-country	Totals
JV	22	32	
Varsity	18	24	
Totals			

   Percent of JV athletes in soccer: ______

   Percent of JV athletes in cross-country: ______

4. Use the data in Item 3, and round your answer to the nearest whole percent. What percent of the athletes are in cross-country? What percent of the athletes are varsity athletes?

   ______ in cross-country

   ______ varsity athletes

5. Use the data in Item 3. What does the conditional frequency $\frac{18}{40}$ represent in this context?

   Ⓐ the percent of soccer players who are JV athletes

   Ⓑ the percent of varsity athletes who are in the cross-country program

   Ⓒ the percent of soccer players who are varsity athletes

   Ⓓ the percent of athletes in the cross-country program who are varsity athletes

Name ______________________________

10 Topic Assessment Form A

For Items 1 and 2, use this data set: 2, 4, 6, 9, 14. If necessary, round your answer to the nearest tenth of a unit.

1. Find the mean absolute deviation.

2. Find the standard deviation.

Use these box plots for Items 3 and 4.

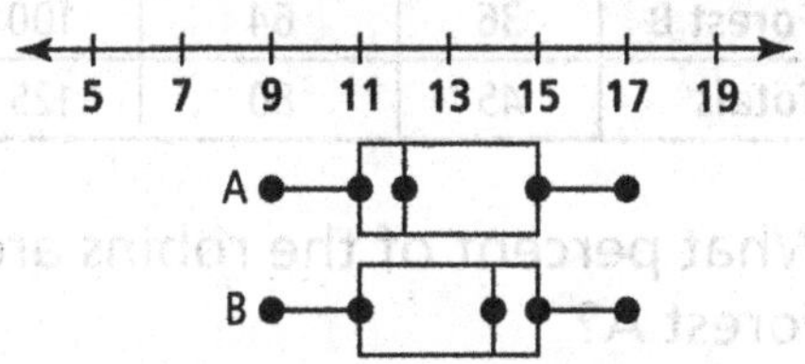

3. Which data set has more of its values less than 13?

4. In which data set is the mean less than the median?

Use this two-way frequency table for Items 5–7.

	Rock	Rap	Totals
Grade 9	4	6	10
Grade 10	30	10	40
Totals	34	16	50

5. How many 9th graders like rock?

6. What percent of the students in the survey are 10th graders?

Ⓐ 90% Ⓑ 80% Ⓒ 20% Ⓓ 10%

7. Complete the table for the conditional relative frequencies.

	Rock	Rap	Totals
Grade 9	40%	60%	100%
Grade 10			100%
Totals	68%	32%	100%

8. Which of the following best describe the box plot? Select all that apply.

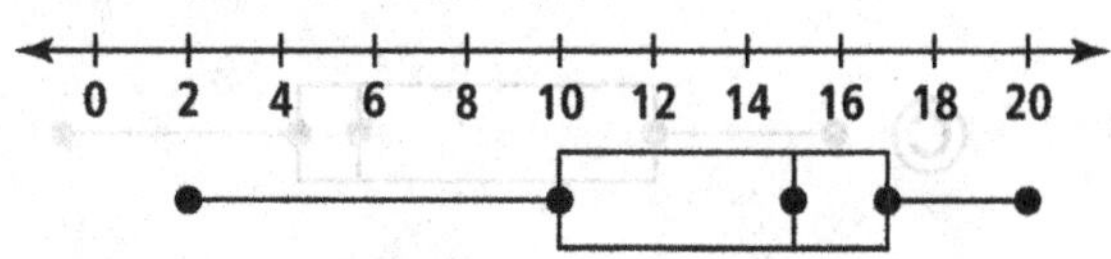

Ⓐ The data set is skewed to the right.

Ⓑ The data set is skewed to the left.

Ⓒ About 50% of the values are between 10 and 17.

Ⓓ About 50% of the values are between 2 and10.

9. In a data set, the mean is less than the median. What does that indicate about the data?

Ⓐ It is skewed to the right.

Ⓑ It is skewed to the left.

Ⓒ It is symmetric.

Ⓓ It is bell-shaped.

10. Data Set A is a normal distribution with mean 10 and mean absolute deviation 2. Data Set B is a normal distribution with mean 10 and a mean absolute deviation 5. Which best describes the data sets? Select all that apply.

Ⓐ They both have the same shape.

Ⓑ The both have the same median.

Ⓒ They are both symmetric about the mean.

Ⓓ Data Set A is more spread out than Data Set B.

11. Which box plot represents the data set 1, 1, 4, 4, 4, 9, 10, 10, 10, 14, 14?

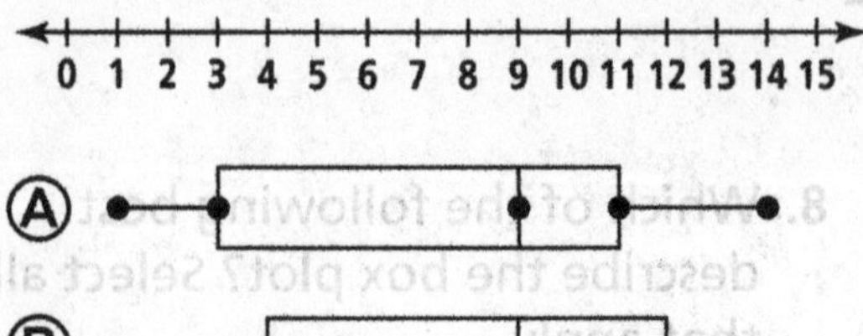

Use the histogram for Items 12–14.

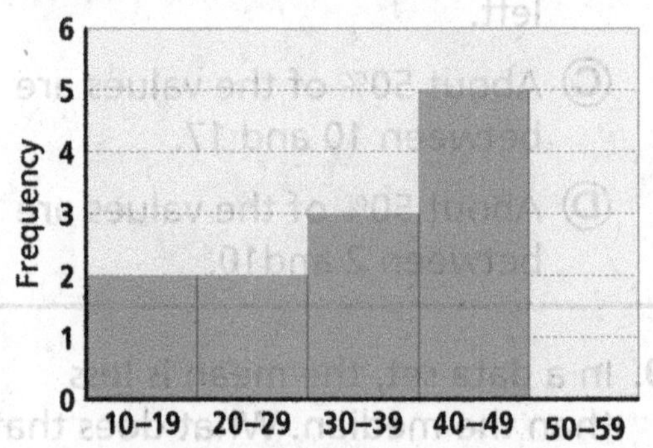

12. How many values are in the data set?

13. What percent of the values are between 10 and 30? Round to the nearest tenth of a percent.

14. The median value of the data set is 39. What could be the mean of the data set?

Ⓐ 48.5 Ⓒ 39.0

Ⓑ 45.2 Ⓓ 32.5

Use this dot plot for Items 15–17.

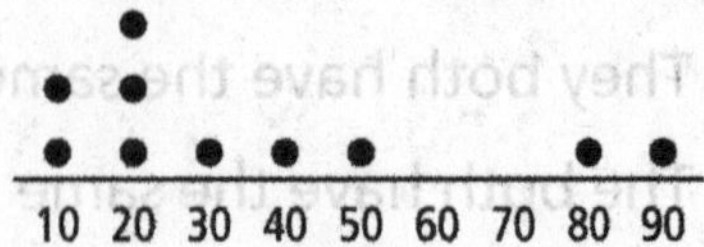

15. What is the mean of the data in the dot plot?

16. What is the standard deviation of the data? Round to the nearest tenth.

17. Will the median value be to the right or to the left of the mean?

A survey of birds in Forests A and B counted the number of robins and sparrows. Use the resulting frequency table for Items 18–20.

	Robins	Sparrows	Totals
Forest A	9	16	25
Forest B	36	64	100
Totals	45	80	125

18. What percent of the robins are in Forest A?

19. What percent of the birds in Forest A are robins?

20. What percent of the birds are robins?

21. During one month, the mean high temperature in Boise, Idaho, was 52.1° F with a standard deviation of 6.5° F. During the same month, the mean high temperature in Death Valley, California, was 81.9° F with a standard deviation of 6.4° F. Which of the following are true? Select all that apply.

Ⓐ About 95% of the high temperatures measured in Boise ranged from 45.6° to 58.6°.

Ⓑ The average high temperature in Death Valley was greater than the average in Boise.

Ⓒ The variation of high temperatures in Death Valley was about the same as the variation in Boise.

Name ______________________

10 Topic Assessment Form B

For Items 1 and 2, use this data set: 2, 4, 6, 7, 8, 9. If necessary, round your answer to the nearest tenth of a unit.

1. Find the mean absolute deviation.
2. Find the standard deviation.

Use the box plots for Items 3 and 4.

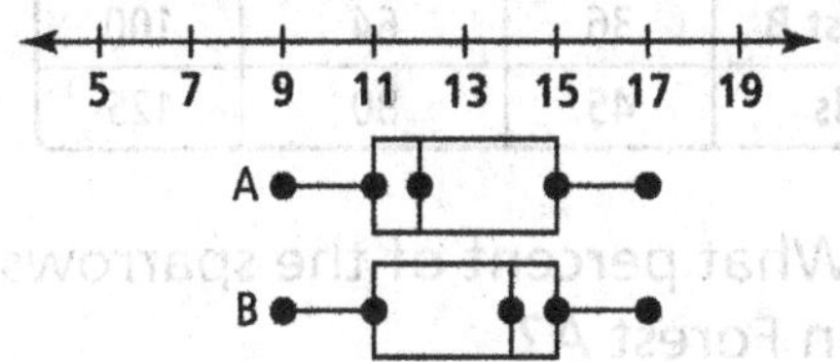

3. Which data set has a greater percent of its values less than 12?
4. In which data set is the median less than the mean?

Use the two-way frequency table for Items 5–7.

	Rock	Rap	Totals
Grade 9	4	6	10
Grade 10	30	10	40
Totals	34	16	50

5. How many 10th graders like rock?
6. What percent of the students in the survey are 9th graders?

   Ⓐ 90% Ⓑ 80% Ⓒ 20% Ⓓ 10%

7. Complete the table for the conditional relative frequencies.

	Rock	Rap	Totals
Grade 9			100%
Grade 10	75%	25%	100%
Totals	68%	32%	100%

8. Which of the following best describe the box plot? Select all that apply.

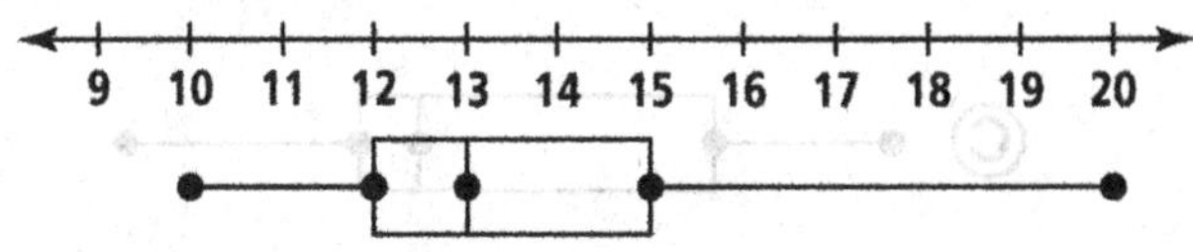

   Ⓐ The data set is skewed to the right.

   Ⓑ The data set is skewed to the left.

   Ⓒ About 50% of the values are between 13 and 20.

   Ⓓ About 25% of the values are between 10 and 12.

9. In a data set, the mean is equal to the median. What does that indicate about the data?

   Ⓐ It is skewed to the right.

   Ⓑ It is skewed to the left.

   Ⓒ It is symmetric.

   Ⓓ It is bell-shaped.

10. Data Set A is a normal distribution with mean 20 and mean absolute deviation 2. Data Set B is a normal distribution with mean 10 and a mean absolute deviation 2. Which best describes the data sets? Select all that apply.

   Ⓐ While they are not identical, they have the same shape.

   Ⓑ The both have the same median.

   Ⓒ They are both symmetric about the mean.

   Ⓓ Data Set A is more spread out than Data Set B.

11. Which box plot represents the data set 1, 4, 4 ,9, 10, 10, 14?

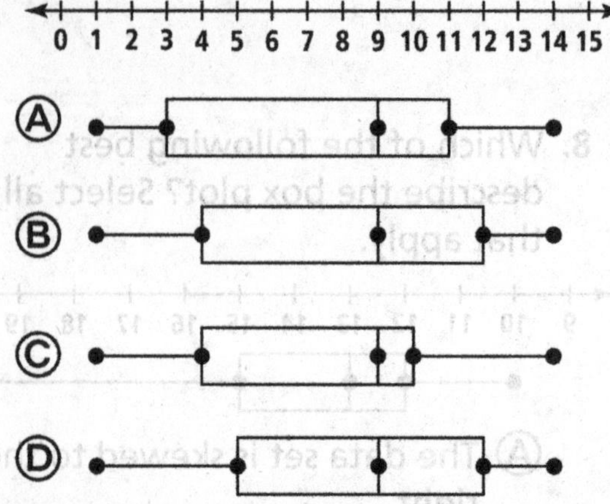

Use the histogram for Items 12–14.

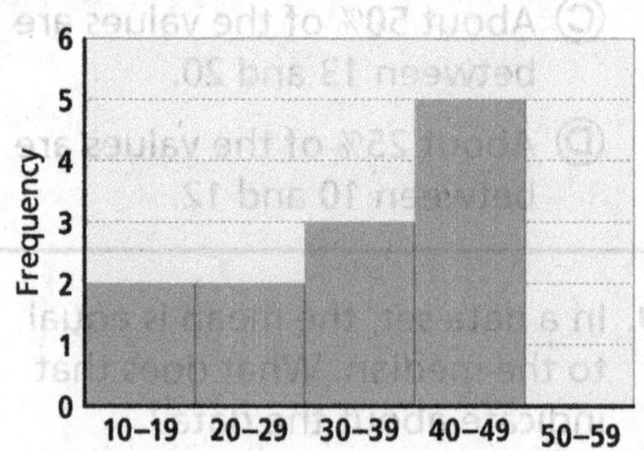

12. How many values are between 30 and 50?

13. What percent of the values are between 10 and 20?

14. The mean value of the data set is 32.9. What could be the median value of the data set?

Ⓐ 39.0

Ⓑ 32.5

Ⓒ 30.5

Ⓓ 30.0

Use this dot plot for Items 15–17.

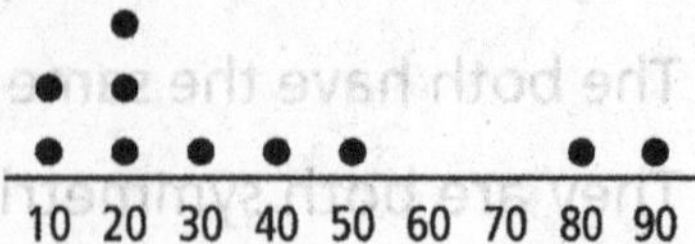

15. What is the median of the data in the dot plot?

16. What is the mean absolute deviation of the data in the dot plot?

17. Will the mean value be to the right or to the left of the median?

A survey of birds in Forests A and B counted the number of robins and sparrows. Use the resulting frequency table for Items 18–20.

	Robins	Sparrows	Totals
Forest A	9	16	25
Forest B	36	64	100
Totals	45	80	125

18. What percent of the sparrows are in Forest A?

19. What percent of the birds in Forest A are sparrows?

20. What percent of the birds surveyed are sparrows?

21. During one month, the mean high temperature in Stowe, Vermont, was 56.0° F with a standard deviation of 3.6° F. During the same month, the mean high temperature in Bend, Oregon, was 56.2° F with a standard deviation of 2.4° F. Which of the following are true? Select all that apply.

Ⓐ About 95% of the high temperatures measured in Stowe ranged from 48.8° to 63.2°.

Ⓑ The variation of high temperatures in Stowe was greater than the variation in Bend.

Ⓒ The average high temperature in Stowe was about the same as in Bend.

Name ______________________________

10 Performance Assessment Form A

Amelia collects and analyzes weather data. Here is part of her presentation for an environmental science class.

1. On May 3, 1999, fifty-nine tornadoes hit Oklahoma in the largest tornado outbreak ever recorded in the state. The data in the table show sixteen of those tornadoes that were classified as strong (F2 or F3) or violent (F4 or F5).

Part A

Create a dot plot of the data for length of the path of each tornado. List any outliers by their length.

0 2 4 6 8 10 12 14 16 18 20 22 24 26 28 30 32 34 36 38 40

Major Tornadoes in Oklahoma, May 3, 1999

Time	Length of path (miles)	Intensity
5:20 pm	6	F3
5:46 pm	9	F3
6:12 pm	4	F2
6:26 pm	37	F5
7:53 pm	7	F2
9:41 pm	12	F3
9:48 pm	8	F2
10:05 pm	7	F2
10:10 pm	15	F4
10:25 pm	39	F4
10:57 pm	1	F2
11:03 pm	22	F3
11:10 pm	15	F3
11:18 pm	8	F2
11:56 pm	13	F3
12:33 am	2	F2

Part B

Make a box plot of the data for length of path. Amelia was asked if more than half of the tornadoes had a path length of at least 15 mi. How should she respond?

Part C

Remove the outliers from the data set given in Parts A and B, and make a revised box plot. How does the removal of the outliers affect the box plot? How does it affect the median of the data set?

2. Amelia researches average rainfall data for two nearby cities during a twelve-month period from January to December. The data are recorded in the table below.

Inches of Rainfall

	J	F	M	A	M	J	J	A	S	O	N	D
City A	3.2	3.1	4.5	5.0	4.1	2.9	1.8	0.8	2.2	2.3	3.1	3.0
City B	4.2	4.0	4.7	4.8	4.5	4.3	4.0	3.9	4.3	4.4	4.6	4.5

Part A

Amelia displayed the data to show values grouped into ranges or intervals *without* showing any individual values. Do you think she used a dot plot, histogram, or box plot to display the data? Create a data display for each city with the type of display that gives the clearest picture of the information.

Part B

The consensus opinion of the class is that, because City A had the greatest amount of rain in April, 5.0 in., City A had more rainfall during the year. Analyze the distribution of values in each data set by completing the table. Tell the class whether the data support the consensus. Also tell them whether the data sets appear to be influenced by outliers.

Box Plot Values

Data Measures (in.)	City A	City B
Minimum		
First Quartile		
Median		
Third Quartile		
Maximum		
Interquartile Range		

Part C

Amelia discusses the predictability of rainfall amounts in both cities with her class. State the mean and the standard deviation to compare the variability of the data sets. Use those measures to discuss the predictability of rainfall in each city.

Name ______________________________

10 Performance Assessment Form B

The data in the table show the bowling averages for all 20 players in each of two different leagues. Bowling officials want to organize and display averages for each league using various methods of data analysis.

League 1	League 2
158	172
99	141
178	160
157	68
119	103
125	81
74	126
133	117
179	144
133	105
157	141
134	123
176	121
118	121
135	119
158	139
178	64
129	143
178	122
99	92

1. Create a box plot of the data for League 1.

2. Create a box plot of the data for League 2.

3. Use the data displays in Items 1 and 2 and the data in the table above.

   Make observations and comparisons about the data sets in terms of the following:

   - ability of the bowlers in each league
   - how the data are affected by any outliers
   - key pieces of information in the box plots (median, first quartile, third quartile, interquartile range)
   - spread of data based on standard deviation

4. Create a histogram for each set of data. Describe each data distribution. What does the shape of the distribution tell you?

5. Both leagues want to create a third league for the most skilled players. They will start a separate league if there are 20 players who average at least 140. Complete the two-way frequency table below. What trends do the results suggest with respect to joint and marginal frequencies? Should there be a separate league for players who average 140 or more? Explain.

	Below 140	Above 140	Totals
League 1			
League 2			
Totals			

6. Complete the table that shows the joint relative frequencies and marginal relative frequencies from the data in Item 5. What suggestions would you give for new members who want to join League 1? League 2?

	Below 140	Above 140	Totals
League 1			
League 2			
Totals			

Name ______________________________

End-of-Course Assessment

1. Which of the following is an arithmetic sequence?

Ⓐ 7, 11, 15, 19, 23, 28, ...

Ⓑ 3, 6, 12, 24, 48, ...

Ⓒ 0, 3, 0, 6, 0, 9, ...

Ⓓ −3, −7, −11, −15, −19, −23, ...

2. Which box plot represents the data set 1, 1, 3, 3, 3, 7, 9, 9, 9, 9, 15?

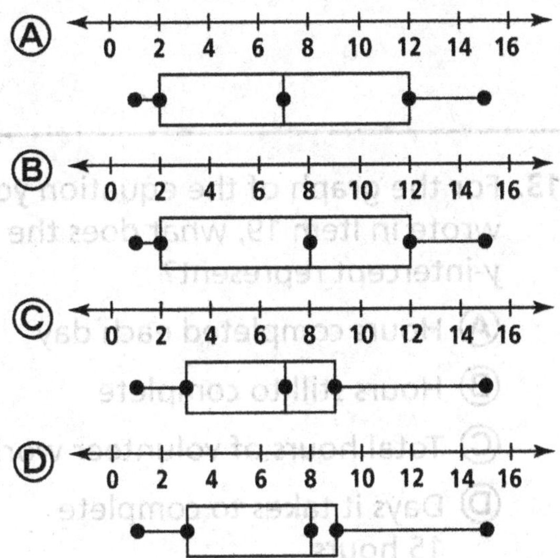

3. What are the x-intercept and the y-intercept of the graph of $8x - 7y = -56$?

Ⓐ x-intercept: 8; y-intercept: −7

Ⓑ x-intercept: −8; y-intercept: 7

Ⓒ x-intercept: 7; y-intercept: −8

Ⓓ x-intercept: −7; y-intercept: 8

4. Which lines are parallel to $8x + 4y = 5$? Select all that apply.

Ⓐ $y = -2x + 10$

Ⓑ $16x + 8y = 7$

Ⓒ $y = -2x$

Ⓓ $y - 1 = 2(x + 2)$

5. Triangle $A'B'C'$ is the image of $\triangle ABC$ under a reflection. Given $A(-2, 5)$, $B(0, 9)$, $C(3, 7)$, $A'(5, -2)$, $B'(9, 0)$, and $C'(7, 3)$, what is the line of reflection?

Ⓐ x-axis

Ⓑ y-axis

Ⓒ $y = x$

Ⓓ $y = -x$

6. If point (p, q) is $\frac{1}{3}$ of the way from A to B, what are the values of p and q?

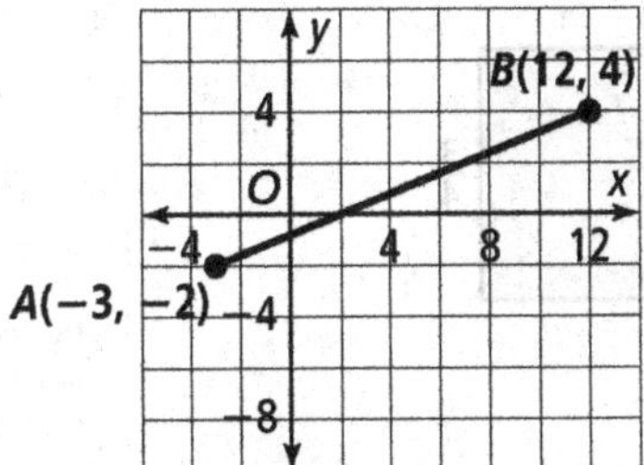

7. What is the equation for the line perpendicular to the line represented by the equation $y = \frac{1}{3}x - 2$ that passes through the point (4, −7)?

Ⓐ $y = -3x - 2$

Ⓑ $y = -3x - 5$

Ⓒ $y = 3x + 2$

Ⓓ $y = -3x + 5$

8. Solve the system of equations.

$y = 3x$

$y = x^2 + 3x - 16$

9. Solve $2x^2 + 3x - 5 = 0$ by factoring.

10. The area A of the rectangle shown is described by the inequality $12 \leq A \leq 60$. Write and solve a compound inequality for x.

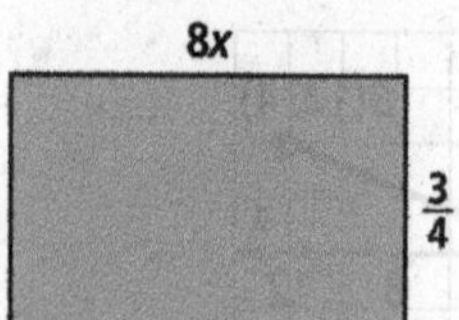

11. Abdul invests \$5,000 at an interest rate of 4%, compounded quarterly. How much is the investment worth at the end of 3 years?

Ⓐ \$624.32

Ⓑ \$5624.32

Ⓒ \$634.13

Ⓓ \$5634.13

12. Rebecca must complete 15 hours of volunteer work. She does 3 hours each day. Write a linear equation in slope-intercept form to represent the hours Rebecca still has to work after x days.

13. For the graph of the equation you wrote in Item 19, what does the y-intercept represent?

Ⓐ Hours completed each day

Ⓑ Hours still to complete

Ⓒ Total hours of volunteer work

Ⓓ Days it takes to complete 15 hours

14. The table shows test scores for five students. Do the data show a *positive* or a *negative* correlation? Do the data show *causation* or *no causation*?

Chemistry	78	64	82	75	93
Geography	84	71	87	81	99

15. The cost of renting a kayak for one hour is \$23. Each additional hour is \$8 more. Write the formulas to represent the situation.

explicit formula: ____________

recursive formula: ____________

16. How does the graph of $g(x) = 2^{x+3}$ differ from the graph of $f(x) = 2^x$?

Ⓐ It is moved up 3 units.

Ⓑ It is moved down 3 units.

Ⓒ It is moved right 3 units.

Ⓓ It is moved left 3 units.

For Items 17 and 18, use the map shown.

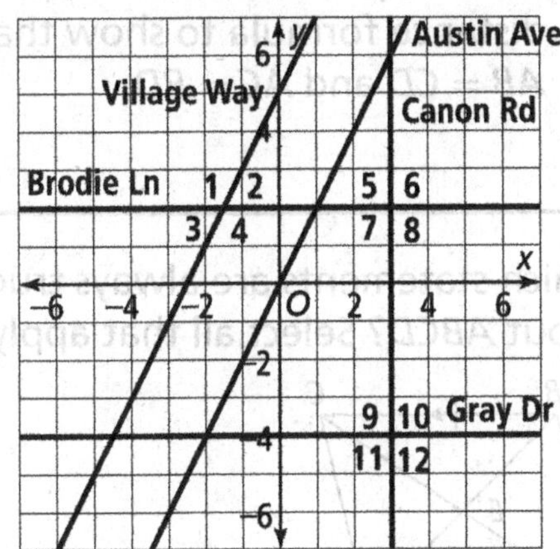

17. The city plans a new road that will be parallel to Brodie Lane. What is the slope of the new road?

18. Let $m\angle 6 = x°$. Which angles have a measure of $180° - x°$?

Ⓐ $\angle 1$

Ⓑ $\angle 3$

Ⓒ $\angle 8$

Ⓓ $\angle 12$

19. What is the equation of a line that is perpendicular to the line $y = -3x + 2$ and passes through the point (6, 8)?

Ⓐ $y = 3x + 2$

Ⓑ $y = 3x - 10$

Ⓒ $y = \frac{1}{3}x + 2$

Ⓓ $y = \frac{1}{3}x + 6$

20. What is the value of x?

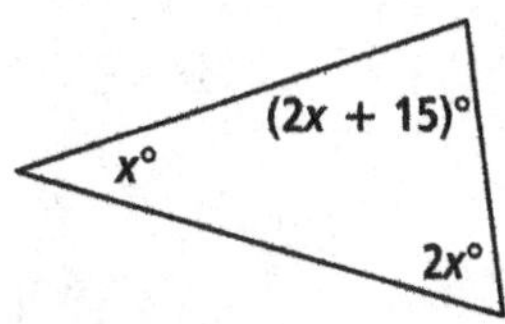

Ⓐ 24

Ⓑ 33

Ⓒ 72

Ⓓ 75

21. Jordan has saved \$15. He doubles the amount he saves each week. Does this represent an exponential function? Complete:

This ____________ represent an exponential function, because his savings increase by a constant ____________.

22. Write $\sqrt[4]{7}$ using rational exponents.

Ⓐ $4^{\frac{1}{7}}$

Ⓑ $7^{\frac{1}{4}}$

Ⓒ 4^7

Ⓓ 7^4

23. Solve the equation
$\left(\frac{1}{16}\right)^{x+3} = \left(\frac{1}{4}\right)^{x+1}$.

Ⓐ $x = -5$

Ⓑ $x = -\frac{1}{4}$

Ⓒ $x = 5$

Ⓓ The equation has no solution.

24. Line GH is tangent to $\odot T$ at N. If $m\angle ANG = 54°$, what is $m\widehat{AB}$?

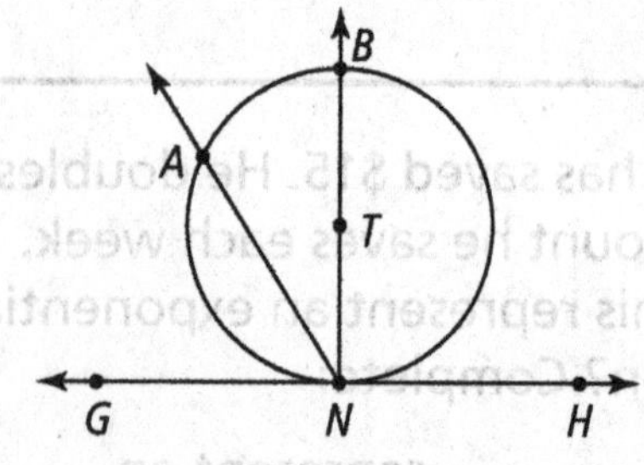

25. Point Q is equidistant from $\overline{AB}$ and $\overline{AC}$. What must be true about Q?

Ⓐ It is on the perpendicular bisector of $\overline{AB}$.

Ⓑ It is on the perpendicular bisector of $\overline{AC}$.

Ⓒ $BQ = CQ$

Ⓓ It is on the angle bisector of $\angle BAC$.

26. If you are given the coordinates of A, B, C, and D, how could you prove that $ABCD$ is a rectangle? Select all that apply.

Ⓐ Use the slope formula to show that $\overline{AB} \parallel \overline{CD}$, $\overline{BC} \parallel \overline{AD}$, and $\overline{AC} \perp \overline{BD}$.

Ⓑ Use the distance formula to show that $AB = CD$, $BC = AD$, and $AC = BD$.

Ⓒ Use the distance formula to show that $AB = CD$ and $BC = AD$, and use the midpoint formula to show that the midpoint of $\overline{AC}$ and the midpoint of $\overline{BD}$ are the same point.

Ⓓ Use the distance formula to show that $AB = CD$, and use the slope formula to show that $\overline{AB} \parallel \overline{CD}$ and $\overline{AB} \perp \overline{BC}$.

Ⓔ Use the slope formula to show that $\overline{AB} \parallel \overline{CD}$, and use the distance formula to show that $AB = CD$ and $AC = BD$.

27. Which statements are always true about $ABCD$? Select all that apply.

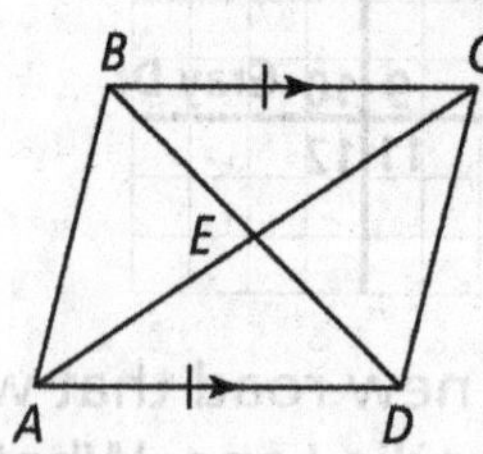

Ⓐ $\angle ABC \cong \angle CDA$

Ⓑ $\overline{BD} \perp \overline{AC}$

Ⓒ $\overline{BE} \cong \overline{ED}$

Ⓓ $m\angle ABC + m\angle BCD = 180°$

Ⓔ $\overline{AB} \cong \overline{CD}$

28. What rigid motion maps the solid-line figure onto the dotted-line figure?

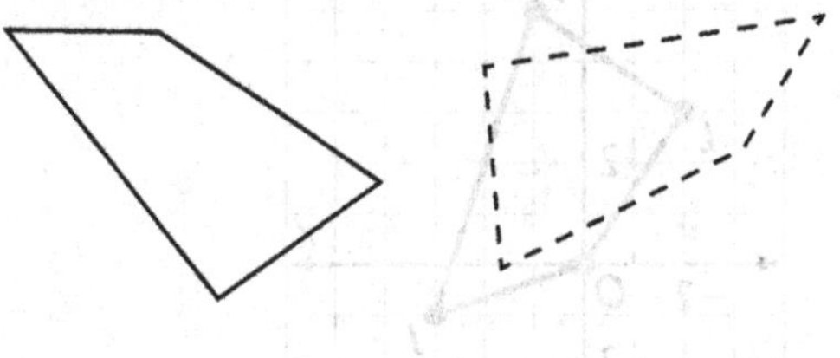

29. Which equation represents a line that is parallel to the line with equation $y = 2x + 1$? Select all that apply.

Ⓐ $y = 2x - 8$

Ⓑ $y = -2x + 1$

Ⓒ $2x + y = 7$

Ⓓ $-2x + y = 2$

Ⓔ $-2x - y = 9$

30. Which criteria can be used to prove triangles are congruent? Select all that apply.

Ⓐ ASA

Ⓑ AAS

Ⓒ SAS

Ⓓ SSA

Ⓔ HL

31. Which theorem can you use to prove that $\triangle GHJ$ and $\triangle GKJ$ are congruent?

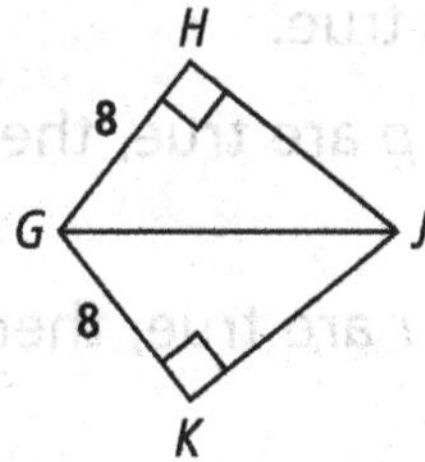

Ⓐ ASA

Ⓑ SAS

Ⓒ SSS

Ⓓ HL

For Items 32 and 33, use the diagram shown.

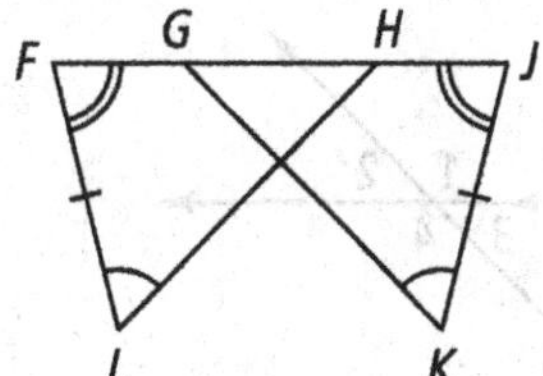

32. ______ is congruent to $\overline{GK}$.

33. The intersection of $\overline{GK}$ and $\overline{HL}$ is point P. Which triangle must be an isosceles triangle?

Ⓐ $\triangle FHL$

Ⓑ $\triangle GPH$

Ⓒ $\triangle JGK$

Ⓓ No triangle is isosceles.

34. What is $m\angle DBC$?

D

$(3x + 22)°$ $(x - 4)°$

A B C

35. Which statement must be true? Select all that apply.

Ⓐ If $p \rightarrow q$ and $q \rightarrow r$ are true, then $p \rightarrow r$ is true.

Ⓑ If $p \rightarrow q$ and p are true, then q is true.

Ⓒ If $p \rightarrow q$ and r are true, then $q \rightarrow r$ is true.

Ⓓ If $p \rightarrow q$ and q are true, then p is true.

36. Which angle is congruent to $\angle 8$? Select all that apply.

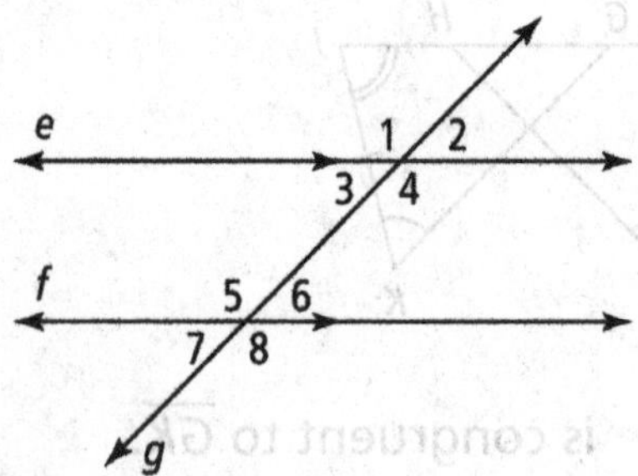

Ⓐ $\angle 1$

Ⓑ $\angle 2$

Ⓒ $\angle 3$

Ⓓ $\angle 4$

For Items 37 and 38, use quadrilateral *JKLO*.

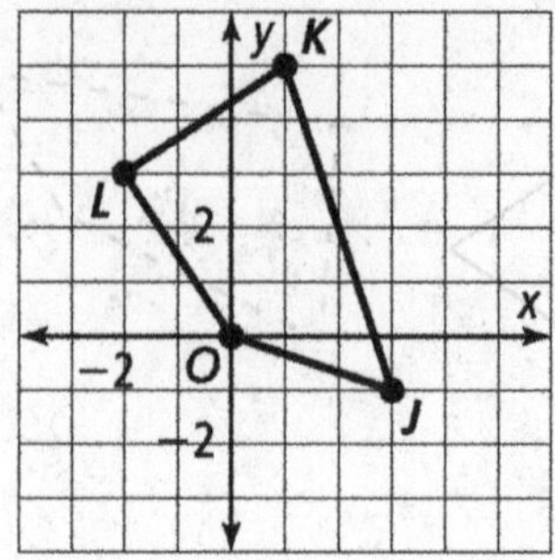

37. What are the coordinates of the vertices of $R_{y\text{-axis}}(JKLO)$?

38. What are the coordinates of the vertices of $r_{(90°,\, O)}(JKLO)$?

39. The lengths of the diagonals of a rhombus are 6 and 8. What is the perimeter of the rhombus?

40. What should be the first assumption in an indirect proof of the following conjecture?

If $\overleftrightarrow{AB}$ is the perpendicular bisector of $\overline{CD}$, then $AC = AD$.

Ⓐ $AC = AD$

Ⓑ $AC \neq AD$

Ⓒ $\overline{AB}$ is the perpendicular bisector of $\overline{CD}$.

Ⓓ $\overline{AB}$ is not the perpendicular bisector of $\overline{CD}$.